MW00609124

Probing the Sky

Selected NACA Research Airplanes
and Their Contributions to Flight

Curtis Peebles

*With Contributions
by Richard P. Hallion*

Library of Congress Cataloging-in-Publication Data

Peebles, Curtis.
  Probing the sky : selected NACA/NASA research airplanes and their contributions to flight / by Curtis Peebles.
    pages cm
  Includes bibliographical references and index.
  1. Research aircraft--United States--History. 2. United
States.--National Aeronautics and Space Administration--Research. I. Title.
  TL567.R47P4349 2015
  629.133'3--dc23
                                    2014039331

This publication is available as a free download at
http://www.nasa.gov/ebooks.

ISBN 978-1-62683-021-9

National Aeronautics and Space Administration
Washington, DC

Table of Contents

The scale of what's involved in undertaking research flights is made clear in this iconic image of the D-558-2, the B-29 launch plane, and the ground support personnel and equipment. The photo was taken in front of the NACA hangar at South Base shortly before the move to the present facilities. (NASA Photo)

Introduction

Toward—and Into—the Unknown

In the decades since the Wright brothers' first flights, a body of knowledge and tools, created in an evolutionary process of small steps, had been built up to guide engineers and researchers in developing new aircraft. The early wood-and-fabric biplanes had given way to all-metal monoplanes. Aircraft size, range, and payload had also grown, until the oceans could be spanned in a fraction of the time a ship would take. Speed became the critical factor in both commercial and military operations.

But by the early 1940s, speed itself had become the problem. With aircraft flying near the speed of sound, the old rules of subsonic aerodynamics no longer applied and the old tool of aeronautical research—the wind tunnel—no longer worked. Consequently, engineers lacked the means to determine if their designs would withstand actual flight conditions.

The technology, tools, and procedures needed in this new realm of flight completely transformed the fields and practices of aerodynamics, propulsion, structures, design theory, materials, flight control systems, life-support systems, escape systems, safety procedures, wind tunnels, and data collection systems and methodologies. The body of knowledge for the supersonic era was effectively recast and made anew.

Thomas Kuhn's term "paradigm shift" is now much overused both as an expression and as an intellectual concept, but, in the case of the midcentury high-speed revolution, it is certainly appropriate. What aeronautical science had accrued for subsonic flight following the Wrights' first flight in 1903 was rendered almost entirely irrelevant by the late 1940s and the onset of the supersonic era.

The engine of transformation was the turbojet. It spelled the end of one era in aviation and the dawn of another, pushing people and machines across the sonic divide faster than they had gone before, forcing transonic and supersonic researchers to address the mysteries that were affecting airplanes entering this new and unknown realm.

Ironically, while it was this new form of propulsion that drove the supersonic breakthrough, the turbojet itself could not yet take the researchers and pilots far enough into the realm to conduct the vital research data they sought.

The turbojet of the 1940s was a new and still immature technology. The temperatures in its combustion chambers (burner cans) and which the spinning turbine blades endured approached the limits of contemporary metallurgical science, making them unsuited then for supersonic flight. In order to explore the supersonic regime, researchers turned to rocket planes, relegating turbojets to slower speeds. Some of these turbojets became famous, such as the XS-1 (later designated simply the X-1, the first of the postwar "X-series" research airplanes). Others are little remembered today—but each played its own distinctive part in taking aviation from the subsonic to the supersonic era. Collectively, these first research aircraft are known as "Round One," the transonic and supersonic probers of the 1940s and 1950s that preceded "Round Two," the hypersonic North American X-15 of the 1960s.

This story is not simply one of strange-looking airplanes and their courageous test pilots. It offers, as well, insights into the history of aerospace technology and science and of shifting technology and (yes) paradigms within that field. The turbojet and the rocket changed the rules. Together, they led to the X-1 and the other research airplanes. These airplanes were also why a small group of engineers came to a vast dry lakebed in the Mojave Desert, establishing there, arguably, the world's premier center for aeronautical research and development, the Air Force Test Center–NASA Armstrong Flight Research Center complex (and the associated airspace) at Edwards Air Force Base, CA.

Creating the new era, with its own rules and tools, took place against the dynamic background of the Cold War, forcing and feeding the need for ever-higher performance. But at the onset of that era, lacking reliable tools to determine what would work and what would not, engineers had few means to decide what paths they should follow. In a real sense, they faced the same situation as the Wright brothers, when they were building their first kites and gliders in 1899–1902, with little reliable information, much of which was contradictory and misleading. They discovered that little of the available information was reliable. They discovered that they had to reject treasured assumptions and awake to new realities. They had to rethink their concepts of stability and control. For the test pilots, there was yet something more: since the potential of failure and death was very real, when they went aloft, their skill had to be matched by even greater courage. Knowledge, dedication, expertise, and courage: of the mix of such was the crafting of the transonic and supersonic revolution, made manifest in the skies over the Mojave over a half century ago.

A semispan airplane model on the wing of a P-51 in January 1946. In an adaptation of the wing-flow technique, a half-scale model of an airplane was attached to the upper surface of a wing. As the airplane made a dive, airflow over the wing accelerated to high transonic or supersonic velocity. (NASA)

CHAPTER 1

Confronting the "Sound Barrier": The Bell XS-1

The resistance of a wing shoots up like a barrier as we approach the speed of sound.
—W.F. Hilton[1]

In 1935, when British aerodynamicist W.F. Hilton inadvertently coined the phrase "sound barrier," the piston engine aircraft was nearing its performance peak, producing approximately one horsepower per pound of engine weight. But aeronautical engineers were already outrunning the knowledge they had acquired in the three decades since the Wright brothers' first flight at Kitty Hawk, NC, in December 1903. Up to this time, designers had always treated the airflow over wings as if it were an "inviscid" or incompressible fluid. This simplified their calculations, and the errors induced by this convenient (if false) assumption were too small to be of significance.

With aircraft now exceeding 400 miles per hour (mph), the compressibility of air could no longer be ignored. But engineers and scientists lacked the insight on how the required revolutionary changes could be accomplished. The wind tunnel, the aerodynamicist's standard tool since before the Wright brothers, was of little help. As the airflow neared the speed of sound, shock waves formed on the models and supports and reflected onto the tunnel walls, rendering the data questionable from Mach 0.8, just below the speed of sound, to approximately Mach 1.2, just beyond the speed of sound. While tunnels could hint at some of the flow changes induced by high-speed flight—for example, a dramatic loss of lift and simultaneous sharp increase in drag—they could not furnish precise quantified data that would permit accurate analysis.

Thus, very suddenly, a new realm of flight loomed—mysterious, unknown, dangerous, and destructive. Pilots making high-speed dives found that control surfaces would not move or did so to little effect. In some cases, their airplanes broke up or dove uncontrollably into the ground. Others, more fortunate, found that the controls would respond normally once the airplanes reached lower altitudes. The phrase "sound barrier" encapsulated the mystique of this realm. Very quickly, a mythology developed regarding supersonic flight. Myths unsupported by scientific fact gained traction, some of which bordered on the bizarre: Some held that a pilot's voice would become caught in the throat as the plane "broke" the sound barrier, while others alleged that time would reverse and the pilot would become younger after going supersonic.[2]

The Onset of Transonic Research

The first indications of these problems appeared in 1918. Aircraft of that time had top speeds of about 100 mph. However, the tips of their propellers were rotating at speeds as high as 300 to 650 mph. It was Frank W. Caldwell and Elisha N. Fales, of the Army Air Service Engineering Division, who made the first realistic measurements of propeller aerodynamics. Using a wind tunnel able to reach speeds of 450 mph, they discovered that "[w]hen the stress reaches a certain value, two adjoining layers of air begin to slide past each other and the character of the flow is changed."[3]

They had observed flow separation, which occurs as airflow passing over an airfoil accelerates. As a consequence, the airfoil's drag increases, reducing its efficiency. Because a propeller's airfoil and that of a wing are similarly affected, the propeller tests gave the first indications of what would occur as aircraft reached the same speeds.[4]

Lyman J. Biggs and Dr. Hugh L. Dryden of the Bureau of Standards expanded upon this initial work over the next decade. Between 1924 and 1931, Biggs and Dryden undertook four separate studies. The first study used the same six airfoils Caldwell and Fales had tested, but at speeds of 375 mph to 682 mph, confirming their earlier results.[5] Biggs and Dryden's second set of tests also involved the six airfoils, but at speeds of 383 mph (Mach 0.5) to 830 mph (Mach 1.08). This reconfirmed the earlier results, determined that flow separation was the cause of the increased drag, and expanded the speed range.[6]

Hugh L. Dryden undertook some of the first research into aerodynamics at transonic speeds during his research on propeller airfoils. The aerodynamic effects the propeller airfoils experienced gave indications as to what would occur as aircraft flew close to the speed of sound. (NASA)

This was followed by a third, much more expansive study of 24 propeller airfoil shapes, tested at speeds of Mach 0.5, 0.65, 0.8, 0.95, and 1.08. The study's results showed a general rule: thin airfoils had lower drag at higher speeds, making them more effective. In contrast, thick airfoils showed greatly increased drag at higher speeds. Another general observation was that when flow separation occurred, all the airfoils' efficiencies were reduced "nearly to the same level irrespective of their efficiency when the flow is smooth."[7] As a result, "[t]he efficient sections therefore suffer most."[8] Because of the different Mach numbers that were used for each test, Biggs and Dryden were able to show that the rate of the increase in drag rose abruptly at speeds well below Mach 1, while the flow separation occurred above Mach 0.8 in most cases.

Biggs and Dryden's fourth and final research study was on the advantages of "circular arc" airfoils. One of the airfoils used in the third study was of this type. A circular-arc airfoil has a flat lower surface, while the upper surface is a segment of a circle. Despite its being a thick airfoil, Biggs and Dryden found that the circular-arc shape was more efficient than conventional airfoil shapes at high speeds. They wanted to see if this applied as a general rule. The tests involved eight circular-arc airfoils at Mach 0.5, 0.65, 0.8, 0.95, and 1.08. By using the same speeds as the earlier tests, they could make a systematic comparison. The results were surprising—one circular-arc airfoil was "extremely inefficient" at low speeds but had only 80 percent of the drag of a conventional airfoil at speeds between Mach 0.85 and 1.08. Biggs and Dryden realized that this result offered an elegant solution to the loss of propeller efficiency. They wrote, "These results indicate that it would be beneficial to use circular-arc sections for the outer part of a propeller blade intended for use at high tip speeds, retaining sections of the conventional type nearer the hub where the thickness ratio is large and the speed low. It seems not unreasonable to expect that a circular-arc section can be used profitably over the outer third of the blade."[9]

Although these studies were conducted by the Army Air Corps and the Bureau of Standards, their results were all published by the National Advisory Committee for Aeronautics (NACA), which was established in 1915 "to supervise and direct the scientific study of the problems of flight with a view to their practical solution."[10] The NACA was created in response to the advances in aeronautical research and aircraft design being made in Europe. Over time, the NACA increasingly focused its efforts on finding "practical solutions" that could advance aeronautics, establishing a pattern of inquiry that constitutes one of the foundational underpinnings of the more recent NASA, which was created in 1958 to address the challenges of the emergent post-Sputnik space age. The propeller-airfoil research represented milestones in the understanding of compressibility effects at transonic and supersonic speeds. Although it was not done to make supersonic flight possible, but rather for the seemingly mundane goal of improving propeller efficiency, it nevertheless had profound significance for the future assault on the "sound barrier."[11]

This focus on practical applications and incremental improvements would serve the NACA well in the 1920s and the Depression years of the 1930s. It reflected the evolutionary nature of aviation technology in this period.

Wood-and-fabric biplanes were giving way to all-metal monoplanes, aircraft ranges and speeds were steadily increasing, and passenger comfort and safety were improving.[12] The wooden Fokker trimotors of 1929 had, a decade later, been replaced by all-metal DC-3s.

In all of these endeavors, the NACA played a significant role. Its work in airfoil development transformed aircraft design practice and established a global standard. While agency researchers did miss—as many others in America and elsewhere did as well—the potential significance of the gas turbine engine, the agency did support studies on reaction propulsion systems, and its many investigations of conventional aircraft propulsion and propulsion systems design resulted in much more efficient engine installations on aircraft, typified by nacelle and cowling location, and the nearly ubiquitous NACA cowling of Fred Weick. As well, the NACA's detailed studies on flight structures, bolstered by its persistent analysis of foreign research, hastened the transformation of the airplane from a wooden, braced biplane to a metal, cantilever, and monocoque monoplane.

The Turbojet Revolution

Serious interest within the NACA in reaction propulsion began at the same time as the propeller-efficiency studies and likewise involved piston-engines, not pure turbojets. In both America and abroad, early concepts for a "jet" engine involved using a piston engine to power a reciprocating air compressor. The resulting high-pressure air was then fed into a combustion chamber, where fuel was added and ignited. The hot gas efflux exited via a convergent-divergent nozzle to produce thrust.[13]

Edgar Buckingham of the Bureau of Standards undertook a study of jet propulsion for the Army Air Service using this conceptual engine. (No actual hardware or subscale engine existed.) His conclusions were published in 1923 by the NACA.[14] Buckingham found that the hybrid piston engine/jet concept had numerous flaws, which included high fuel consumption, a much heavier weight than a piston engine, an increased number of moving parts, and the resulting lower reliability and higher maintenance requirements. Buckingham concluded, "There does not appear to be, at present, any prospects whatever that jet propulsion of the sort here considered will ever be of practical value, even for military purposes."[15] Buckingham's conclusions were incorrect, both for this hybrid concept and, more significantly, for the higher-performance (and more technologically demanding) turbojet. It should be noted, however, that the Bureau of Standards and the NACA were far from alone in such judgments, which, generally, were accepted more broadly by the global engineering and scientific community as a whole.

Subsequent NACA studies in the 1920s and early 1930s used the same flawed, conceptual engine and reached the same flawed conclusions. In part, this was due to the inefficient hybrid design, incorrect assumptions about the large size and weight of the compressor, and the research culture at the NACA. The Langley Memorial Aeronautical Laboratory, which was the only NACA research facility until 1941, had only a small engine research division, and its members were largely focused on the piston engine. Thus, it was three European countries—Nazi Germany, Great Britain, and Fascist Italy—and not the United States, that made the most significant jet-related technology breakthroughs of this era. (It should be noted, however, that the same complacency afflicting American aeropropulsion experts was likewise generally found overseas. Only after inventors outside the aeropropulsion mainstream—Hans von Ohain in Germany and Frank Whittle in Great Britain—demonstrated the value of the gas turbine was it effectively "seized" by the aeropropulsion community and subsequently made a normative element of aircraft design.)[16]

Neither von Ohain nor Whittle was aware of the other's work until after the outbreak of the Second World War. Hans von Ohain, a young physicist, began his work on jet engines in 1933. Von Ohain's engine was a more advanced axial-flow turbojet engine design than Whittle's concept, but, even so, he finished first, thanks in large measure to the support of Ernst Heinkel, a leading aircraft manufacturer in Germany. Von Ohain's turbojet engine powered the He 178, which made the world's first flight by a pure jet aircraft on August 24, 1939.[17] Frank Whittle, von Ohain's equivalent in Great Britain, began working on a turbojet engine design earlier, in 1928. He persevered in the face of official skepticism, metallurgical challenges, and a lack of serious financial support, and finally he successfully ground-tested a centrifugal-flow jet engine in 1937, following this with a flying example four years later, the Gloster E28/39, which flew on May 15, 1941, as the first British jet aircraft. At first glance, Whittle's engine resembled a Moss or Rateau-type turbosupercharger in design, but it had very great differences, notably, of course, in its direct connection, via a single drive shaft, of the "hot" turbine and the "cold" compressor.[18]

Despite growing interest in gas turbine propulsion, the NACA remained focused on the original ducted fan design, assisted by downstream burning with the jet efflux passing through a convergent-divergent nozzle. In early 1940, Albert E. Sherman undertook a second look at Buckingham's report on jet propulsion. Sherman examined a jet's feasibility in terms of flight at 500 mph. His conclusion was that jet propulsion offered the possibility of high speeds without the heavy machinery Buckingham had thought necessary 17 years previously. Sherman's report was discussed at an April 11, 1940, meeting in the office of Henry Reid, the head of the Langley Aeronautical Laboratory.

The senior staff in attendance accepted the report and concluded that Langley should undertake jet research.

Dr. George W. Lewis, the NACA Director of Aeronautical Research, sent a letter to Langley on April 22, 1940, approving the start of work on a combustion test rig for what was now called the "Jeep" engine, but which was still, at heart, simply a refined version of the conceptual design Buckingham had examined in 1923. This was a piston-engine/combustion-chamber design, rather than a true turbojet. It was built using sheet iron and a salvage engine, but the low priority and demands of other work meant 2 years passed before Jeep test runs would begin.

Europe was now engulfed by war, and, while the United States was still officially neutral, a close watch was kept on Germany's aircraft developments.[19] General H.H. "Hap" Arnold, chief of the U.S. Army Air Corps (shortly to be reorganized as the U.S. Army Air Forces [AAF]), sent a letter on February 25, 1941, to Dr. Vannevar Bush, the chairman of both the NACA and the National Defense Research Committee. Arnold warned that the Germans had made considerable progress on rocket propulsion, which threatened to make existing fighter aircraft obsolete. He continued, "Further investigation by a large group of able scientists is immediately needed."[20] Bush formally established the NACA Special Committee on Jet Propulsion, with retired professor William F. Durand as chairman. Durand had been a member of the NACA since it was organized and was still active at the age of 82. Bush told him in a March 18, 1941, letter about the Jeep engine and commented, "It seems to have great possibilities and I cannot find any flaw in their arguments."[21]

Eastman N. Jacobs, an engineer in Langley's airflow research branch who had been studying reaction propulsion and thrust-augmented systems since the late 1920s, wanted to do more than ground-test the Jeep engine. He wanted to use the Jeep to power a specially designed high-speed research aircraft. His concept, which emerged from the drawing tables in July 1942, had a cylindrical fuselage, a nose-inlet, a shoulder-mounted straight wing, and a V-tail, and it sat on tricycle landing gear. The pilot's cockpit was just behind the inlet. The research plane used a wing with a 15-percent thickness-chord ratio (i.e., the wing's depth from top to bottom was 15 percent of the distance from the wing's leading edge to its trailing edge) and an NACA high-speed airfoil. The power came from an 825-horsepower Pratt & Whitney R-1535 radial piston engine, to compress the incoming air, and the downstream fuel-injection and burning Jeep propulsion system. The drag due to compressibility effects above 550 mph made the airplane's top speed uncertain. However, the team felt confident that the airplane could reach transonic speeds.

Ironically, the driving force behind the proposal was not propulsion experimentation itself, but the loss of aircraft in high-speed dives. Lockheed

P-38 Lightnings, Republic P-47 Thunderbolts, and Bell P-39 Airacobras had all suffered fatal tail failures. The Navy's Curtiss SB2C Helldiver had similar problems (and some foreign aircraft did as well). Tests at both Langley and the new Ames Research Center (the second NACA center, created in 1941 to support the West Coast aircraft industry) showed that the P-47 and P-39 needed to have their tail structures strengthened to withstand the higher-than-predicted air loads at high speeds. With the SB2C, compressibility at high speeds was distorting the wing surface, causing flow separation and buffeting turbulence, which in turn caused the horizontal stabilizers to flutter, exceeding their structural strength and breaking them off. To cure the problem, the wing structure was stiffened, preventing the distortions. Additionally, the tail had to be redesigned to withstand the 13-g loads experienced in dives.[22]

This design, proposed by Eastman Jacobs in 1941, constituted the first NACA research aircraft. The airplane was powered by a Jeep engine, which combined a piston engine to compress the air and a combustion chamber to produce thrust. The Jeep engine had already been made obsolete by British and German turbojet engines. (NASA)

Despite the need, Jacobs's proposed research aircraft and the Jeep engine would never be built. In April 1941, Hap Arnold had visited Britain and been informed of British work with the Whittle engine. He immediately arranged for the importation of Whittle engine technology to the United States. Out of this came the first American "black" aircraft program: to develop a highly secret jet engine test bed. Bell Aircraft Corporation was awarded a contract to develop the plane, and General Electric another contract to develop its engines. The plane itself was assigned an abandoned propeller-driven fighter designation (P-59) used for another program to mask its own development.

On October 1, 1942, at Muroc Army Air Field, California (now Edwards Air Force Base), the Bell XP-59A jet made its first flight. The aircraft was powered by a pair of General Electric I-A Whittle turbojet engines. Durand was on hand for the airplane's first flight at Muroc and had known about the airplane from its beginning. Due to the secrecy of the project, however, he could not discuss it with the other committee members. With an advanced turbojet already in production, the research aircraft and the Jeep engine project were obsolete. The Jeep was formally canceled in March 1943, marking the end of formal American interest in ducted fan approaches. From now on, America would be firmly fixed on the turbojet—and the rocket.

During the summer of 1943, Jacobs went to England and visited the Royal Aircraft Establishment, where he learned about the state of British turbojet engine technology. When Jacobs returned to Langley, he drafted a letter strongly protesting the military services' refusal to fund a research aircraft. In the letter, he stated that the United States was making the same mistake that the British had, namely, applying a revolutionary engine to a conventional airframe. But it was his final comment that carried the most weight. In his warning, Jacobs demonstrated uncharacteristic perception for someone from an agency increasingly being seen as having failed to meet its primary mission of advancing American aviation technology. "The development of the jet power units themselves," he warned any and all, "had progressed beyond the development of suitable airplanes to employ them."[23]

Jacobs realized that the unknowns of compressibility were no longer the single issue facing designers. The revolutionary turbojet engine had to be matched with an equally revolutionary airframe design. He argued that a unified effort involving the military services, aircraft manufacturers, and the NACA was needed to solve the multiple unknowns of high-speed flight. This effort would be done "with a view to producing quickly extreme-performance aircraft of several types to be developed around existing units and suitable to exploit to the full the capabilities of those existing jet-propulsion power plants."[24]

Two Roads Toward the Transonic

The Jacobs research aircraft was not the only such proposal being discussed. John Stack, the head of the Compressibility Research Division, met with Lewis in the spring of 1942 to discuss the development of such an aircraft. Lewis did not like the idea of a research aircraft, but he did respect Stack's ability, self-assurance, ambitions, and skills as a researcher. Lewis did not approve development work on a research airplane due to wartime pressures on the NACA. Stack came away from the meeting with a sense that Lewis did not object to a low-priority effort to identify the design features that a transonic research aircraft should have.

As Jacobs had done, Stack also assembled a team to define the research aircraft. The members included engineer Milton Davidson and junior engineering aide Harold Turner, Jr. (Turner had worked on Jacobs's aircraft design.) Stack's design had a top speed of Mach 0.9, as he was not interested in actual supersonic flight. The limited performance of early turbojet engines made a successful Mach 0.9 flight marginal in any event. By early summer of 1944, the team had completed a preliminary design of a small turbojet-powered research aircraft capable of Mach 0.8 to Mach 1 speeds.[25]

John Stack, the NACA researcher who masterminded the design and construction of the D-558 series. He was determined to get a jet-powered/transonic research airplane and was opposed to the rocket-powered/air-launched/supersonic XS-1. In this 1946 photo, a D-558-1 wind tunnel model is in the background and Stack is holding a swept-wing D-558 model. This eventually led to the D-558-2 Skyrocket. (NASA)

Stack informed selected friends within the AAF and Navy aeronautical communities of the study; the only military officer who expressed strong support for his research aircraft was Captain Walter Stuart Diehl of the U.S. Navy, a noted aeronautical engineer, author of an influential aerodynamics textbook, expert on seaplane design, and senior naval representative to the NACA. During late 1943, Diehl met several times with the chief of the Navy's Bureau of Aeronautics' structural branch. He argued that a research airplane was the only means to convince people that the "sound barrier" was "only a steep hill."[26]

Support for a research airplane also came from an industrial source. On December 18, 1943, Durand held a special meeting at the NACA Headquarters on the subject of jet propulsion. At the meeting, he asked a basic question: What should the United States do with the turbojet propulsion technology being developed?

Among those in attendance was Robert W. Wolf of Bell Aircraft, who was the designer of the XP-59A's airframe, cockpit, and propulsion system. Wolf had also traveled to Britain in 1943 to review its progress in turbojet technology. He knew more powerful engines were under development that would allow aircraft to reach transonic speed in level flight.

During the discussion, Wolf suggested that a high-speed, jet-powered research aircraft be designed. These data were urgently needed, as new jets would soon be facing the same structural and control problems in level flight that had befallen the P-38, P-39, P-47, and SB2C during dive tests. After the meeting concluded, Wolf put his ideas into a letter sent to Lewis on December 29, 1943. He wrote:

It appears quite possible to construct a single engine aircraft based on available gas turbine jet power plants which will fly at speeds in level flight exceeding the critical Mach numbers of currently used types of wings. If this aircraft were designed with enough inherent versatility to changes in control surfaces, wings, etc., it should be possible to develop usable control surfaces such as ailerons, dive control flap, tail surfaces, etc., which would work satisfactorily at or above the critical speeds of the wings. Furthermore, this could be done in level flight and would not be subject to the dangers and difficulties associated with the high accelerations encountered in current dive programs.[27]

Lewis's response was more positive than that he had given Stack in 1942. He wrote Wolf that the NACA was highly interested in learning more regarding compressibility and aircraft stability and control at transonic speeds by means of a turbojet-powered research aircraft. Lewis continued that the NACA was giving this project "our very serious concern."[28]

A 1944 photo of John Stack when he was the head of Langley's Compressibility Research Division. With wind tunnels incapable of providing reliable transonic-speed data, attention began to focus on building a research aircraft to provide the needed data. This resulted in a conflict between the NACA and the Army Air Forces, as well as within the NACA over the aircraft's design—subsonic and jet powered versus supersonic and rocket powered. (NASA)

The AAF had some intelligence reports on Germany's rocket and jet-powered aircraft, though these often offered sketchy and in some cases contradictory information. It was also clearly interested in transonic flight research. In mid-January 1944, the Development Engineering Branch of the Materiel Division at AAF Headquarters authorized a study of a research airplane for investigating aerodynamic phenomena between 600 and 650 mph. At the same time, Ezra Kotcher requested that the Design Branch of the Aircraft Laboratory at Wright Field conduct a comparative study of two different research airplane concepts. The first would be powered by a General Electric TG-180 axial flow turbojet engine with a thrust of 4,000 pounds. The other aircraft design would use a proposed 6,000-pound-thrust Aerojet rocket engine.[29]

While this study was underway, two joint military-NACA conferences took place at Langley on March 15 and 16, 1944, to deal with the issue of a transonic research aircraft. One meeting was chaired by Navy Captain Diehl and the other by Colonel Carl Greene of the Materiel Command. Greene was Diehl's AAF equivalent, functioning as the permanent AAF liaison officer at Langley. While the NACA leadership had now accepted the need for a specialized research aircraft, the military services—with numerous responsibilities for waging a global war against ruthless foes—were still divided over the need, design, and objectives: was, for example, the aircraft to be purely experimental? Or might it have operational features or even be the basis of an operational design?[30]

The AAF's Design Branch completed its studies for the supersonic research airplanes in April 1944. Kotcher's design was dubbed the "Mach 0.999 study," a reference to the popular belief in an impenetrable sound barrier. A rocket-powered aircraft was seen as offering the best approach to collect supersonic flight data. The thrust of the rocket engine meant higher speeds could be reached at higher altitudes, eliminating the need to make dive tests, as well as the associated risks for both pilot and plane.

This question of using a turbojet versus a rocket motor for the research airplane sharply divided research airplane proponents in the AAF and the NACA. Kotcher had presented the preliminary results of the Mach 0.999 study at a May 15–16 meeting with the NACA. Stack was critical of the design in large part because of the rocket engine. NACA researchers believed this form of propulsion would be unsafe. If the rocket failed during the takeoff from a runway, they argued, the heavily loaded airplane would crash and explode.

A rocket-powered aircraft, Stack believed, could not meet the research requirements. Its flight time would be brief compared to that of a turbojet-powered aircraft (he did not envision the air-launching that would make them highly productive). This meant a rocket-powered aircraft would not be able to collect the volume and quality of data the researchers needed. While the AAF vehicle was designed to fly above Mach 1, the NACA's research airplane was limited to flying at transonic speed. Finally, the NACA objected that the performance of a rocket-powered vehicle would not be representative of an operational aircraft's. In contrast, the experience of flying a turbojet research aircraft would be applicable. Kotcher countered that the XP-59A had shown that existing turbojet engines lacked the thrust needed to fly at transonic speeds, while the Mach 0.999 study showed that rockets could reach such speeds.

The AAF gave its reply in a final round of meetings at Langley on December 13–14, 1944. Not surprisingly, the AAF rejected the NACA jet-powered aircraft proposal, as the subsonic concept was too conservative. The AAF wanted the airplane to reach Mach 1.2 (approximately 800 mph, depending on the altitude), and, as NACA researcher John V. Becker later observed, "The Army was putting up the money and they decided to do it their way."[31] In late December 1944, 1 week after the meeting, the AAF began negotiations with Bell Aircraft Corporation to build the XS-1 (Experimental Sonic-1) rocket-powered research aircraft, the result of a fortuitous chance meeting at Wright Field between Kotcher and Bell chief engineer Robert J. Woods.[32]

Stack was committed to acquiring a turbojet-powered research aircraft, for if it did not have the fullest performance of the rocket-powered one, it would nevertheless have greater endurance and might well, in his view, be safer and more reliable as well. Thus, after Kotcher (whom Stack highly respected) made it clear that the AAF was determined to build a rocket-powered research aircraft based on his Mach 0.999 study, Stack turned to the Navy's Bureau of Aeronautics. His message was dire: he told Navy personnel that the AAF's rocket-powered aircraft was unlikely to survive enough flights to provide significant data. His efforts had the desired results.

Abraham Hyatt, a Marine Corps officer and aeronautical engineer, proposed a research aircraft design in September 1944 that matched the NACA concept. It would have a top speed of 650 mph at sea level, use a turbojet engine, have thin 10-percent thickness-chord wings, take off and land under its own power, have room for flight instrumentation, and have excellent low-speed handling. These requirements were not surprising, as the Bureau of Aeronautics stated that the Navy "was only interested in obtaining an airplane which met with the full approval of the NACA."[33]

In late December 1944, Diehl, Hyatt, and Captain William "Bill" Sweeney, of the Bureau of Aeronautics, showed L. Eugene "Gene" Root, of the Douglas Aircraft Corporation, the preliminary specifications for the jet-powered research aircraft. Douglas was a major contractor for Navy aircraft, and Gene Root took the Navy specification to Douglas's El Segundo plant and met with its chief engineer, Edward Henry "Ed" Heinemann. Heinemann formed a small design team and, by February 1945, had completed a preliminary design for the Douglas Model 558 High-Speed Test Aircraft.

This aircraft would be the first of a three-part effort. The D-558 phase 1 would have a top speed of about Mach 0.89. In the phase 2 effort, two of the aircraft would be modified to have both a Westinghouse 24C turbojet engine and a Reaction Motors Incorporated rocket. This would allow them to fly at speeds between Mach 0.89 and about Mach 1 in level flight. The data from the phase 1 and 2 aircraft would be used by Douglas to produce engineering drawings and a mockup of a phase 3 operational Navy combat aircraft.

The Bureau of Aeronautics approved the new design of the D-558 phase 1 and 2 aircraft. To differentiate the two aircraft designs, the phase 1 aircraft were given the Douglas model number D-558-1, while the phase 2 aircraft were called the

The scale of what is involved in undertaking research flights is made clear in this iconic image of the D-558-2, the B-29 launch plane, and the ground support personnel and equipment. The photo was taken in front of the NACA hangar at South Base shortly before the move to the present facilities. (NASA)

D-558-2. The Bureau of Aeronautics also outlined a development program that gave the NACA a major role in the management of the flight research program.

The NACA, the Navy, and Douglas would each have access to one of the D-558-1 aircraft. The NACA research pilots would use their aircraft to collect data on air loads, flutter, engine performance, and stability and control at transonic speeds. Douglas test pilots would fly the company's D-558-1 for information useful for the D-558-2 operational aircraft. In early March 1945, the NACA sent a letter to the Navy giving its observations: "The Committee is certain that the procurement of these two models of high-speed research airplanes will permit making of a large advance in aerodynamic knowledge in the transonic region of flight and every attempt should be made to make these aircraft available to the NACA for flight research as soon as possible." After several inspections of the D-558-1 mockup and revisions of the design to correct what NACA representatives saw as shortcomings, the D-558-1 design was approved.[34]

While Navy-NACA-Douglas relations were smooth, the same was not completely true of the AAF–NACA–Bell XS-1 effort. The initial disagreement was within the Langley staff and concerned the best wing to use on the aircraft. Both groups knew that a thin wing was preferable to a thick wing for high-speed flight. The reason was that thick wings have a lower "critical Mach number," the velocity at which a shock wave forms, leading to an immediate large increase in drag, causing the so-called "shock-stall."

Stack and fellow wind tunnel researchers wanted the XS-1 to have a wing with a 12-percent thickness-chord-ratio wing. The group took this position because the thicker 12-percent wing would encounter flow changes at speeds of Mach 0.75 to 0.9. The aerodynamicists wanted data in this speed range to correlate with their wind tunnel data. As a result, they recommended that Bell fit this thicker wing to the XS-1 to deliberately cause it to fly within the risky shock-stall flight regime.

The opposite viewpoint was expressed by Robert R. Gilruth, a researcher at Langley, who argued for a very thin wing, with a thickness as low as 5 per-

Robert R. Gilruth invented the wing-flow technique to collect transonic data from an airplane in a dive, and he supported the rocket-powered XS-1. Stack effectively designed the jet-powered D-558-1. Their activities following the establishment of NASA reflected their outlooks. Gilruth worked on piloted space flight activities, and Stack retired when the NACA ceased to exist. (NASA)

cent. He believed the XS-1 and its pilot would need every advantage they could get to survive the unknowns of transonic flight. If a thin wing was used, the airplane would be much safer to fly.

The thick/thin wing debate had a larger importance. If the 12-percent-thickness wing was selected, the XS-1 would only be able to reach Mach 0.9; it could not go supersonic. In contrast, Gilruth was arguing that to increase safety, a very thin wing should be used to lessen the inherent unknowns and dangers of transonic flight. Ironically, this safe approach also meant that the XS-1 could exceed Mach 1.

Floyd Thompson reviewed the arguments and evidence and decided that Gilruth's thin-wing concept was preferable. Stack responded by suggesting that the XS-1 be fitted with two different sets of wings. The first would be a 10-percent-thickness wing, less than what Stack had wanted but more than what Gilruth recommended. The second wing would have an 8-percent thickness-chord ratio. This was slightly thicker than Gilruth had argued for, but much less than what Stack wanted. The logic was clear to Thompson and other Langley managers, and, in March 1945, they decided to have Bell build the two sets of wings.[35]

A far more serious set of objections arose as Bell Aircraft began construction of the XS-1. The original design had cylindrical internal fuel tanks for the liquid oxygen and alcohol/water fuel positioned fore and aft of the wing carry-through structure. A turbopump fed the oxidizer and fuel into the rocket engine. Difficulties in building this turbopump led to the cylindrical tanks' being replaced by two spherical tanks. High-pressure nitrogen gas would now feed the fuel into the engine. The nitrogen gas was carried in multiple spherical tanks. To withstand the pressure of the nitrogen gas, both the storage tanks and the oxygen and alcohol/water fuel tanks had to be made of thick metal. The result was that the XS-1's landing weight was increased by a ton and the fuel supply dropped due to the lesser volumetric efficiency of spherical tanks. As a result, a ground takeoff would reduce the XS-1's maximum speed to below Mach 1.

Larry Bell had decided at an early stage that the XS-1 should be air-launched from a four-engine mother ship such as a Douglas C-54 Skymaster transport or Boeing B-29 Superfortress. Air-launching avoided the risk of the heavily loaded XS-1's suffering an engine failure on takeoff, undoubtedly resulting in the loss of both plane and pilot. With the war still underway, however, no aircraft were available. Langley researchers, in contrast, expected the airplane to take off from a runway, fly the speed run, and make a normal runway landing. Due to the lack of a mother ship, the launch issue was still open.

With the redesign of the fuel system, the only option to reach the AAF's planned Mach 1.2 top speed was an air launch from a mother ship. This would carry the XS-1 to an altitude of 30,000 feet, at which point the XS-1 would be released. Although an air-launch profile had earlier been considered as a safety measure, it was now mandatory to meet the AAF's speed goals. An additional problem was that the smaller fuel supply meant that the rocket's burn time had dropped from 5.4 minutes to around 2.6 minutes. These changes reopened the disagreements between the NACA and the AAF.[36]

Upon hearing of the changes, Stack sent a memo to Langley's chief of research. The XS-1 "may prove to be unsuitable."[37] Stack listed five basic requirements the research airplane had to meet before he would be satisfied:
- Speed greatly in excess of the critical Mach number.
- Duration at full power for complete observations in level flight at steady conditions.
- Takeoff, flight, and landing with self-contained power units.

- Flexibility to permit changes of all principal components such as wings, tail surfaces, and canopies.
- Space for adequate instrumentation.[38]

Stack then noted that the XS-1 fell short of these basic requirements. In particular, the aircraft lacked the needed duration at full power as well as the ability to take off, fly, and land with self-contained engines. It also probably could not now meet the requirement for adequate instrumentation.

Because the XS-1 did not meet the required duration at full power, Stack continued, it also now failed to meet the requirement for speed in excess of the critical Mach number. The fuel supply was so limited that the XS-1 would burn its entire fuel supply to reach 35,000 feet and then be unable to make the level speed run. While speed runs could be made at lower altitudes, their research value was minimal, as it was only at altitudes of around 35,000 feet that speeds in excess of the critical Mach number could be reached. In closing, he urged that a major effort be made to develop the turbopump needed for the original fuel system design.

Another factor that disturbed engineers at Langley, perhaps Stack most of all, was control of the program. The AAF began looking for possible test sites other than Langley. Langley was a busy airport located in a heavily populated area, and any emergency ran the risk of killing and injuring people on the ground. A possible move meant the Langley researchers would not have the direct control over the flight research program that they wanted and were accustomed to.[39]

The initial test sites considered for the XS-1 other than Langley were Muroc Army Air Field in California and Wendover Field in Utah. Both were in isolated areas ideally suited for safety and security. The move to a remote site prompted objections from both NACA Headquarters and Langley personnel. Stack dashed off an angry memo to John Crowley, chief of research at Langley, on June 14, 1945, which said, "This airplane originated here as did the P-80 program. If we are to do research of this kind we must have the airplane here. I do not believe we should again be treated as a service as was in the case with the P-80. If the shifting of this aircraft to a western station materializes I propose that we transfer *all work* beginning right now so we can free our people to do research with our present equipment."[40]

By late summer of 1945, the issue of the test site was still unresolved. The candidate sites being checked by Bell test pilot Jack Woolams included Muroc Army Air Field; Wendover Field, UT; Salina Field, KS; Daytona Beach, FL; Marietta Field, OH; and several airfields in Texas. Stan Smith of Bell thought Muroc, deep in the Mojave desert, 100 miles from Los Angeles and over 2,100 miles from Buffalo (Bell Aircraft headquarters), was too far away and recommended Daytona Beach.[41]

Why Not Swept Wings?

By this time, a much larger issue had arisen that damaged the NACA's reputation even more than its earlier neglect of jet-engine technology or any disagreements with the AAF over rocket planes and tests sites. Ironically, it also represented a major breakthrough in the design of supersonic aircraft. It was the result of theoretical calculations by Robert T. Jones at Langley.

Jones's accomplishment began with a study of a dart-shaped missile in late 1944. The missile's slim delta shape required a new approach to calculate its lift. Jones saw that he could apply the mathematical studies of the airflow around airships that Max Munk had made in 1924 to analyze the flow around the missile, buttressed by studies by Hsue-Shen Tsien, a von Kármán associate from the Guggenheim Aeronautical Laboratory at the California Institute of Technology, for supersonic flow around projectiles and slender bodies.

Jones began studying the mathematics of "potential flows" at supersonic speeds in early 1945. This term refers to fluid motion where there is no rotation of the fluid element. Jones realized he was deriving the same equations as he had using his earlier lifting theory. These new equations now also included compressible flow. Jones recalled that Tsien had said that some slender projectiles exhibited no effects of compressibility when rotated. Jones took his earlier calculations out of the desk drawer and incorporated the compressible flow equations. Jones found that very slender wings lacked compressibility effects.

Trying to find a physical explanation, Jones undertook a series of elaborate calculations and eventually found that this lack of compressibility effects was the result of sweepback on the lift generated by large-span wings. Again, it was a paper by Munk that gave Jones an understanding of the physical process. Munk's paper had dealt with the effects on aircraft stability due to wing dihedral and sweepback at low subsonic speeds. Munk noted that for an airplane in level flight, only the component of velocity at a "normal angle" (i.e., at a perpendicular angle) to the wing's leading edge affected the production of lift. Although Munk's paper only applied to subsonic aerodynamics, Jones believed it could apply to slender wings in supersonic flows.

When Jones finished his calculations, he had a unified theory that encompassed swept wings with angles ranging from 0 degrees to 90 degrees and covered all possible wing configurations rather than solely slender wings. By late April of 1945, Jones had completed a report on his calculations. Jones noted, "The analysis indicates that for aerodynamic efficiency, wings designed for supersonic speed should be swept back at an angle greater than the Mach angle and the angle of sweepback should be such that the component of velocity normal to the leading edge is less than the critical speed of the airfoil sections. This principle may also be applied to wings designed for subsonic speeds near the speed of sound, for which the induced velocities resulting from the thickness might otherwise be sufficiently great to cause shock waves."[42]

The physical explanation of these results was complex, but the results were astonishing. With the Mach line ahead of the wing, the "streamlines," a smooth, nonturbulent flow over the upper surface of a wing following a set pattern, would curve and follow paths consistent with a flow at subsonic speeds, even though the velocity was actually supersonic.

This meant the *effective* Mach number was reduced compared to the *actual* Mach number of the airplane. Jones had suspected that this would occur, but he was surprised by the size of the reductions his calculations indicated, which showed that the effective Mach number would be three to five times smaller than that on a straight wing. This limited the amount of wave drag, which was due to changes in velocity through a shock wave. Also reduced were the effects of compressibility shock, which involved significant changes in the patterns of airflow pressures, densities, and temperatures.

The advantages of swept wings were not limited to supersonic flight, Jones found. He noted the sudden increase in drag when the airflow "may be avoided by increasing the angle of sweepback so that the normal component of the velocity not only is subsonic but is also less than the critical speed of the airfoil sections. This principle may also be applied to wings designed for subsonic speeds near the speed of sound."[43]

Jones wrote a memo to Crowley telling him he had "made a theoretical analysis which indicated that a V-shaped wing would be less affected by compression than other planforms. In fact, if the angle of the V was kept small relative to the Mach angle, the lift and center of pressure remain the same at speeds both above and below the speed of sound."[44]

The next step was to test the theory in actual flight. Jones concluded the memo by asking Crowley to approve wing-flow and drop-body testing of different wing shapes "designed to minimize compressibility effects."[45] These alternative techniques had been developed in response to the inaccurate data from wind tunnels at transonic speeds. Gilruth had developed the wing-flow technique. A model connected a balance mechanism located in the starboard gun bay of a P-51 Mustang protruded above the upper surface of the wing, and an NACA pilot then dove the plane to over Mach 0.80. While the aircraft itself was still subsonic, the airflow over the model was supersonic, to as high as about Mach 1.4. While this produced useful results, the short duration of the test methodology—and the obvious dangers attending diving into the dense lower atmosphere at compressibility-inducing Mach numbers—limited its appeal.

A semispan airplane model on the wing of a P-51 in January 1946. In an adaptation of the wing-flow technique, a half-scale model of an airplane was attached to the upper surface of a wing. As the airplane made a dive, airflow over the wing accelerated to high transonic or supersonic velocity. (NASA)

A second approach was drop-body tests. These were streamlined shapes with either rectangular or swept wings, dropped from 40,000 feet by a B-29. During their fall, the shapes reached Mach 0.9 to Mach 1.27. The forces acting on the wings were measured using onboard instruments, and the measurements were transmitted to ground stations. Their trajectories were followed by radar and optical tracking. Crowley gave his approval, and Gilruth's flight research section began testing to verify or refute the advantages of swept wings.

While these tests were still underway, Jones's draft paper met with strong opposition from Dr. Theodore Theodorsen, head of the Physical Research Division, a leading theoretical physicist, and chairman of the Langley publication committee. He had had a contentious dispute with Eastman Jacobs in the 1930s over the use of wind tunnels versus theoretical calculations. Theodorsen was similarly critical of Jones's results.

Theodorsen did not agree with Jones's arguments or his conclusions, calling them "hocus-pocus" and demanding that they be clarified with some "real mathematics." Worse, he dismissed Jones's results as "a snare and a delusion." At the end of the publication committee meeting, Theodorsen demanded that the material on Jones's swept-wing theory be removed from the paper. Considering the weight he carried because of his stature and term of service, Langley management agreed with Theodorsen's objections and decided publishing the paper without experimental proof could not be justified.[46]

The debate was settled by the end of May 1945, and Jones's reputation was redeemed with the completion of the wing flow and drop-body tests. They showed that Jones's predictions were valid. The data showed a reduction of wing drag by a factor of almost four using a swept-wing configuration. The results were also confirmed by Macon C. Ellis and Clinton Brown, using a section of wire at a large angle of sweep in Langley's supersonic wind tunnel.[47]

A 35° swept-wing model mounted on the wing of a P-51 Mustang. The "wing flow" technique provided data on airflow at transonic speeds that were otherwise unobtainable through wind tunnel tests. (NASA)

Langley's engineer-in-charge, Henry Reid, sent Jones's completed paper to NACA Headquarters in early June 1945. Reid noted that Theodorsen *still* did not agree with Jones's arguments and conclusions and had refused to participate in the paper's editing. The paper, titled "Wing Plan Forms For High-Speed Flight," was issued on June 21, 1945, as a Confidential Memorandum Report. A second edition was issued 3 weeks later, as an Advanced Confidential Report, with a wider distribution to both the military services and specific personnel in the aviation industry.[48]

At this same time, Allied intelligence teams were searching for documents and other data on advanced technology developed by Germany. They soon discovered that extensive work on high-speed airfoils and sweptback wings had been done. In contrast, the NACA had done virtually no research in these fields during the 1930s and 1940s. The failure to anticipate the advantages of swept wings was seen by the military and aircraft contractors as still another NACA failure to keep pace with European aviation advances, and it caused an angry response.

Brigadier General Alden R. Crawford, chief of the AAF's Production Division, asked NACA Chairman Jerome Hunsaker in October 1945 why no mention of Jones's swept-wing theory had been made during earlier XS-1 design reviews. Had the AAF known about this, General Crawford claimed, the XS-1 design could have been changed to incorporate swept wings. The general was incorrect—the AAF *had* been told about Jones's paper before the first XS-1 mockup review. The AAF had specified straight wings for the XS-1 because its planned jets used straight wings. For its part, the NACA had rejected using a swept planform because, in the minds of Langley researchers (as they informed the AAF), logically, it made little sense to further burden the research airplane with yet another unproven design concept. Even so, the NACA's reputation was again damaged, and, for the record, Jones himself had hoped that the XS-1 might incorporate a swept-wing planform.[49]

Flight Tests and Unresolved Issues

As 1945 drew to a close, the XS-1 project neared the flight-test phase. Colonel George F. Smith, chief of the Engineering Division's Experimental Aircraft Project Division at Wright Field, who oversaw the XS-1 project, sent a letter to Lewis on November 23 to outline the AAF's position on several issues. The initial Bell glide flights would be made at Pinecastle Army Air Field in Florida. This base had a 10,000-foot runway; was being equipped with an SCR-584 radar and optical tracking equipment; had predictable weather; and was nearer to the Bell, AAF, and NACA facilities than Muroc. Pinecastle's remote location also provided security. Colonel Smith's letter also made clear that the inability to develop a turbopump would not be allowed to delay the project and that the XS-1 would be flown using the high-pressure fuel system. Not surprisingly, Stack had very different ideas about the NACA's role and was not willing to change them.[50]

Stack wrote a three-page memo on December 28, 1945, to research director Crowley regarding the NACA's views on XS-1 flight research program management. Stack wrote that the Pinecastle flights were "to determine the feasibility of operating from Langley Field," a notion he and other NACA engineers still harbored. Stack added that after the Bell contractor flights were completed, Langley would take over pilot responsibilities for the tests. His earlier objections to the XS-1 design still remained. He wrote that the NACA should not take possession of the XS-1 project until the aircraft was flown with the turbopump system and fuel for a powered landing and was capable of a ground take-off. Finally, he emphasized in the memo to Crowley that the NACA had to insist that these conditions be met.[51]

On January 8, 1946, NACA Headquarters sent a reply to Colonel

Senior officials with the XS-1 research program included, from left, Joseph Vensel (head of operations), Gerald Truszynski (head of instrumentation), Capt. Charles Yeager (XS-1 pilot), Walter C. Williams (head of NACA Muroc Flight Test Unit), Maj. Jackie Ridley (XS-1 project engineer), and De E. Beeler (chief engineer). (NASA)

Smith's letter. Although the NACA letter supposedly agreed with the AAF position on the XS-1 program, in fact, it was "accepting" Stack's rejection of the Army position. The NACA letter stated the following:

- The final Army acceptance would occur after the rocket motor was demonstrated and without the need for the B-29 launch aircraft.
- The Pinecastle flights were to determine if Langley Field operations were feasible.
- Bell Aircraft would supply the pilot until the NACA decided to take over the program.[52]

By the time the NACA's letter was sent, the Bell glide flights were underway at Pinecastle Field. Bell test pilot Jack Woolams made 2 captive flights and 10 free flights between January 25 and March 6, 1946, flying the first Bell XS-1 (AAF serial 46-062), equipped with a 10-percent thickness-chord wing and 8-percent thickness-chord tail (changed subsequently to an 8-percent thickness-chord wing and 6-percent thickness-chord tail before it began its powered flights). The Pinecastle glide flights provided the answers to several issues. The XS-1 had good low-speed flight characteristics but poor visibility through the flush windshield, and the air-launched concept was practical.

More important, the Pinecastle flights eliminated the use of either Langley Field or Niagara Airport for subsequent XS-1 powered test flights. A much wider landing area was required for safe operations. Of the 10 glide flights, the first landed short of the runway. On the fourth flight, the left main gear retracted after touchdown and the XS-1 went off the runway and suffered minor wing and fuselage damage. On the fifth landing, the nose gear retracted, causing minor damage. Even a 10,000-foot runway lacked the qualities needed for a consistently acceptable unpowered touchdown. Additionally, bad weather caused numerous canceled flights. The XS-1 required a site with better and more predicable weather conditions.[53]

Despite the hopes of both Langley's Stack and Bell Aircraft's Smith, the only site that met the requirement was Rogers Dry Lake at Muroc Army Air Field in California. With a surface area of 44 square miles, Rogers was the largest dry lake in the world. Its surface was dried silt, able to support 250 pounds per square inch. The lakebed's north-south distance was 11 miles. It enjoyed clear skies some 350 days a year. The lakebed was located in the middle of the Mojave Desert, far from prying eyes, yet was less than a hundred miles from Los Angeles and its aircraft contractors. The XP-59A had first flown there, and the advantages of the site for flight testing were clear to project personnel.[54]

The next step was the powered flights, using the Reaction Motors, Inc., four-chamber XLR-11 6,000-pound-thrust rocket engine.[55] As part of its contract with the AAF, Bell Aircraft had to demonstrate that the XS-1 was controllable to a speed of Mach 0.8 and could withstand an 8-g pullout. Although this concluded Bell's obligations under the contract, company management assumed they would also make the first Mach 1 flight. The longstanding practice was that contractor test pilots made the envelope expansion flights, up to the airplane's maximum speed.

The powered XS-1 flights would not be made by Woolams, who had been killed while practicing for the 1946 Thompson Trophy air race. His replacement was Chalmers H. "Slick" Goodlin. He was only 23 years old when assigned to be the XS-1 test pilot, but he had amassed extensive flight experience. He had soloed before turning 17; he had served in the Royal Canadian Air Force as a flight instructor, in the Royal Air Force as a Spitfire pilot, and in the U.S. Navy as a test and ferry pilot—all before joining Bell in December 1943 as a production test pilot.[56]

The NACA was also preparing for the Muroc tests. In September, Hartley Soulé, chief of the Stability Research Branch at Langley, selected Walter C. Williams to oversee a small team, including engineers, instrument technicians, and technical personnel, who were to support the Bell XS-1 powered flights. They were called the NACA Muroc Flight Test Unit. Williams and four other NACA engineers arrived at Muroc in September 1946. Six more arrived in

Group photo of the groundbreaking for the new main building at the High-Speed Flight Research Station. From left to right are Gerald Truszynski (head of instrumentation), Joseph Vensel (head of operations), Walter C. Williams (director of the High-Speed Flight Research Station), Marion Kent (administration officer), and California state official Arthur Samet. (NASA)

October, and the two women "computers," who reduced the data from the onboard instrumentation into charts and graphs, arrived in December. The 13 personnel were initially considered to be a unit on a temporary assignment to the desert base. The NACA Muroc Flight Test Unit gained permanent status on September 7, 1947. It became the High-Speed Flight Research Station on November 14, 1949, and was later renamed simply the NACA High-Speed Flight Station.

They found themselves in a place very different from Virginia. Facilities at Muroc were meager, with the initial NACA facilities consisting of a single hangar shared with the AAF, plus two rooms. Darkroom facilities were lacking. Support facilities were the loading pit for the XS-1, the liquid-oxygen and liquid-nitrogen tanks, and a fuel trailer to mix the alcohol/water fuel.

Housing was also marginal. Williams found an apartment in Palmdale, 40 miles from Muroc. He was the exception. Single engineers and technicians lived in "Kerosene Flats," the decaying wartime housing in the town of Muroc near the edge of the lakebed. In late 1946, the Marine air station in Mojave was closed, and married NACA personnel moved into the base housing. In both cases, the housing was low-quality wartime construction, cold at night, and in dilapidated condition.

The biggest change from Langley was the landscape. Muroc was in the wide-open spaces of the southwestern desert, with hot, dry weather during the summer, while winter saw freezing temperatures and occasional snow. It was so bleak that some Langley engineers and their families outright refused to leave the familiar shores of Tidewater, VA. Of those who came west, some adapted and thrived, while others soon returned to the Chesapeake.[57]

The second XS-1 (AAF 46-063) arrived at Muroc on October 7, 1946, under the belly of the B-29 launch aircraft. The aircraft had the thicker 10-percent thickness-chord wings and 8-percent thickness-chord horizontal tail flown on the first airplane at Pinecastle 9 months earlier. Goodlin initially made a series of glide flights to become familiar with the XS-1's handling and flight characteristics. The first glide-flight attempt was made 2 days later but was aborted before launch. It was rescheduled and successfully made on October 11. A total of four glide flights were made by December 2, 1946. The way was now clear for the initial powered flights. The first attempt, on December 9, was aborted before launch. The next try, on December 20, was successful. Goodlin made a total of 12 powered flights in the second XS-1 over the next 3 months, with a final flight on February 21, 1947. Two more attempts were aborted before launch.

Settling Differences, Building a Program

While Bell's powered flight tests were going smoothly, the internal differences continued. The Bell and NACA personnel had different concepts of the role of the contractor XS-1 glide and powered flights. For Bell, these were to prove the basic airworthiness of the XS-1, within the contract specifications. This was to be a quick program, which Richard Frost of Bell Aircraft noted did not "envision any lengthy series of scientific tests to investigate all the byroads of stability in its various forms."[58]

In contrast, Williams told Frost and Robert Stanley (also with Bell) during a September 1946 meeting at Muroc that the NACA wanted complete stability and control data from the upcoming powered flights, as well as aerodynamic and structural load data. The data needed, he continued, included longitudinal stability characteristics, control in both steady and accelerated flight conditions, and the buffet boundary.[59] Frost responded that no special flights would be made to collect such data. Bell would accept its test pilot's assessment of stability and control issues to meet the contract requirements. There would be no delays in the flight to accommodate the NACA's research requirements.

On April 11, 1946, Colonel Smith wrote to Lewis to outline the AAF's position regarding its understanding and plans for the XS-1 project. Once the Bell test flights were completed, the NACA would undertake the high-speed flights and supply a pilot and data collection system and personnel. If the NACA concluded the aircraft was unsafe, the XS-1 could be returned to AAF control. The letter also stated that the AAF position was for the air launch to continue, as this was the most practical and safest method of flight testing for the XS-1. Colonel Smith made it clear that the AAF wanted a "firm understanding" between the AAF and the NACA on these issues before the end of the Bell powered flights.

Williams wrote a memo to Melvin N. Gough, chief of the Flight Research Division at Langley, in response to the AAF letter. Williams stated that the NACA should not accept the XS-1 until the turbopump had been successfully tested. He also rejected the use of the B-29 launch aircraft. Williams also noted that Bell was planning to make the initial powered flight at Muroc, having rejected operating from Langley.

Gough had his own requirements, which included the capability to take off and climb to 35,000 feet under its own power. While he suggested that the NACA might waive this requirement once the B-29 operations gained experience, Gough insisted that the NACA not accept the XS-1 without the turbopump and reserve fuel capacity for emergency landings. Langley's engineer-in-charge, Henry Reid, in a letter to NACA Headquarters written on April 29, 1946, noted that unless these requirements were met, the NACA "will not undertake to supply a pilot and operate the airplane." Reid asked NACA Headquarters to press the AAF to begin the construction of XS-1 fueling and handling facilities at Langley. Doing so would allow the transonic research flights to begin soon after the acceptance testing was completed. Despite the results of the Pinecastle glide flights, Langley personnel still intended to fly *their* XS-1 from *their* facility.

As for the XS-1 test plan itself, Williams outlined a two-phase approach on June 7, 1946, to Gough. The first phase would determine stability and control at high Mach numbers. Flight would be made in increasing Mach number increments, with eight flights made for each speed increment. A total of 48 "successful flights" would be made in the first phase to reach the XS-1's "operational limits." If a change in wing thickness was needed,

Melvin N. Gough, chief test pilot at Langley, was among the group of staff members who wanted the XS-1 to take off and land on the Langley runway and who opposed the air-launch technique, supporting development of the D-558-1. (NASA)

the entire sequence would have to be repeated, requiring another 48 flights. A "successful flight" was defined as one in which all systems functioned correctly, the pilot flew the mission exactly as planned, and all the instrumentation operated properly. The odds of this were about 50/50, indicating that as many as 100 flights might actually be needed.

The second phase would be to measure aerodynamic loads on the wings and tail and collect additional drag and performance data along with stability and control measurements. This phase would be much shorter, with only 16 flights being planned for each wing thickness. Reid forwarded the plan to NACA Headquarters on June 24, 1946. What was not in the plan was just as important. The XS-1 would be flown to its "operational limits." Williams never mentioned making supersonic flights. His plan was also a long, deliberate, step-by-step effort, requiring a year or more to complete.[60]

The differing viewpoints between Bell, the NACA, and the AAF were such that insignificant matters gave rise to anger. As 1946 ended and the first powered flights were made, both the AAF and Bell began to publicize the XS-1 project (even though the XS-1 was a classified project and was being flown at a restricted base). Stories were carried in the *New York Times* and later in *Time* magazine, which focused on Bell, the AAF, and Goodlin.

On December 12, 1946, the day after the *New York Times* article was published, Williams sent a letter to Soulé at Langley. Williams complained that the Bell-AAF publicity was about an airplane that, he claimed, did not really exist. They "should admit that the airplane was not designed as a supersonic aircraft but rather a high transonic airplane."[61] He continued that the supersonic capability was only because they were "forced" to use the B-29 launch plane to achieve the altitude and flight time. The issue of straight wings versus swept wings also raised Williams's ire. He dismissed comments that straight wings were on the XS-1 because it was not known if swept wings could be used "for the birds." The real reason was that no one knew much about swept wings when the aircraft was being designed.[62]

Both Williams and James Voyles, the civilian AAF representative for the XS-1 project, believed Stanley might go as far as to authorize Goodlin to "accidentally" exceed Mach 1. While the suspicions were unjustified, they reflected the sharp disagreements emerging among all players over the program's goals and future direction.

Even the test site still seemed subject to debate. In January 1947, a group of Ames researchers came to Muroc and were shown around by Gough. They were impressed by the XS-1 support facilities, including the loading pit. Lawrence Clousing of Ames commented about it, and Gough replied that a similar pit would be built at Langley. Clousing was surprised, but Gough told him Goodlin had landed the XS-1 on the paved Muroc runway. Operating the rocket plane from Langley, Gough said, would not be a problem.[63]

The NACA's plans for the XS-1 had also undergone a change from those in Williams's June 7, 1946, letter. NACA management expected to acquire one of the XS-1s in July 1947, which would mark the start of phase 1 of the three-phase research effort. The first phase was built around the XS-1 and the D-558-1 aircraft. Reflecting Stack's preferences, phase 1 involved only transonic flights. Phase 2, using the as yet unbuilt Bell XS-2 and Douglas D-558-2 swept-wing research aircraft, would reach speeds up to supersonic. Not until phase 3 would flights above Mach 1 be made by the NACA. The third phase would use the XS-3, a jet-powered aircraft with low-aspect straight wings, and a proposed third derivative of the D-558-1 (which was never built).[64]

Both Bell Aircraft and the AAF felt that the NACA approach was too slow and cautious, and indeed it was. Robert Stanley told Larry Bell that the NACA was only marking time until the D-558 was ready. Stanley also feared that the NACA would follow the earlier pattern of testing done with the P-80 and P-84 aircraft. Stanley believed the NACA planned to fly the XS-1 at altitudes of 20,000 to 30,000 feet until the pilot encountered trim changes or buffeting, at which point the NACA flights would stop. Stanley pointedly added, "At these low altitudes, they could do the same with a P-84 since it reaches Mach trouble at part[ial] throttle." Little wonder, then, that Stanley saw no point in testing the XS-1 in this manner.[65]

The AAF had its own issues with both Bell and the NACA. From the beginning, reaching Mach 1 was the Army's primary goal for the XS-1 project. This was to be accomplished in the shortest time possible. The NACA seemed, at best, reluctant to take on the challenge. Williams's initial flight plan and the later three-phase effort were both going to be slow, long-term efforts. In contrast, the AAF's focus was on the near term. The swept-wing XP-86, then under development, would be approaching supersonic speeds as early as late 1947, and the AAF had to have data on the possible risks it faced and needed the data sooner, not in a year or more.

The AAF also had management and monetary issues regarding Bell's efforts. The contractor's proposal included no specifics on the length of its project or any guarantees of results. Colonel Smith also objected to Goodlin's "bonus money." The practice itself was not unusual, and contractor test pilots had long been paid extra money for risky flights. Bell management and Goodlin had reached a "handshake agreement" that he would receive $150,000 for making the first supersonic flight in the XS-1, a not-unreasonable sum given the risks involved. But the AAF was suffering from the postwar funding cutbacks, and money for the XS-1 was running short. The AAF was unable to meet the proposed payment, and Smith would not agree to so large a pilot bonus.

Instead, he offered Bell a fixed-price contract, which included specific requirements Bell had to meet during the tests. At the same time, the NACA's perceived foot-dragging and continued objections to AAF decisions convinced Smith and other AAF personnel that they had to pursue a new approach to meet the AAF's research needs.[66]

The new AAF plan was a two-part complementary program. The AAF would reach Mach 1 in a minimum number of flights, using a service test pilot. The NACA would conduct a detailed, incremental flight research effort using its pilots. Bell's involvement would end once the company's original contractual obligations were completed.

By the spring of 1947, as the AAF was debating the future of the XS-1 flight program, the Flight Test Division personnel were confident that AAF test pilots were ready for the challenges that the XS-1 posed. Colonel Osmond J. Ritland recommended to Colonel Smith that the Flight Test Division be given responsibility for the supersonic test flights.[67] Based on Ritland's assessment, Smith asked Colonel Albert Boyd, chief of the Flight Test Division at Wright Field, if his pilots could undertake the accelerated flight test plan for the XS-1. Boyd's reply was, "You bet."

Bell turned down the proposed fixed-price contract, and on May 1, 1947, Smith notified AAF Headquarters of the company's decision, adding, "As a result of this notification, discussion is now underway with [the] view of having this program taken over by [the AAF Air Mobility Command] Flight Test Division."[68] Larry Bell appealed to General Carl Spaatz, the AAF commander, to reverse the decision (ultimately to no avail).

Following this interchange, the Flight Test Division began planning for the AAF program. The instrumentation on the XS-1 would be the minimum required for measuring the speeds and altitudes reached during its flights. As many as five glide and powered flights were planned just to reach Mach 0.8. While the AAF flights would be done in parallel with the NACA's effort, the Army would focus on achieving a Mach 1.1 flight in the shortest time possible. The first XS-1, fitted with the thinner 8-percent thickness-chord wings and 6-percent thickness-chord horizontal stabilizers, had a higher critical Mach number and speed capability than the thick-wing second XS-1 and was thus better suited for the AAF's accelerated assault on Mach 1. A key decision made by the AAF flight planners was to make the supersonic flights at high altitudes, thereby reducing the dynamic pressure the XS-1 would experience and minimizing the loads encountered should it experience abrupt transonic pitching and buffeting. Boyd and Lieutenant Colonel Fred Ascani now reviewed the records of the 125 pilots at the Flight Test Division and compiled a list of candidates to fly the plane.[69]

They selected Captain Charles E. "Chuck" Yeager as the primary XS-1 pilot. Yeager was then 24 years old, married, and a P-51 ace from World War II. While Yeager lacked both a college degree and formal engineering training, Boyd considered him the best instinctive pilot he had ever known. Yeager was the engineers' choice because he had an uncanny ability to return from a test flight and tell the engineers exactly what the airplane had done in response to what control input at what stage of the flight, in language the engineers immediately understood, and all after a flight was over, no matter what else had transpired during the flight. Yeager was clearly a standout, even among the very select group of test pilots composing the AAF's Flight Test Division at Wright Field.

For Yeager's backup, Boyd selected First Lieutenant Robert A. "Bob" Hoover, another outstanding intuitive fighter test pilot. The AAF's engineer-in-charge/project manager was test pilot Captain Jackie L. "Jack" Ridley, holder of a master's degree in aeronautical engineering from the California Institute of Technology, who could furnish the engineering support the two pilots required.[70]

On June 24, 1947, General Spaatz concurred with Smith's accelerated plan for XS-1 testing, and the following day, Yeager, Hoover, and Ridley joined personnel from the Flight Test Division and the Aircraft Projects Section to develop the accelerated test plan, preparing as well for a meeting with NACA personnel at the end of the month to finalize the two-phase test plan.

Langley's personnel proved less than enthusiastic in the change of program direction. In a June 13, 1947, letter to NACA Headquarters, Henry Reid indicated that Langley researchers had never liked the Bell Aircraft Corporation's XS-1 flight program and had only agreed to it in order to establish a good working relationship with the company, thereby ensuring they got the modifications that agency engineers wanted before finally accepting the aircraft. The Bell Aircraft Corporation's test program would also have shown that the XS-1 was safe—as far as the NACA was concerned—before the NACA flew the airplane. Neither of these goals really mattered now that Bell was out of the project. The result, Reid drily noted, "is considered unfortunate by the Laboratory."[71]

Reid was also skeptical about the AAF's plans. While promising NACA Headquarters that Langley would cooperate with the joint effort and that the agency had no objection to the AAF's taking over the project, he did want the AAF to acknowledge that Langley disagreed with the expedited flight plan and still preferred its own plan, as it would provide the largest amount of research data.[72]

It was this last point that turned out to be the redeeming element for the NACA in all this, although no one knew it at the time. In the rush to Mach 1, the AAF made it clear that the details were of secondary concern, while to the NACA those details were the only concern, and this had been the source of so much friction between the two groups. In time, knowing exactly what was happening all along the way turned out to be essential, at which point the NACA's methodical, ever-so-slow approach to increased speeds was its trump card. But in mid-1947, the logic of more rapidly accelerating the drive through Mach 1 was unassailable, particularly given the urgency of new high subsonic and transonic aircraft programs such as the XF-86.

AAF and NACA representatives met at Wright Field on June 30 and July 1, 1947, to discuss the coordination of their respective XS-1 plans. Colonel P.B. Klein opened the meeting by stating that the AAF planned to undertake an accelerated flight plan with the XS-1 to achieve speeds of Mach 1.1 at altitudes of 50,000 to 60,000 feet in the shortest possible time. AAF personnel were aware of Reid's comments and stressed that the XS-1 was a joint effort. Colonel Boyd emphasized that the Flight Test Division would "appreciate all of the assistance the NACA personnel could give them in conducting this program."[73] AAF personnel also asked Bell Aircraft for the help of Richard Frost, who had been part of the Bell XS-1 team. He had provided technical advice during the Bell flights and urged that all the AAF tests parties cooperate with him.

Hartley Soulé presented a summation of what had been learned thus far, the possible technical problems that lay ahead, and the NACA-recommended procedures that should be used. He noted that no significant compressibility effects on the XS-1 had been identified up to Mach 0.82. He added, "It is apparent from the flight and wind tunnel data that above M-0.85 large changes in stability and control and vibrational changes are to be expected. These have been anticipated in the Langley flights, which will be made at an altitude of 30,000 feet, and plans have been made to increase speed cautiously in small increments and to explore conditions at each increment thoroughly before proceeding to a higher speed."[74]

NACA researchers had concerns about the AAF's plan to make the tests at high altitudes, and Soulé focused on this in his remarks. He noted that the Mach 0.8 flight had been made at 30,000 feet, which resulted in a dynamic pressure on the XS-1 of about 250 pounds per square foot. "At 60,000 feet for the same Mach number of 0.8, the dynamic pressure would be about 65 pounds per square foot. It appears doubtful, therefore, that any inadvertent attitude to which the airplane might go as a result of stability and control changes could result in any structural failures at 60,000 feet."[75]

Reflecting how little was then known of transonic flying, Soulé cautioned, "The pilot should avoid prolonged glides to lower altitudes where the density is higher because conditions may change critically between the acceleration and deceleration phase of the flight, and consequently such glides may be extremely dangerous."[76] He also recommended that AAF personnel read several NACA flight-data reports, the results of wind tunnel testing, and other testing results.

He also provided AAF personnel with a copy of the NACA flight plan and asked for a copy of theirs in return. The Flight Test Division representatives told them no flight plan had been developed listing specific Mach numbers and altitudes. Decisions on such matters would not be made until the flights were underway and would be based on data analysis and Yeager's recommendations after each flight.

Aware of the rising tension in the room, Boyd assured Soulé and the rest of the NACA contingent that the Flight Test Division flight planning was to be guided by common sense, sound engineering experience, and a focus on safety. He stressed, however, that the flight plan would be progressive and brief; the goal remained to fly supersonic in the shortest time, and they would not be diverted from this objective. The official start of the AAF accelerated plan was July 10, 1947. The time required to reach Mach 1 was estimated to be 60 to 90 days. As events would prove, the high end of this estimate was right on the mark.[77]

Toward—and Beyond—the Unknown

Following briefings at Bell Aircraft, Yeager, Hoover, and Ridley traveled to Muroc, arriving there on July 27. Frost began a 4-day XS-1 "familiarization schooling" for the new arrivals. Frost later summed up the unknowns of supersonic flight in the summer of 1947. Regarding an impregnable sound barrier, "At best, I was ambivalent about it. In hindsight, people may well say that the so-called 'sound barrier' really didn't prove to be a barrier at all…but let me assure you, the conditions Chuck was facing going into those flights were very much a barrier in our minds at that time…. It wasn't within our power to give Chuck any real assurances about what might happen in any one of a multitude of different circumstances."[78]

As with Woolams and Goodlin, Yeager began by making glide flights in the first XS-1. Three of these were made between August 6 and August 9, 1947. Yeager commented that the little saffron speedster was "graceful, responsive, and beautiful to handle."[79]

Due to a shortage of B-29 parts, it was 3 weeks before the powered flights could begin. Yeager made his first powered flight on August 29 and reached Mach 0.85. This was followed by four more powered flights in September. Yeager increased the XS-1's speed in small increments, going from Mach 0.89 to 0.91, and then to Mach 0.92. In the process, Yeager was assessing the XS-1's stability and control, elevator and stabilizer effectiveness, and buffet. This continued with another two flights, on October 5 and 8. While there had been problems, the accelerated effort made good progress. The October 8 flight reached Mach 0.925.

The next flight was made on October 10, 1947, reaching an indicated airspeed of Mach 0.94 at 45,000 feet. Yeager then pulled back on the control column and was surprised when the aircraft failed to respond. The shock wave on the horizontal stabilizers had moved aft until it was on the elevator hinge line. The elevators had lost all effectiveness, and, as a result, Yeager had no pitch control of the XS-1. He wrote in his flight report, "[T]he control column could be moved to the limits of travel each way with little force and very slow response in airplane attitude."[80]

In fact, things were far less bleak than this report suggests. Aerodynamicists had predicted that the XS-1 would pitch up or down at Mach 1 and that without the elevator's pitch control, the aircraft might be lost. That had been, after all, the reason that the XS-1 had an adjustable horizontal tail installed in the first place. Significantly, NACA testing had already indicated that the XS-1 had to use the adjustable stabilizers in order to fly through the speed of sound. At the request of the AAF, the NACA had tested a $\frac{1}{16}$-scale Bell model of the XS-1 in the Langley 8-foot high-speed tunnel at speeds of up to Mach 0.945 and Reynolds numbers of 1.18×10^6.

The tests clearly revealed the steady decrease in elevator control effectiveness above Mach 0.87, Langley researcher Axel T. Mattson noted in a report issued in May 1947 (5 months before Yeager's flight): "*At a Mach number of 0.9, however, the airplane, because of an indicated diving tendency with loss and reversal in elevator control, will require the use of the stabilizer as a trim control.* Control by the use of the stabilizer is effective at least up to a Mach number of 0.93, the limit for these tests."[81] (Emphasis added.) So available data clearly indicated both the necessity for using stabilizer trim in the transonic region and the likelihood that it would resolve any pitch control problems. In any case, Yeager's associate Jack Ridley reassured the airman that by moving the stabilizers in very small increments of ¼ to ⅓ of a degree, Yeager could retain pitch control without the elevators.

A genuine surprise came from John Mayer while he was reducing the data from the flight. After correcting for errors in the XS-1's airspeed system, he found that the aircraft had reached a true airspeed of Mach 0.957. After working through the weekend, he again revised his analysis, concluding the XS-1's true airspeed was Mach 0.997 at 37,000 feet. Only the narrowest of margins still remained.

On the morning of October 14, 1947, the B-29 with the XS-1 attached underneath took off from the Muroc runway. Due to the loss of pitch control on the previous flight, NACA engineers told Yeager to limit his speed to Mach 0.96 unless he was certain he could safely fly faster. Yeager himself was not in the best condition as he climbed into the XS-1 cockpit. The previous weekend, he had fallen from a horse at aviatrix Florence "Pancho" Barnes's notorious Happy Bottom Riding Club and had broken two ribs. In pain, Yeager went to a civilian doctor in Rosamond to have them taped up, rather than go to an Air Force flight surgeon and risk being grounded. Ridley, by now a firm Yeager friend, knew about the mishap and cut a 10-inch length of broom handle to help Yeager lock the hatch from inside the rocket plane, despite his broken ribs.

The drop was made at 10:26 a.m., at an altitude of 20,000 feet and an airspeed of 250 mph. This was slower than expected, and Yeager had to lower the XS-1's nose to avoid stalling. He fired the four rocket chambers in rapid succession and began to accelerate and climb. He shut down two of the rocket chambers and began using the movable stabilizer for pitch control, finding it "very effective."

Yeager leveled out at approximately 42,000 feet and fired a third rocket cylinder. The XS-1 accelerated rapidly to an indicated airspeed of Mach 0.98. The Machmeter needle fluctuated and jumped off scale. There was no violent buffeting. The aircraft did not pitch up or down. There were no indications that something unusual had happened. Yeager held the speed for 20 seconds before shutting off the engine. Yeager radioed, "Ridley! Make another note.

There's something wrong with this Machmeter. It's gone screwy!" Ridley replied, "If it is, we'll fix it. Personally, I think you're seeing things."[82] NACA personnel analyzed the flight data and determined that the XS-1 had reached a speed of Mach 1.06. The task had taken 96 days since the AAF took over the program on July 10, 1947. Within hours, the achievement was classified, and no public announcement was made.[83] Not quite three months later, at the express direction of Air Force Secretary Stuart Symington, the Army Air Forces held a secret conference at Wright Field to present the results of the program to a select audience of the Nation's leading designers, engineers, and aeronautical researchers.[84] NACA's Muroc Flight Test Unit harvested the technical results of the flight in a series of analytical reports issued over the next several years, buttressing the quick look afforded by the Air Force's accelerated flight test program.[85]

Beyond Yeager's landmark achievement awaited a new series of unknowns. There were many design ideas about how a supersonic airplane should be configured. However, there was little solid information and, with wind tunnels still unable to provide reliable data, few means to find out more. There remained an interrelated series of problems in aerodynamics, propulsion, and aircraft configurations to bedevil and bother the aeronautical community in the years ahead. Nevertheless, if there were many challenges and unknowns ahead, there was one major bedrock accomplishment: the myth of an impenetrable barrier had been forever vanquished.

Endnotes

1. Opening quote from Louis Rotundo, *Into the Unknown: The X-1 Story* (Washington, DC: Smithsonian Institution Press, 1994), p. 6.

2. James R. Hansen, *Engineer in Charge: A History of the Langley Aeronautical Laboratory, 1917–1958* (Washington, DC: NASA SP-4305, 1987), p. 253; Richard P. Hallion, *Supersonic Flight: Breaking the Sound Barrier and Beyond—The Story of the Bell X-1 and Douglas D-558* (London: Brassey's, 1997), p. x. When asked about these stories, John McTigue, a former X-15 engineer, recalled reading such claims in newspaper articles and letters to the editor circa 1944–45. The stuck-voice story was false, as the air in the cockpit was not moving with respect to the pilot. The time-reversal story represents a misunderstanding of the theory of relativity. As an object nears the speed of light, time slows down. The crew of a starship traveling at nearly the speed of light would experience a flight as lasting only a few months. Simultaneously, back on Earth, years, decades, or even centuries would pass. In no case, however, can time actually be "reversed."

3. F.W. Caldwell and E.N. Fales, "Wind Tunnel Studies in Aerodynamic Phenomena at High Speeds," Report No. 83 (NACA, 1920), p. 59.

4. Ibid., pp. 60, 77, 86, 89.

5. L.J. Briggs, G.F. Hull, and H.L. Dryden, "Aerodynamic Characteristics of Airfoils at High Speeds," Report No. 207 (NACA, 1924), pp. 465, 478.

6. L.J. Briggs and H.L. Dryden, "Pressure Distribution Over Air Foils at High Speeds," Report No. 255 (NACA, 1926), p. 555.

7. L.J. Briggs and H.L. Dryden, "Aerodynamic Characteristics of Twenty-Four Airfoils at High Speeds," Report No. 319 (NACA, 1929), pp. 327–328, 345–346.

8. Ibid.

9. L.J. Briggs and H.L. Dryden, "Aerodynamic Characteristics of Circular-Arc Airfoils at High Speeds," Report No. 365 (NACA, 1931), pp. 67, 69.

10. NASA, "The National Advisory Committee for Aeronautics: Tracing NASA's 95-Year-Old Roots," *http://www.nasa.gov/centers/ames/news/features/2010/95_anniversary_prt.htm*, updated March 3, 2010.

11. Hansen, *Engineer in Charge*, pp. xxviii, 2, 126–133.

12. Eric Schatzberg, *Wings of Wood, Wings of Metal* (Princeton: Princeton University Press, 1998). This book looks at the social factors, as

opposed to engineering requirements, behind the switch from wooden construction toward all-metal aircraft. These include a perception that metal was "modern," while wood was a "preindustrial" material. Another factor was the influence of the U.S. military on aircraft design.

13. For a discussion of these, see G. Geoffrey Smith, *Gas Turbines and Jet Propulsion for Aircraft* (New York: Aircraft Books Inc., 1946), pp. 34–50. For the jet engine more generally, see Edward W. Constant II, *The Origins of the Turbojet Revolution* (Baltimore: Johns Hopkins University Press, 1980), pp. 63, 64, 70–72, 77, 89, 93, 95; and Robert Schlaifer and S.D. Heron's *Development of Aircraft Engines and Fuels* (Boston: Harvard Business School, 1950). The best-known of these hybrid concepts was the "Campini engine," after the Italian engineer Secondo Campini, who successfully flew one in 1940–41, but many other concepts for such engines existed as well. In England, the term "motorjet" was also used. For Campini's work, see Gregory Alegre, *Campini Caproni*, no. 5 of the Ali d'Italia series (Turin: La Bancarella Aeronautica, n.d.).

14. For American work, see James St. Peter, *The History of Gas Turbine Development in the United States…A Tradition of Excellence* (Atlanta, GA: International Gas Turbine Institute of the American Society of Mechanical Engineers, 1999).

15. Edgar Buckingham, "Jet Propulsion for Airplanes," Report No. 159 (NACA, 1923), p. 85.

16. For a particularly useful introduction to the history and development of the jet engine, see Walter J. Boyne and Donald S. Lopez, eds. *The Jet Age: Forty Years of Jet Aviation.* Washington, DC: National Air and Space Museum in association with the Smithsonian Institution Press, 1979.

17. Margaret Connor, *Hans von Ohain: Elegance in Flight* (Reston, VA: American Institute of Aeronautics and Astronautics, 2001).

18. For Whittle's view of his work, see his autobiographical *Jet: The Story of a Pioneer* (New York: Philosophical Library, 1954) and John Golley's (in association with Whittle and with technical assistance from Bill Gunston) semiautobiographical *Whittle: The True Story* (Washington, DC: Smithsonian Institution Press, 1987). See also John Grierson's memoir-history *Jet Flight* (London: Samson Low, Marston & Co., Ltd., 1944); and Andrew Nahum's thought-provoking *Frank Whittle: Invention of the Jet* (Duxford, U.K.: Icon Books, 2004).

19. For the impact (in both directions) of turbojet development and combat requirements, see Sterling Michael Pavelec, *The Jet Race and the Second World War* (Annapolis, MD: Naval Institute Press, 2007).
20. Hansen, *Engineer in Charge*, pp. 230–231.
21. Hansen, *Engineer in Charge*, pp. 231–232. Dr. Vannevar Bush's interest in the Jeep engine concept also reflected his own technological conservatism and academic mindset. Despite his accomplishments as a scientist, he endorsed the same jet concept the NACA was studying. For the record, Bush consistently displayed a pattern of being too quick to dismiss the possibilities of technological breakthroughs. In late 1945, for example, he told a congressional committee that a long-range rocket armed with a nuclear weapon was impractical and that the Congress and the American people should leave it out of their thinking. In 1949, he predicted it would be many years before the USSR would build an A-bomb. The Soviets tested their first A-bomb that year.
22. Ibid., p. 260; Hallion, *Supersonic Flight*, pp. 19–20.
23. Hansen, *Engineer in Charge*, p. 244.
24. Ibid., pp. 236–245; Hallion, *Supersonic Flight*, pp. 18–21. The XP-59A itself was an example of what Jacobs was describing. It was initially intended to evolve into an operational combat aircraft rather than remain a technology demonstrator. The goal was to have a combat aircraft ready sooner than first building an experimental aircraft, followed by an operational fighter. (Much like the Durand Committee had proposed for Jacobs's research aircraft.) While the turbojets were revolutionary, the XP-59A's airframe was a late-1930s high-drag design. This limited it to a top speed of 389 mph. As a result, the few P-59s built were used as jet trainers to introduce pilots into the higher-performance Lockheed P-80A that succeeded it.
25. John V. Becker, *The High-Speed Frontier: Case Studies of Four NACA Programs, 1920–1950* (Washington, DC: NASA SP-445, 1980), p. 90.
26. Hansen, *Engineer in Charge*, p. 260.
27. Hallion, *Supersonic Flight*, p. 22.
28. Ibid., pp. 20–23.
29. Ibid., pp. 24–25.
30. Hansen, *Engineer in Charge*, pp. 260–261.
31. Becker, *The High-Speed Frontier*, pp. 91–92.
32. Becker, *The High-Speed Frontier*, p. 91; Hansen, *Engineer in Charge*, pp. 271–273. "XS-1" continued to be used into 1948, when the Air Force revised its designation system. The "S" was dropped for all of

the research aircraft (XS-1, XS-2, XS-3, and XS-4), and they became the X-1, X-2, X-3, and X-4.

33. Hallion, *Supersonic Flight*, pp. 31–32, 61, quotes the Hyatt memo at length, which was USN Bureau of Aeronautics AER-E-225-AH, "Proposed High-Speed Research Airplane" (September 22, 1944). See also Rotundo, *Into the Unknown*, p. 21; and Hansen, *Engineer in Charge*, pp. 273–274.

34. Ibid., pp. 65–67, 69, 70; Hansen, *Engineer in Charge*, pp. 290–291. Unlike the AAF or the Air Force, the U.S. Navy never had a specific designation for a purely experimental aircraft. Until September 1962, the Navy and Air Force had separate aircraft designation systems, even for the same aircraft.

35. Hansen, *Engineer in Charge*, pp. 275–279; Hallion, *Supersonic Flight*, pp. 71–72. Stack and Gilruth also jointly recommended that the thickness-chord ratio of the XS-1's horizontal stabilizer be less than that of the wing. This was to prevent them from both experiencing shock wave formation at the same time, with attendant changes such as turbulence, loss of control effectiveness, etc. They also recommended attaching the horizontal stabilizer midway up the vertical fin to avoid a loss of effectiveness due to the wing wake impinging upon it. A final joint recommendation was to have the horizontal stabilizer be adjustable, effectively making the combined stabilizer and elevator surface almost an "all-moving tail." As an airplane's speed increased, the shock wave moved aft on the horizontal stabilizer. When it reached the hinge line of the movable elevator, the control surface would be blanked out and the pilot would lose pitch control to such a degree that, in many cases, he could freely move the elevator without his control inputs having any effect upon flight path control. To avoid this, the stabilizer's angle could be changed by the pilot, giving a measure of control. The same design approach was also applied to the D-558-1 and the Air Force's F-86E Sabre jet fighter. Later supersonic aircraft such as the American F-100A and Soviet MiG-19 had a one-all-moving horizontal stabilizer.

36. Hallion, *Supersonic Flight*, pp. 52–53.

37. Hansen, *Engineer in Charge*, p. 288.

38. Ibid., p. 288.

39. Ibid., pp. 288–289.

40. Rotundo, *Into the Unknown*, p. 31.

41. Ibid., pp. 35–36. Stan Smith and Bell Aircraft management had a private reason for rejecting Muroc Army Air Field in California.

The West Coast was the home, by the mid-1940s, of many U.S. aviation contractors. Had the XS-1 gone to Muroc, many of the engineers might have decided to forego the Buffalo winters for the California sunshine.

42. Robert T. Jones, "Wing Plan Form for High-Speed Flight," in *Collected Works of Robert T. Jones*, TM X-3334 (Washington, DC: NASA, 1976), p. 379.

43. Ibid., p. 379; Richard P. Hallion, "Lippisch, Gluhareff, and Jones: The Emergence of the Delta Planform and the Origins of the Sweptwing in the United States," *Aerospace Historian* 26, no. 1 (spring 1979), passim; Hansen, *Engineer in Charge*, pp. 282–283; MSN Encarta, "Sound Barrier," *http://uk.encarta.msn. com/text_781533139__3/Sound-Barrier.html*, accessed November 30, 2009 (cached page). The development of Robert T. Jones's wing planform paper shows the complex process by which technological and scientific breakthroughs are made. It started with Jones's efforts to develop a lift theory for a dart-shaped missile. This, in turn, led Jones to a pair of very different studies. The first, by Max Munk, was of low-speed airflow around dirigibles, while the other, by Hsue-Shen Tsien, was on supersonic airflow around spinning projectiles, which indicated a lack of compressibility effects on these bodies. When Jones factored Tsien's equations into his calculations, it appeared that very slender wings would also show no compressibility. Next, Jones recalled another paper by Munk, which dealt with the effects on aircraft stability due to dihedral and wing sweep. This was the first paper to describe the basic effects of sweepback on a wing. But because it only dealt with low subsonic speeds, the implications for transonic and supersonic flight went unrealized. Once Jones incorporated Munk's second paper into the calculations, he was able to create a general theory that was valid for all wing-sweep angles.

What Jones *did not* know was also important. Adolf Busemann, a German aerodynamicist, was among those giving papers at the Volta Congress on High-Speed Aeronautics in 1935. Part of his highly theoretical paper dealt with "arrow wings" as a means of reducing wave drag. Busemann's theory did not include the idea of positioning the wing behind the Mach line, however. As a result, the cross flow over the wing was still supersonic. Three American scientists attended the Volta Congress—Eastman Jacobs, Hugh Dryden, and Theodore von Kármán. None of them viewed Busemann's idea as important. Not until after Jones had written an initial draft of his paper was a 1942 British translation of Busemann's paper found in the Langley library. Jones incorporated a citation listing it in the revised text. See Richard P. Hallion, "Sweep and Swing: Reshaping the Wing for the Jet and Rocket Age," in Richard P. Hallion, ed., *NASA's Contributions to Aeronautics, vol. 1: Aerodynamics, Structures, Propulsion, Controls, SP-2010-570-Vol 1* (Washington, DC: National Aeronautics and Space Administration, 2010), pp. 5–17.

Of the three papers by Munk and Tsien, written in the 1920s and 1930s, only one was related to supersonic flight. Despite this, they played a role in Jones's development of this swept-wing paper. This influence was due to Jones's ability to realize their relevance to the problems he was investigating, despite their subject matter. The use of swept wings on the German Me 262 jet fighter and the Me 163 rocket fighter also had no influence on Jones's paper, as these aircraft were subsonic and the swept wings were used primarily to maintain their center of gravity. Indeed, the Me 163 had profoundly poor— even dangerous—high-speed stability and control characteristics induced by its tailless swept-wing planform, as discussed subsequently in the chapter on the Northrop X-4 Bantam.

44. Hansen, *Engineer in Charge,* p. 284.
45. Ibid., p. 284.
46. Ibid., pp. 105–107, 284–285.
47. Ibid., pp. 281–284; Hallion, *Supersonic Flight*, p. 45.
48. Hansen, *Engineer in Charge*, pp. 284–285.
49. Ibid., pp. 289–290; Hallion, *Supersonic Flight*, pp. 46–47.
50. Rotundo, *Into the Unknown*, pp. 43–44.
51. Ibid., p. 50.
52. Ibid., pp. 51–59, 62. Langley's location near the ocean and nearby rivers, as well as its humid climate, all ruled out operating the XS-1 from the site. Pinecastle had better weather than Langley, but this still interfered with the glide flights. Given the poor visibility from the XS-1 cockpit and the landing accidents during the Pinecastle glide flights, it seems the loss of the airplanes would have been nearly certain had the flights operated from Langley's runway.
53. Hallion, *Supersonic Flight*, p. 91.
54. John Ball, Jr., *Edwards: Flight Test Center of the USAF* (New York: Duell, Sloan and Pearce, 1962), pp. 38–41.
55. For the story of this remarkable engine, see Frank H. Winter, "'Black Betsy': The 6000C4 Rocket Engine, 1945–1989," a paper presented at the 23rd Symposium on the History of Astronautics, 40th International Astronautical Congress of the International Astronautical Federation, Malaga, Spain, October 1989.

56. Hallion, *Supersonic Flight*, pp. 89–91.

57. Ibid., pp. 91–92, 98–102; Richard P. Hallion and Michael H. Gorn, *On the Frontier: Experimental Flight at NASA Dryden* (Washington, DC: Smithsonian Books, 2003), pp. 21–24.

58. Rotundo, *Into the Unknown*, pp. 102–103.

59. Ibid., pp. 118–119.

60. Ibid., pp. 104–109, 120, 125–126; James O. Young, *Meeting the Challenge of Supersonic Flight* (Edwards Air Force Base, CA: Air Force Flight Test Center History Office, 1997), p. 35.

61. Rotundo, *Into the Unknown*, p. 151.

62. Ibid., p. 152.

63. Ibid., p. 162. The reality was that the airplane Williams described was the one that did not exist. The turbopump would not be ready for several more years, no provisions for a reserve fuel supply were ever included in the aircraft, and a ground takeoff capability was impractical and unsafe.

64. Ibid., pp. 39, 181.

65. Ibid., pp. 191, 193–194; Young, *Meeting the Challenge of Supersonic Flight*, p. 36.

66. Young, *Meeting the Challenge of Supersonic Flight*, pp. 34–37.

67. Ibid., pp. 38–39.

68. Ibid., p. 40.

69. Young, *Meeting the Challenge of Supersonic Flight*, pp. 39–41.

70. Ibid., pp. 41–42.

71. Rotundo, pp. 230–231.

72. Ibid., pp. 230–231.

73. Young, *Meeting the Challenge of Supersonic Flight*, p. 45.

74. Ibid.

75. Ibid.

76. Ibid.

77. Ibid., pp. 45–46.

78. Ibid., p. 47.

79. Ibid., p. 48.

80. James O. Young, *Supersonic Symposium: The Men of Mach 1*, Air Force Special Code (AFSC) Special Study, September 1999, p. 219.

81. Axel T. Mattson, "Force and Longitudinal Control Characteristics of a 1/16-scale Model of the Bell XS-1 Transonic Research Airplane at High Mach Numbers," NACA RM L7A03 (May 21, 1947), p. 9–10. All NACA Research Memorandums in this book can be found on the NASA Technical Reports Server (*http://ntrs.nasa.gov/search.jsp*) or within Dryden Flight Research Center's archives.

82. From flight transcript, reprinted in Young, *Meeting the Challenge of Supersonic Flight*, p. 73.

83. Hallion, *Supersonic Flight*, pp. 113–119, 124–125; Rotundo, *Into the Unknown*, pp. 274–279; Young, *Meeting the Challenge of Supersonic Flight*, pp. 52–59. The secret held until December 22, 1947, when the *Los Angeles Times* carried a front-page story. The headline read, "U.S. Mystery Plane Tops Speed of Sound." The story had a number of significant errors: Captain Charles "Yaeger" had broken the sound barrier at 70,000 feet, NACA research pilots Herbert Hoover (true) and Howard Lilly (false) had also flown supersonic, and Goodlin had made the first 30 flights (false). Not until June 15, 1948, was the flight officially confirmed in a joint press conference by General Hoyt S. Vandenberg, Air Force Chief of Staff, and Dr. Hugh L. Dryden, NACA Director of Research. On December 17, 1948, the Robert J. Collier Trophy, aviation's most prestigious award, was given to the XS-1 project. Its citation read: "To Robert Stack, Research Scientist, NACA, for pioneering research to determine the physical laws affecting supersonic flight, and for his conception of transonic research airplanes; to Lawrence D. Bell, President, Bell Aircraft Corporation, for design and construction of the special research aircraft X-1; and to Captain Charles E. Yeager, U.S. Air Force, who, with that airplane, on October 14, 1947, first achieved human flight faster than sound."

It is ironic that Stack, who preferred the D-558 over the X-1 and who objected to its propulsion system, its launch method, and its test site, should win the Collier Trophy for its achievements. In contrast, Ezra Kotcher, whose "Mach 0.999 study" and whose support of a rocket engine over a turbojet led directly to the X-1, was most unfortunately ignored, at least in the Collier citation.

84. The symposium papers were subsequently published by the USAF as *Air Force Supersonic Research Airplane XS-1 Report No. 1* (Wright Field, Dayton, OH: USAF Air Materiel Command, January 9, 1948). This historic report was subsequently reprinted and reissued in October 1997 by Richard P. Hallion, then the Air Force Historian at the Air Force History and Museums Program, Headquarters Air Force, Washington, DC, in commemoration of the 50th anniversary of the first piloted supersonic flight.

85. These reports included the following: Ellwyn E. Angle and Euclid C. Holleman, "Determination of Longitudinal Stability of the Bell X-1 Airplane from Transient Responses at Mach Numbers Up to 1.12 at Lift Coefficients of 0.3 and 0.6," NACA RM L50I06a (November 7,

1950); De E. Beeler and John P. Mayer, "Measurements of the Wing and Tail Loads During the Acceptance Tests of Bell XS-1 Research Airplane," NACA RM L7L12 (April 13, 1948); L. Robert Carman and John R. Carden, "Lift and Drag Coefficients for the Bell X-1 Airplane (8-Percent-Thick Wing) in Power-Off Transonic Flight," NACA RM L51E08 (June 25, 1951); Hubert M. Drake and John R. Carden, "Elevator-Stabilizer Effectiveness and Trim of the X-1 Airplane to a Mach Number of 1.06," NACA RM L50G20 (November 1, 1950); Hubert M. Drake, Harold R. Goodman, and Herbert H. Hoover, "Preliminary Results of NACA Transonic Flights of the XS-1 Airplane with 10-Percent-Thick Wing and 8-Percent-Thick Horizontal Tail," NACA RM L8I29 (October 13, 1948); Hubert M. Drake, Milton D. McLaughlin, and Harold R. Goodman, "Results Obtained During Accelerated Transonic Tests of the Bell XS-1 Airplane in Flights to a Mach Number of 0.92," NACA RM L8A05a (April 19, 1948); Harold R. Goodman and Hubert M. Drake, "Results Obtained During Extension of U.S. Air Force Transonic-Flight Tests of XS-1 Airplane," NACA RM L8I28 (November 16, 1948); Harold R. Goodman and Roxanah B. Yancey, "The Static-Pressure Error of Wing and Fuselage Airspeed Installations of the X-1 Airplanes in Transonic Flight," NACA RM L9G22 (August 12, 1949); Walter C. Williams and De E. Beeler, "Results of Preliminary Flight Tests of the XS-1 Airplane (8-Percent Wing) to a Mach Number of 1.25," NACA RM L8A23a (April 6, 1948); and Walter C. Williams, Charles M. Forsyth, and Beverly P. Brown, "General Handling-Qualities Results Obtained During Acceptance Flight Tests of the Bell X-1 Airplane," NACA RM L8A09 (April 19, 1948).

The third D-558-1 parked on the South Base ramp with three ground personnel. The Skystreak was one of two concepts for how best to gain data on transonic flight. It represented a traditional design, had straight wings, and was jet-powered, with a top speed just below Mach 1. It was funded in part by the Navy and built by Douglas to NACA specifications. In contrast, the Army Air Forces XS-1 was rocket-powered, with a top speed well above Mach 1. (NASA)

CHAPTER 2

Flying Test Tube:
The Douglas D-558-1 Skystreak

The Model D-558 gives the impression of being an outstandingly excellent job of design and engineering, and a very sound airplane for research purposes....
—Captain Frederick M. Trapnell, U.S. Navy[1]

If the D-558-1 could have been promoted in the early forties, it would have been timely. But coming into the flight picture as it did in 1947, it was unnecessary.
—John V. Becker, NACA

The Douglas D-558-1 Skystreak always flew in the shadow of the Bell XS-1.[2] If radical by the standards of conventional propeller-driven airplanes, then by the standards of the rocket-powered XS-1 the Skystreak was a very conservative design, reflecting the NACA's desire for a turbojet-powered research airplane that could effectively "loiter" in the transonic regime, nibbling at the sonic frontier. If overshadowed by its flashier rocket-powered contemporary, it admirably fulfilled the expectations of the NACA, playing a significant role in the early years of high-speed research with its capability to undertake a wide range of research activities over a 6-year period, effectively "freeing up" its higher-performance rocket-powered rivals to explore the frontiers of the supersonic regime while it generated detailed information on the high-subsonic and transonic.

In performance, appearance, mode of operation, and systems, the D-558-1 appeared little different in design from the first generation of U.S. jets. Chief engineer Edward H. Heinemann, L. Eugene Root, Kermit Van Every, A.M.O. Smith, Robert C. Donovan, R.G. Smith, and the other members of the Douglas design team faced a number of challenges if the D-558-1 was to be capable of accomplishing the research goals that the NACA and the Navy's Bureau of Aeronautics had set for it.[3]

The first of these tasks was to minimize the fuselage's frontal area so as to maintain a *high fineness ratio*, the ratio of the fuselage's length to its diameter. Drop-body tests showed that a high fineness ratio reduced drag at transonic speeds. At the same time, the fuselage shape had to prevent airflow from being accelerated to supersonic speeds, which would cause a flow-disrupting shock wave to form in the vicinity of the wing. To address these issues, the best solutions were also the simplest.

The team selected a cylindrical fuselage, one with a diameter just big enough to hold the TG-180 turbojet engine; indeed, afterwards, A.M.O. Smith (who determined the wing planform and airfoil section and did much of the work on the aerodynamics of the nose inlet) recalled the design process as "a case of wrapping the smallest airplane around the largest jet engine that was available."[4] This shape also minimized airflow acceleration over the wing. A final design requirement was that of the fuselage/wing fillet, which needed a critical Mach number as high as that of the wing but which would not exhibit poor stall characteristics. Meeting this specification would require considerable NACA wind tunnel testing.

The wings used the NACA's 65-110 airfoil (a symmetrical "65-series" wing section with a thickness-chord ratio of 10 percent), as it had a high critical Mach number, had good high-speed characteristics, and had been used previously by the Douglas engineers for their A-26 medium bomber, the highest-performance twin-engine medium bomber developed during the Second World War. As with the XS-1, the Douglas team employed a straight-wing planform. But in contrast to the relatively high aspect ratio of the XS-1's wings, the D-558-1 had low-aspect-ratio wings (a short wingspan with a wide chord). Further, all the D-558-1s employed a 10-percent thickness-chord section, not the lower 8-percent thickness-chord section employed on the first of the XS-1s. The horizontal stabilizer was similar to that on the XS-1. It had a thinner airfoil than did the wing (6 percent for the stabilizer versus 10 percent on the wing) and was mounted higher up on the vertical tail, with the forward section made movable to retain control at high transonic speeds. The pilot had a switch on the control wheel for moving the stabilizer up and down.[5]

The D-558-1 structural design was described by Heinemann as being comparatively conventional and straightforward. It did have some unusual features, however, that were different from those of contemporary aircraft structures. In an era dominated by aluminum skinning, the Skystreak's fuselage skin was a magnesium alloy slab 1/10-inch thick, which eliminated the need for formers or stringers, both used in conventional fuselage designs, thus ensuring a light yet rigid and strong fuselage tube, saving at least 60 pounds in structural weight over a conventional rib-stringer-skinning design. The only internal reinforcement used was at points of concentrated structural loads. As a result, the D-558-1's internal volume was relatively large.

The wings and the tail were of standard aluminum construction, using high-strength alloy in a conventional rib and spar matrix. To ensure that their external skins were as smooth as possible, sheet-metal fabricators and craftspeople attached the fuselage and wing skins to rigid contoured frames and then attached the internal framework directly to the skin.

The thin wings posed several design problems. First was fuel capacity, for the aircraft had to carry enough fuel for a research flight lasting about 30 minutes from takeoff through landing. The solution designers chose was to make the front half of the wing into an integral fuel tank, a so-called "wet wing." Technicians sealed the wing interior using a synthetic rubber compound, which required 5 weeks to cure and dry. Once ready, the tank formed by this process held 230 gallons of kerosene fuel. To extend flight time and altitude, a pair of 50-gallon tip tanks could also be carried, which when used added another half hour to flight duration (and which were, in fact, employed at various points during the test programs flown on the three Skystreak aircraft).

The D-558-1 had tricycle landing gear, but, here, too, the thin wing created a challenge. While the nosewheel could retract into the forward fuselage behind the cockpit, the tightly packed fuselage—occupied by the engine, controls, instrumentation, and other systems—lacked any room for the twin main wheels. Accordingly, the only place for the main landing gear was inside the wings, but, given the thin airfoil, the wheels had to be much thinner and smaller than would have been typical for an aircraft of the D-558-1's size. Douglas engineers approached the Goodrich Corporation to produce special 20-by-4.4, 8-ply nylon tires. Originally, the tires were intended to operate at 230 pounds per square inch (psi), though this was later reduced to a more forgiving 175 psi. As Heinemann later noted, "It was realized from the outset that this wheel and tire size was much smaller than desired for the load, but the selection was considered justified due to the serious effect larger wheels would have had upon the size of the airplane."[6]

Additionally, Douglas engineers had the issue of pilot escape from the D-558-1 at high speeds to consider. Aeromedical experts were asked about escape options and indicated they doubted a human could withstand a normal bailout at high speeds. The air blast was considered too great for a pilot to survive, and the acceleration needed to propel both an ejection seat and the pilot clear of the vertical tail was in excess of human anatomical limits.

The approach taken was to use a capsule escape system. The capsule's nose was attached to the fuselage at four points. In an emergency, the pilot would pull a handle to release the four attachments, freeing the nose section. Once it fell away and slowed, the pilot pulled a second handle that dropped the seat back, then fell out of the nose section and opened his parachute. Similar capsules were later fitted to the D-558-2 and the Bell X-2 research aircraft. In both X-2 crashes, the capsules proved ineffective, and both pilots died.[7]

To aid optical tracking from the ground, the D-558-1 was painted insignia red (though this was subsequently changed to white, as the red actually made the aircraft far less visible against the dark blue Mojave sky). The aircraft carried standard U.S. "star-and-bar" markings, and the words "Douglas Skystreak" were painted on the nose in a stylized typeface suggesting speed and modernity. With its red paint finish, cigarette-like cylindrical fuselage, nose inlet, and rounded silver jet nozzle, the aircraft was not surprisingly nicknamed the "Crimson Test Tube."[8]

"The arrangement of the airplane was quite conventional," Heinemann subsequently recalled, "as it was believed the best way to obtain the largest amount of useful data in the shortest period of time was to employ only design features that were well known and did not involve uncertainty."[9] He also noted, "It is considered necessary that all of the high speed aerodynamic data be obtained in level flight instead of vertical or near vertical dives as in the past."[10] These stipulations were a reflection of the NACA's viewpoint, goals, and influence.

First Flights and Speed Records

In January of 1947, the D-558-1 #1 (Bureau of Aeronautics number [BuNo] 37970) was completed and several months of ground testing was begun. Two trucks then transported the disassembled aircraft from the Douglas plant at El Segundo over the San Gabriel Mountains to the Mojave Desert and Muroc Army Air Field. After reaching Muroc on April 10, the aircraft was reassembled, the engine and other systems were tested, and preparations were made for the first flight.

Veteran Douglas test pilot Eugene F. "Gene" May, who had flown for the company since 1941, was selected for the initial flights. The airplane was ready by April 15 for the first flight. May took off from the lakebed and immediately ran into trouble. The TG-180 engine suffered a partial power loss, and May landed straight ahead on the lakebed. When he applied the brakes, the left brake disintegrated and he had to hold the left rudder to keep rolling forward in a straight line. On April 21, similar problems plagued the second attempt, grounding the D-558-1 until the end of May 1947.

Landing gear problems were encountered on the next six flights, with the gear either not retracting or locking in place. Even so, by the 12th flight, on July 12, 1947, the aircraft had demonstrated satisfactory low-speed flight characteristics. Douglas engineers began modifications needed for transonic research flights. The low-speed, clear-bubble canopy was replaced with a V-shaped, reinforced high-speed hooded windscreen. The new canopy design was found by several pilots to be too small to allow them to wear a helmet, and they flew without one. With the work complete, the aircraft made an airspeed calibration check on its 13th flight.

May now began a buildup to transonic speeds, beginning with the 14th flight made on July 17. During the course of the next six flights, May reached a speed of Mach 0.85 on August 5. During this same period, the second D-558-1

From left to right, Eugene May (Douglas Aircraft) and Howard Lilly (NACA research pilot) pose in front of the second D-558-1, which was destroyed in a crash on May 3, 1948. Lilly was killed in the accident, the first NACA research pilot lost in the line of duty. (NASA)

(BuNo 37971) was completed and delivered to Muroc Army Air Field, where it was to be used by NACA pilots. The next step, however, was an attempt at the world's airspeed record.[11]

The Navy was interested in using the second D-558-1 to best the existing airspeed record of 615.778 mph, set by British Royal Air Force Group Captain E.M. Donaldson in a modified Gloster Meteor in September 1946. The rules for an official record recognized by the Fédération Aéronautique Internationale (FAI) required that an aircraft fly at an altitude below 250 feet (75 meters) and make four passes along a 1.864-mile (3-kilometer) course. While the discussions were underway, Donaldson's record had fallen to the AAF. Colonel Albert Boyd broke the record on June 17, 1947, in a modified P-80R jet, reaching a speed of 623.738 mph, the last speed record set by the service before it transformed into the independent United States Air Force in September of that year. The higher speed increased the challenges both the airplane and pilots would have to overcome.

With the second D-558-1 delivered and test-flown, the way was clear for the record attempts. Navy Commander Turner F. Caldwell made the first record attempt on August 20, 1947, in the first D-558-1 and achieved an average speed in the four passes of 640.663 mph, breaking the standing record by 16.924 mph. Marine Major Marion E. Carl's turn came on August 25. He had an idea for a way to squeeze a little more speed from the second D-558-1.

On Caldwell's flight, the TG-180 engine had produced 100 percent rotations per minute (rpm) on the ground, but power readings dropped to 98 percent rpm once he took off. Carl convinced the Douglas ground crew to raise the engine's rpm to 102 percent on the ground. As expected, the same rpm drop occurred after takeoff, leaving Carl with 100 percent rpm in flight. When his four passes were averaged, he had achieved 650.796 mph, raising the record by 10.133 mph, small but enough.[12]

With the world speed record now in Navy/Marine hands, attention shifted back to the test-and-research effort. The first D-558-1 resumed its contractor flights, piloted by May. Another 18 flights were flown before it was turned over to the NACA on October 23, 1947, a week after Chuck Yeager and the rival XS-1 had broken the sound barrier.

The NACA D-558-1, the second of the three Skystreaks, had not been fitted with data instrumentation, so the first step in preparing the aircraft was to install a standard NACA recording package, overseen by the Muroc Flight Test Unit's chief instrumentation and telemetry tracking engineer, Gerald M. "Gerry" Truszynski:[13]

Instrumentation	Data Collected
Airspeed-altitude recorder	Indicated airspeed and pressure altitude
Three-component accelerometer	Normal, longitudinal, and transverse acceleration
Angular-velocity recorder	Rolling velocity
Sideslip-angle recorder	Sideslip measurement
Wheel-force recorder	Aileron and elevator forces
Pedal-force recorder	Rudder-pedal force
Control-surface position recorder	Aileron, elevator, rudder, and stabilizer position
Consolidated oscilloscope	Wing-bending moment/sheer load and horizontal tail sheer load
Common timing circuit	Synchronize collected data

It was not until late November that the work had progressed far enough for a flight to be made. NACA research pilot Howard C. "Tick" Lilly had been selected to fly the second D-558-1. The first NACA flight was made on November 25, 1947, for pilot familiarization, but it was cut short after instrumentation problems. Lilly made a second flight the following day, but it also had to be aborted due to both instrumentation problems and the failure of the landing gear to lock properly after retracting. With the onset of the winter rainy season, Rogers Dry Lake was flooded. Engine modifications also had to be made. Taken together, all these factors halted flight operations for several months.[14]

Project managers used the winter downtime to make another modification. As mentioned previously, on the ground and at low altitudes over the desert the Skystreak was eye-catching in its dark red finish, but optical and photographic trackers had a hard time spotting it when it flew at higher altitudes, against the dark blue Mojave sky. Walter C. Williams later wrote,

> It was found…that very little photographic contrast was being obtained between the red airplane and the relatively dark blue sky conditions prevalent in this area[,] with the result that photographs could not be obtained to ranges greater than the order of 25 to 30 thousand yards. It was reasoned that the photographic contrast could be increased by using the lightest color possible against the darker sky. On this basis, the aircraft was test painted white and both visibility and photographability were found to be greatly increased. With proper filtering techniques, photographs of the airplanes are now taken to greater than 60,000 yards and are generally visible over their entire test flight range.[15]

Disaster: The NACA Loses Its First Pilot

The second D-558-1 had a history of landing gear problems. On November 26, 1947, on the second NACA flight, the landing gear door would not lock. Between March 31 and April 7, 1948, the problem caused NACA flights 4 through 7 to be aborted. After several successful research flights, the gear problem reoccurred on April 28 when the right landing gear did not retract, forcing an abort of the 16th NACA flight.[16]

The problem reoccurred on May 3, 1948. At noon, after takeoff on the 18th NACA flight, the landing gear failed to lock in the full-up position. Lilly landed the aircraft, and the next several hours were spent troubleshooting the problem. When that was finished, the ground crew towed the D-558-1 to the west end of the runway; Lilly started the engine and took off heading east. The landing gear retracted normally, and the aircraft accelerated to a speed of about

250 mph at an altitude of 100 to 150 feet above the runway. Several ground crewmembers continued watching the D-558-1 and saw "a large piece of white material" separate from the fuselage.[17]

Smoke and flames began coming from the fuselage as the aircraft maintained level flight for several seconds. The D-558-1 began a left yaw and right sideslip roll, which continued until the left wingtip, canopy, and vertical tail struck the lakebed. The impact point was about 1,800 feet beyond where the large piece of fuselage skin had landed. The aircraft bounced into the air and broke up, hitting the ground about 400 feet farther along the flightpath and scattering debris over a wide area. The fire was extinguished by Air Force personnel. Lilly was killed on impact, the first NACA research pilot killed in the line of duty since the agency's founding in 1915.

Crash investigators began by carefully searching for evidence along the takeoff path, locating and tagging debris and marking it on a grid chart to establish the sequence of events. The first pieces found were fragments of the engine compressor case and blades, bits of the fuselage skin from the top of the engine section, and paint chips, evidence of in-flight engine disintegration. These were located less than 2 miles from where takeoff had begun. About 0.2 miles farther down the flightpath was the 4-foot-square section of white fuselage skin spotted by witnesses. Examination showed no evidence of fire. Instead, it was determined that compressor case and blade debris had torn through the fuselage skin.

These fragments struck a vulnerable spot on the top of the fuselage. The single set of rudder and elevator cables passed between this section of skin and the compressor case. As the fuselage skin separated, the control cables were "plucked," causing a leftward movement of the rudder, a right sideslip, and a left roll. The right rudder cable and the up elevator cable were severed. In contrast, the left rudder cable, down elevator cable, and aileron cables survived the disintegration of the compressor case but broke on ground impact.

Examination of the debris revealed that the fire had broken out after the compressor case had broken apart. The left side of the rudder was badly burned, but the right side showed no sign of fire, confirming that the rudder had moved to the left before impact. The fixed vertical tail, however, had heavy fire damage on both sides. The tail cone bore a burn pattern consistent with flames at an angle approximately that of a full left rudder.

The investigation board examined the TG-180 engine and determined that the rapidly spinning compressor rotor had suddenly stopped turning, causing the compressor shaft to fail. Many of the compressor blades were torn out, and the compressor casing had broken up with apparently explosive force. The board learned that three other TG-180 engines had suffered similar failures in earlier aircraft accidents, a pattern that pointed to fatigue failure of the blades as a potential primary cause. The board noted other possible causes: blades damaged by objects being sucked into the engine, or a failure in a steel spacer ring between the 10th and 11th rotor stages.

The board also learned that three TG-180 engines assigned for use in the D-558-1 aircraft had been rejected by NACA and Navy inspectors after numerous large nicks had been found on the edges of the engines' turbine blades. Inspection of the compressor for such damage is practically impossible as a routine preflight check, but if present, it could lead to blade failure. Additionally, investigators learned that the steel spacer ring had been replaced in later-production TG-180 engines with an aluminum ring to reduce the potential for failure. This change had not been made in the engines for the NACA aircraft.

The investigation board made a number of recommendations aimed at improving flight safety. The board wanted only newly manufactured TG-180 engines fitted in the two remaining D-558-1 research aircraft before flights were resumed. Board members also wanted improvements in preflight inspections, as well as in specifications and manufacturing and inspection procedures for turbine blades.

Further, the recommendation was made that controls, fuel lines and pumps, and electrical circuits located near the compressor section be protected and that control cables should be armored, shielded, or duplicated to protect them from damage.

The board was also critical of the D-558-1 canopy and cockpit design. Lilly had not worn a crash helmet in the aircraft because the narrower high-speed canopy did not leave sufficient room for one. He had earlier removed the shoulder straps because he found them inconvenient. The board also discovered that the cockpit space was restrictive and quite dark. The pilot had to lower his head to see some of the instruments and could not see both outside and inside the cockpit at the same time. The board urged that a study and redesign of the cockpit be undertaken.

Given that the idea of air-launching the XS-1 had been controversial among Langley researchers, and in light of their repeated demands that the aircraft be ground-launched, one of the board's recommendations was ironic: "As a safeguard for personnel and valuable research equipment, the fairly well proven use of air launching should be given more consideration. The great difference in wing loading between take-off and landing, as well as the magnitude of the loading, and the desirability for maneuvering capability at the start of an uncertain flight emphasize the value of air launching."[18]

First Research Results

As the investigation of Lilly's crash was underway, Williams wrote up the first research results from the limited longitudinal-stability and control data taken during the second D-558-1's short operational life. The data, taken during the

Skystreak's airspeed calibration flights, up to Mach 0.85, were published less than 2 months after the crash.[19] The flights involved making level flights at a 30,000-foot-pressure altitude and increasing the aircraft's speed from Mach 0.55 to Mach 0.85. During the flight, changes in elevator position and force required to trim the aircraft were recorded. These were used to determine the aircraft's longitudinal stability and any trim changes caused by the effects of transonic speed, such as the formation and movement of shock waves on the wings and stabilizers. The flights were done at stabilizer incidence angle settings of 1.95° and 2.32°.

Williams wrote, "The results of measurements of the elevator angle and force required for trim at Mach numbers up to 0.85 show that below a Mach number of 0.80 the D-558-1 airplane possesses positive static longitudinal stability. Above a Mach number of 0.82, there is a nose-down trim change."[20] Charting of the elevator force, specifically how many pounds of force the pilot had to use to counter any trim changes, made clear what had occurred. Between Mach 0.6 and 0.75, only minor pressure was needed to keep the D-558-1 level. Once the aircraft reached Mach 0.8, however, the amount of pressure required sharply increased. At Mach 0.85, the pilot had to pull back on the control yoke with nearly 10 pounds of force to keep the airplane level.

As the NACA realized, the report constituted a "quick look," rather than a detailed, incisive examination. The airspeed calibration data had not been completely evaluated, but the error margin was estimated to be 1 percent or less. This estimate was based on comparisons with the airspeed calibrations done with the XS-1, also at Mach 0.85. There were also instrumentation issues; no elevator-position data were obtained above Mach 0.8 for a stabilizer setting of 2.32°, as the recorder's film had run out. Finally, the stabilizer incidence angles were close together, making it difficult to determine the relative elevator effectiveness over various Mach numbers.

The results were considered valid, however, as the elevator force and angle data showed the aircraft had positive longitudinal stability up to a Mach number of about 0.80 with the control wheel both fixed and free. Above a speed of about Mach 0.82, the data showed that a trim change occurred, the first indication of compressibility effects in level flight. A similar trim change also appeared in the data derived with the second XS-1, which also had a 10-percent wing. NACA researchers subsequently issued further reports likewise based on the initial flights of the second Skystreak, following these reports with a more extensive study by Williams examining the aircraft's stability characteristics during sideslips, dated April 18, 1949.[21]

The technique used by the pilot to measure the static directional stability of the D-558-1 was to slowly deflect the ailerons, creating gradually increasing sideslips. At the same time, he added enough rudder and elevator to maintain level flight. The Skystreak was flying level at a constant altitude, but with its nose angled to one side. Two series of tests were flown. One was made at a 10,000-foot-pressure altitude and at indicated airspeeds between Mach 0.50 and 0.80. The second series was made at a 30,000-foot-pressure altitude, at Mach 0.50 and 0.84. (The indicated airspeed was above that where the nose-down trim change occurred.)

Once the data were collected, the rudder, aileron, and elevator positions and the forces and angles of bank were plotted on graphs as functions of sideslip angle. Bank angles were obtained from measurements of transverse acceleration. Variations of rudder position and force with the sideslip angle gave a measure of the aircraft's static directional stability, with both fixed and free control. The dihedral effect, which is the rolling moment of an aircraft caused by the spanwise inclination of the wings, was measured with both fixed and free controls. This was illustrated in the variations of aileron position and force with the sideslip angle. The pitching moment due to the sideslip was indicated by the variation of the elevator position and force with sideslip angle. The variation of angle of bank with sideslip angle gave a measure of crosswind force characteristics. The report concluded:

- "The apparent directional stability of the D-558-1 was high throughout the speed range covered, but was greater at low altitudes than at high altitudes at any given Mach number. There was also an increase in directional stability with an increase in Mach number."
- "The increase in directional stability at lower altitudes was probably due to a decrease in rudder efficiency, caused by distortions of the vertical tail and fuselage by higher dynamic pressure."
- "The dihedral effect was positive but low over the speed range tested."
- "There was little to no change in pitching moment with sideslip and the cross-wind force was positive."[22]

Several issues related to data collection had been neglected. No measurements of rudder forces were recorded at 10,000 feet. There were also discontinuities in the variation of both the aileron force and the position with sideslip angles near zero. Williams concluded that the problems with the force measurements were due to friction in the control system. He believed the position errors were caused by play in the linkage between the aileron and the point of measurement. Despite this, Williams believed the slope of the curves should provide a good measure of dihedral effect.[23] These two reports contained preliminary data drawn from a few early flights. A more detailed report was issued on April 22, 1949, and contained information on the D-558-1's high-speed characteristics, up to Mach 0.89, that was not included in Williams's two early reports.[24]

The stability measurements used in the report were primarily derived from two of Lilly's high-speed flights. The two flights, made at an altitude of 40,000 feet, reached Mach 0.89 and used stabilizer incidence angles of 2.3° and 1.4°. The results of the different settings were significant. The 2.3° stabilizer-incidence angle resulted in the aircraft's becoming increasingly nose-heavy as the Mach number increased above Mach 0.80. During the initial phase of the recovery maneuver, Lilly had to pull back hard on the control yoke to decrease the Mach number. As the Mach number decreased over a 10-second period, nose heaviness was also reduced, and Lilly had to reduce the pull force to avoid too great an acceleration.

The Skystreak's behavior was very different at a stabilizer incidence angle of 1.4°. Above Mach 0.83, the Skystreak became increasingly tail-heavy. During the 24-second recovery phase, Lilly simply reduced the push force; the airplane's speed dropped from Mach 0.88 to 0.834, and he completed a normal recovery. When the sideslip angle and the control forces and positions were plotted as a function of Mach number, the differences were glaringly apparent. Depending on the stabilizer setting, a pull- or push-force of 30 pounds was required to correct trim.

During both high-speed flights, Lilly reported that above Mach 0.84 the right wing became very heavy, and he had to make increased left aileron inputs to correct it. He added that the wing heaviness was not continuous, which made the aircraft's lateral stability feel uncertain at its highest speed. Lilly found it difficult to determine the amount of lateral control needed for trim. His control movements resulted in lateral oscillations. The report's author believed some of this problem to be due to aileron fraction.

Some stability and control data were also collected during several incrementally increasing turns made at an altitude of 30,000 feet, at Mach numbers between 0.50 and 0.80. A single turn was made at 10,000 feet and Mach 0.71. The data from the turns showed positive longitudinal stability throughout the speed range. The lowest value was recorded at Mach 0.675, and beyond this point stability increased with increasing Mach number. These results were also consistent with those from the XS-1 flights.

The single test at 10,000 feet indicated that the apparent stability was higher at this altitude than at 30,000 feet. The report noted, "Some of this difference can be accounted for by the effects of altitude but it is also possible that, because of the higher dynamic pressure at the lower altitudes, the apparent stability is altered by distortion effects."[25] This increase in apparent stability at lower altitude was also noted in Williams's second report, also issued in April 1949.

Buffeting occurred on both of the high-speed runs, beginning at a speed of about Mach 0.85. The D-558-1's buffet boundary was determined not only during speed runs, but also in straight stalls and turns. The normal-force coefficients necessary to cause buffeting were plotted as functions of Mach number, to define the combination at which buffeting began.

Data from the XS-1 flights confirmed the Skystreak results. The XS-1 was also flown with the same two stabilizer incidence angles as the D-558-1, and in both cases the aircraft became nose-heavy at higher speeds. The XS-1 also showed similar wing-heaviness behavior. This similarity was to be expected, as both had 10-percent wings and 65-110 wing sections.[26]

Modifications and Flights Resume

With the death of Lilly and the destruction of the second D-558-1, the two remaining aircraft were grounded until the accident investigation was completed. During this period, the D-558-1 #1 (the Douglas aircraft) underwent modifications to fix the problems identified by the accident board and was returned to Muroc.

Gene May resumed the Douglas flight-test program, which entered a dangerous phase during which stability and control data for speeds of up to the aircraft's maximum Mach number were to be collected. Because of the D-558-1's limited performance capability, May had to make risky dive flights, similar to those done in the P-38s and other aircraft, rather than level speed runs, as were done with the X-1.

The test program involved 10 dive tests, 5 with wingtip fuel tanks and 5 without. A dive would begin at 40,000 feet, with a pullout following at around 30,000 feet. On September 29, 1948, May exceeded Mach 1 in a 35° dive in D-558-1 #1, constituting the only time a Skystreak was to fly supersonic. Stability and control deteriorated badly at Mach 0.84, with the aircraft oscillating laterally. As speed increased, the left wing became heavy. Longitudinal stability decreased above Mach 0.94, with the aircraft "tucking under." This was similar to what had been experienced with piston-powered aircraft during transonic dive flights.

The dive tests with the tip tanks followed in early November 1948. With the stock tank configuration, drag was reduced and range increased. However, top speed was also reduced, and the takeoff roll was longer. The tanks were later fitted with endplates in a study of wing airflow. On November 4, 1948, Gene May made another dive test to Mach 0.945. The flight data showed the endplates had stopped spanwise flow separation over the wings, which disrupted lift. Despite this, the endplates were not used again on the D-558-1. These endplates, in some respects, anticipated the development of the vortex-reducing winglet two decades later.[27]

The third D-558-1, which was assigned to the NACA, had been trucked to Muroc on November 4, 1947, but, with attention focused on the first and second aircraft, it had made only four flights by early 1948. Following Lilly's crash, the third D-558-1 was disassembled and trucked back to the Douglas plant for modifications. The work involved adding duplicate control cables and ¼-inch stainless steel armor to protect the emergency fuel pump and fuel lines. Engineers also tested the vulnerability of the high-pressure fuel hoses to shrapnel from an exploding engine. This was done by firing .22-caliber rifle bullets into the standard fuel hose. The bullets easily punctured the standard hose. As a result, these were replaced by wire-wound fuel hoses, which were better able to withstand high-velocity impacts.

The final change Douglas made was to repaint the third D-558-1 in an overall white finish. This posed a complication with the control surfaces. A letter from R.B. Cox, of Douglas, to Walter C. Williams, dated October 11, 1948, noted:

> When the aircraft was sprayed with the white undercoat…the control surfaces were painted. I had seen a schedule of work, issued by the chief engineer for this division, which called for a white paint coat on the entire ship, except for the control surfaces. I called this to the attention of the aircraft project engineer and investigation proved the shop order was in conflict with the original order. Further investigation showed the reason for not painting the surfaces involved a problem of weight and balance. With the original red color the surfaces were just within the allowable margins and the addition of the white undercoat threw them over the limits. The solution was to remove the white, rubbing down into the red just slightly and then fog a light mist coat of red on the units.[28]

The modified and repainted third D-558-1 was returned to Muroc Army Air Field by Douglas in early November 1948. After the aircraft was reassembled, Douglas pilot Gene May completed a demonstration flight in the modified aircraft. He accomplished this on January 3, 1949, in a flight that included a 6.8-g pullout, left and right maximum sideslips at 580 mph, and a low-level pass at 605 mph indicated airspeed.

The flight was apparently without mishap. However, an NACA safety representative making a postflight inspection discovered a damaged brass safety wire that had passed through the jet engine. Pulling the engine and conducting an inspection would have delayed turning the aircraft over to the NACA. Instead, Douglas simply installed a new TG-180 engine. The NACA took formal delivery of the third D-558-1 on January 22, 1949. The ground crew then began preparing it for research flights, a process that lasted until April.

As this was underway, the Douglas flight tests with the first Skystreak were concluded. A total of 101 flights had been completed. Douglas transferred the aircraft to the NACA, which put it in "dead storage" for use as spare parts. It never flew again. The third D-558-1 was the only one of the three Skystreaks still in use.[29]

Preparing the NACA Skystreak for research flights took much of 1949–50. Robert A. Champine was the first to fly the aircraft after it was turned over to the NACA. He had arrived at Muroc from Langley in October 1948. He made two D-558-1 pilot proficiency flights in April 1949. After Champine's two flights, the aircraft was grounded for an engine change and remained grounded during the spring and summer of 1949. It would not be ready to fly until August.

NACA research pilot Robert Champine climbs out of the D-558-1 after a flight. Champine became an NACA research pilot in December 1947, and he retired in 1979. On December 2, 1948, he became the sixth person to fly supersonic. (NASA)

NACA Research Flights Continue

Once the Skystreak was restored to flight status, the initial research focus was on its handling qualities. Piloting duties were split between Bob Champine and John H. Griffith, an NACA research pilot assigned to Muroc in August of 1949. Between August and September of 1949, the two made seven flights.[30] One issue explored during these flights was the effectiveness of the D-558-1's ailerons. NACA flight 8 was made by Champine on August 31 and involved 22 aileron rolls, of which 4 were at Mach 0.86. On NACA flight 9, made by Griffith on September 28, 16 aileron rolls were made, 4 of them above Mach 0.875. The rolls were abrupt, with the rudder held in a fixed position, and made at speeds between Mach 0.6 and 0.89.

The amount of aileron deflection was between one-eighth and one-half the total available deflection of ±15°. Most of the rolls were made at pressure altitudes of about 35,000 feet, although some were as low as 15,000 feet. The rolls were made in both directions. To make the research pilot's task easier, a mechanical stop was placed in the cockpit to allow the pilot to hold a constant aileron deflection until a constant rolling velocity was established.

As the Skystreak rolled, a yawing oscillation occurred, much like that of a wobbling top as it spins. This yawing was most apparent when the rolling velocity was increasing. Once the rolling velocity reached maximum value, however, the yawing damped out. Several of the roll maneuvers were studied to determine what effects the yawing had on maximum rolling velocity. No significant change was noted.

Complicating the tests was the fact that the ailerons were slightly warped. With no load on them, this amounted to as much as a 1° difference between the aileron-cord line and the wing-cord line at different points along the span of each aileron. Ideally, there should have been a continuation of the airfoil.

The results of the flights were described in a May 1950 NACA research memorandum. Altitude had no effect on the ailerons' ability to control the aircraft. None of the test rolls were executed with more than half the available aileron deflection. The pilot believed the rolling velocities achieved with one-half deflection were enough to meet the maximum requirements for either test or military operations with the aircraft. Indeed, a full aileron deflection at Mach 0.85 at 35,000 feet would result in a complete revolution in 0.95 seconds.

The aileron forces required at a given deflection increased with indicated airspeed. The indicated value of force at maximum rolling velocity depended on the time required to reach maximum rolling velocity and the fraction in the aileron control system (estimated at ±5 pounds). When the force data were graphed, an approximately straight line resulted. This indicated that the total hinge-moment coefficient for a given aileron deflection was independent of the Mach number, at least for the speed range of the tests.

From the earlier stability and control research flights, as well as the aileron tests, a clearer understanding of the Skystreak's lateral trim and handling characteristics at high Mach numbers was now available. The report noted the following:

> As the speed of the airplane is increased a right-wing heaviness becomes apparent to the pilot at about the same time as general buffeting of the airplane is encountered. As the speed is further increased the wing heaviness increases, a change in aileron trim force of about 7 pounds and a corresponding change in total aileron deflection of about one-half degree being required to trim…at a Mach number of about 0.88. The trim force and deflection for the wing-heaviness example quoted are typical, although in a few cases trim changes could not be detected on the

recording instruments and were not noticeable to the pilot. The lateral unsteadiness of the airplane at high speeds is evident on the time history from the rapid variations of force and deflection applied by the pilot in attempting to trim. It was also evident... that the airplane has a short-period rolling-yawing oscillation of small amplitude. In addition to the wing heaviness, pilots have reported an intermittent "wing dropping" which occurs above a Mach number of about 0.86. This sudden rolling of the airplane occurs above a Mach number of about 0.86. This sudden rolling of the airplane occurs in either direction and appears to be associated with the general lateral unsteadiness of the airplane at high Mach numbers.[31]

As earlier reports had noted, the wing heaviness of the X-1 and D-558-1 were similar, but more details were now apparent. On the X-1, the heaviness occurred at about Mach 0.85 and appeared to be related to an abrupt reduction in aileron effectiveness. The stability and control data on the Skystreak showed that aileron effectiveness did not decrease at speeds of up to Mach 0.89. Aileron effectiveness had not been investigated for small deflections, however. The report also noted, "A possible contributing cause of both the wing heaviness and wing dropping is probably asymmetric location and movement of shock waves on the wing resulting from construction asymmetry."[32]

During September and October of 1949, two 60-cell manometers were installed to record right-wing surface-pressure-differential measurements. Six rows of orifices were cut into the upper and lower surfaces of the right wing, running along the chord from front to back. Row 1 was only 6 inches from the fuselage; row 6 was close to the tip. The pressure differential between the upper and lower wing surfaces was measured from rows 1, 2, 3, 4, and 6. Row 5 measured individual surface pressures relative to the instrument compartment, and the instrument compartment pressure was measured relative to the static pressure, which was corrected to the free-stream static pressure by using radar-tracking data. This process calibrated the pressure measurements, eliminating errors and ensuring accuracy.

The "plumbing" installed within the wing was extensive. The flush-type orifices in the wing skin were connected to the instrument compartment with ⅛-inch-inside-diameter aluminum tubing, which was connected to the manometer cells with ³⁄₁₆-inch rubber tubing. The length of the aluminum tubing ranged from 6 feet at the wing-root stations to about 14 feet at row 6, near the wingtip. About 4 feet of rubber tubing was used on each line.

Given the length of tubing, the maneuvers that were planned, and the need for precision data, the effects of instrument lag had to be considered. Ground testing indicated that any lag attributable to tubing length would be negligible. The lag in the airspeed recording system was calculated using established procedures and corrections made in the data. Considerable instrument lag in the airspeed recording system occurred during speed runs and the windup turns. Corrections were calculated and added to Mach-number and dynamic-pressure measurements. For the 1-g-stall measurements, lag was negligible because the pilot used a separate airspeed system.[33]

With the installation of the manometers now complete, the aircraft was returned to flight status on October 28, 1949, with Griffith making the first pressure-distribution flight. Two more pressure-distribution flights, one each by Griffith and Champine, were made by late November, before the year's activities came to a close.

More than 2 months passed before D-558-1 flights resumed. Technical problems continued, grounding the aircraft in February 1950 following an engine malfunction. Repairs took significant time, and it was not until April 5, 1950, that pressure-distribution flights resumed. Griffith flew the third D-558-1 as Champine had returned in 1950 to Langley, where he continued as a research pilot. Following a flight on April 11, 1950, the aircraft experienced hydraulic problems after landing.[34]

Pressure-distribution research involved a large number of flights and a wide range of test maneuvers and procedures. Early research activities involved a 1-g stall at a subcritical Mach number and 15,000 feet, a speed run to Mach 0.90, and a windup turn at Mach 0.86. The 1-g stall was executed by gradually slowing the aircraft until it stalled. Other maneuvers were more complex.

The speed run started with the Skystreak at 37,000 feet and Mach 0.70. The pilot dove to 33,000 feet and a Mach number of 0.90 and then began a gradual left turn, which he tightened until maximum allowable buffeting was reached. During the turn, airspeed dropped to around Mach 0.86. Once at a near-constant Mach number and an increasing normal-force coefficient, the pilot collected several data points. The ailerons were held near neutral during the maneuvers, and rolling velocities due to lateral oscillations were low.[35]

The third D-558-1 was also used to investigate a simple solution for reducing or delaying a range of effects resulting from compressibility, including buffeting, lateral instability, changes in trim, and reduction in control efficiency. Engineers attached "vortex generators" to the upper wing surfaces. Despite their impressive name, these were small airfoils with an NACA 0012 section and a chord of 0.5 inches, and they were positioned at 2-inch intervals. The generators were alternately tilted toward and away from the fuselage. They did not change the wings' section profile and were added following Griffith's April 11, 1950, flight. The work took less than a month.

The first vortex generator research flight was made on May 5 as a continuation of pressure-distribution studies. The vortex generators on the first flight extended only from the wing's mid-flap to the mid-aileron. The flight entailed takeoff and landing followed by a flight to altitude. The goal was to collect data on low-speed handling characteristics with the vortex generators installed. The initial configuration was modified for the second flight, with the vortex generators extending from the mid-flap section out to the wingtip. The final design, for the third flight, stretched the full width of the wing.

The portions of the research flights made at altitude involved low-speed stalls, pull-ups in the buffet regions at speeds of up to Mach 0.89, and abrupt aileron rolls above Mach 0.7. Once the flights were completed, the vortex generators were removed and the flight conditions were repeated to collect baseline measurements. The sixth and final vortex generator flight was made on June 13, during which Griffith reached a speed of Mach 0.98. This marked the end of the pressure-distribution research flights.

NACA researchers analyzed the data and found that the vortex generators produced a number of effects. At speeds above Mach 0.85, the areas of flow separation were reduced. At Mach numbers greater than 0.85, the flow separation and the forward movement of the shock wave on the wing's upper surface were reduced, though no change in the small-amplitude lateral oscillations could be identified. The buffet boundary and wing drop were both delayed by about Mach 0.05. The pilot reported that the intensity of the buffeting was "appreciably reduced" below the stall.[36] No detrimental effects from the vortex generators were found on the Skystreak's longitudinal and lateral control, at least for the conditions of the tests. The only negative result was an increase in drag.

The NACA vortex generator test series had a major impact on aeronautics and aircraft design. Boeing was the first to use vortex generators on production airplanes. Rows of the little metal tabs soon appeared on the wings of B-47 and B-52 bombers, KC-135 tankers, and thousands of airliners.[37] Other companies followed suit as well.

The next research effort undertaken was the measurement of the Skystreak's buffet boundary, which is the combination of speed and lift coefficients at which an aircraft experiences irregular shaking or oscillation due to turbulent flow or flow separation. The Skystreak was grounded for modification during the summer and early fall of 1950. A high-speed photographic manometer was added to measure wing-pressure distribution over a spanwise station, and a downwash vane for airflow measurements was added to determine the wing's contribution to buffeting. A nose boom was also added for angle-of-attack measurements.

While the aircraft was grounded, the engineers replaced its stabilizer with the first D-558-1's instrumented stabilizer. The engineers had noticed a trim change during pressure-distribution flights that was due to a loss of elevator effectiveness. They were uncertain whether this was a result of changes in the actual pressure distribution or of physical distortion of the stabilizer and elevator. The solution was to replace the stabilizer. They completed the work in mid-October 1950, and D-558-1 flights resumed on October 26 with a check flight by Griffith, clearing the way for buffeting, tail-load, and longitudinal-stability flights, which would be made over the course of the coming year.[38] The check flight would be Griffith's last in the D-558-1. He left the NACA in the fall of 1950 to become a senior test pilot on the troubled Chance Vought F7U Cutlass flight test program.

His replacement was A. Scott Crossfield, a World War II Navy fighter pilot and gunnery instructor. Crossfield was a thorough-going aeronautical professional, both a consummate engineer and consummate pilot. He had attended the University of Washington, earning bachelor's and master's degrees in engineering during 1949 and 1950. Soon after, he joined the NACA as an aeronautical research pilot. His arrival reflected the new demands on test pilots wrought by transonic and supersonic flight. It was no longer enough to be a hot-shot fighter pilot with plenty of stick-and-rudder time. Both the new and the old test and research pilots were accomplished aviators, but for the new breed such as Crossfield, engineering knowledge was at least as important as flying skill.[39]

Crossfield made his first D-558-1 flight on November 29, 1950. It was both a pilot checkout flight and the beginning of the buffet, tail-load, and longitudinal-stability research project. He made a total of five flights before year's end. The effort continued into the new year with Crossfield making another four research flights in January 1951.

Another new pilot now joined the D-558-1 project. Walter P. Jones had arrived at the High-Speed Flight Research Station in September 1950 with both undergraduate and graduate degrees in aeronautical engineering from Purdue University. Jones made his first flight in the aircraft on February 13, 1951—a pilot check flight that also included the collection of some buffet, tail-load, and longitudinal-stability data. Jones's second Skystreak flight, on February 20, highlighted the risks of research flying. His oxygen regulator was faulty, and Jones began to suffer from anoxia. He nevertheless recognized his situation, aborted the flight, and landed safely.

These were not the only dangers Crossfield and Jones faced. Engineers discovered that the elevator was twisting by as much as 2° during pull-ups at about Mach 0.80 and was also experiencing undesirable vibrations. Flight data indicated that these vibrations increased in amplitude in direct proportion to the increase in Mach number and occurred in all high-lift conditions over the entire Mach number range, even if the airplane was in a stall. Elevator force and position indicators did not reflect the vibrations until they had reached an undesirable level. Though a precautionary x-ray examination of the elevators showed no sign of fatigue cracks, concerns persisted.

NACA engineers contacted Douglas, as the latter had recorded similar problems during its flight program with the first Skystreak. During a Mach 0.94 dive test, the first D-558-1 had experienced vibrations so severe that a "never-exceed" speed of Mach 0.92 had been established for the aircraft. Douglas engineers said they had attempted to reduce the vibrations by changing the position of the outboard elevators' balance weights. The Douglas contractor flight program was ending, and the engineers admitted that they had not evaluated the change. More serious was the fact that the Douglas engineers had never informed NACA engineers of the speed limitation.

The team at Douglas analyzed data from the NACA flights and discovered that the elevator vibrations had reached nearly 70 percent of the maximum stress limits of the design and could eventually cause a fatigue failure. Between the Douglas and NACA tests, more than a hundred flights had been made with the elevators from the first D-558-1, which had been fitted subsequently to the third D-558-1, and it was questionable how many more flights could be made without a failure. As a precaution, the first D-558-1's elevators were removed and the third D-558-1's elevators were reinstalled, since these had been used on only 22 flights and had a much longer service life. The switch took a significant amount of time, and it was not until late April 1951 that the work was completed.[40]

Jones made the first flight in the reequipped D-558-1 on May 2, 1951. Between May and late June, Crossfield and Jones made a total of six buffet, tail-load, and longitudinal-stability flights at speeds between Mach 0.835 and Mach 0.86. Once more, there was a change in personnel. During the remainder of the NACA Skystreak project, Crossfield made only three more flights, with Jones making a single additional D-558-1 flight. Subsequent research activities were undertaken once several new pilots joined the effort.

Joseph A. Walker was the first of these. An Army Air Forces pilot in World War II, he had flown reconnaissance missions in P-38 Lightnings over Austria, the Black Sea, and southern France. At the war's end, and already holding a bachelor's degree in physics from Washington and Jefferson College, he joined the NACA's Lewis Flight Propulsion Laboratory in 1945 as a physicist. He transferred to the High-Speed Flight Research Station in 1951 as a research pilot.[41]

Walker's first pilot checkout flight came on June 28, 1951, during which he reached a speed of Mach 0.82. He made a second checkout flight on July 3,

The third D-558-1 on the lakebed, being prepared for a flight. A ground crewman is adjusting the pilot's parachute straps, which the pilot cannot see. The aircraft is also positioned close to the lakebed shoreline to allow the maximum distance for a takeoff run. When the NACA contingent first arrived at Muroc Army Air Field in late 1946, they found the facilities of a wartime training base very different from those at Langley. Housing was subpar, the facilities were limited, and the climate was usually either too hot or too cold to work comfortably. Some NACA personnel left, but others adapted. (NASA)

which also included tests of buffeting and tail loads. Walker made a total of 14 D-558-1 flights between June 28 and October 18, 1951. Although the D-558-1 flights represented a significant part of the High-Speed Flight Research Station's activities, they were never routine.

On Walker's third flight in the D-558-1, on July 17, he had to cut the mission short due to low fuel. Two flights later, on July 26, weather forced an inflight abort. Clouds prevented tests at altitudes above 15,000 feet. The next two flights were successful, but on August 10 the airplane suffered a fuel leak due to a malfunctioning vent valve, cutting short still another mission. After a successful flight on August 20, on which Walker reached a true airspeed of Mach 0.9, problems struck again. A hydraulic failure caused his August 22 flight to be aborted. Walker's final D-558-1 flight, on October 18, was for the collection of lateral-stability and landing data. Walker then moved on to other projects.[42]

Stanley P. Butchart took over research duties with the D-558-1. Like Crossfield and Walker, he was a World War II combat pilot, having flown TBM Avenger torpedo planes in the Pacific.[43] Butchart entered the University of Washington after the war, earning bachelor's degrees in aeronautical engineering and mechanical engineering. While there, he and Crossfield served in the same Naval Reserve squadron before both joined the NACA in May 1951. Butchart made his first D-558-1 flight, for pilot checkout, on October 19, 1951. This was followed on November 9 by his first research flight, which was the last flight of the buffeted, tail-load, lateral-stability, and landing-study project.

Skystreak flights made during this period resulted in the publication of several NACA research memorandums between early 1951 and early 1952. Additional tables of wing-pressure measurements were released in January 1951. Like the data issued in December 1950, the new data were collected in windup turns. Unlike in the earlier tests, however, the new information was not limited to collection at a single speed of Mach 0.86. Rather, it covered Mach 0.67, 0.74, 0.78, and 0.82 at an altitude of 35,000 feet. Both reports consisted of tabulated measurements but lacked detailed analysis, in the interest of making flight-test data available to designers as quickly as possible.[44]

During the flights made with the second D-558-1, measurements had been made of the effects of different stabilizer incidents on the aircraft's longitudinal-stability and control characteristics. These preliminary results showed that minor changes in the stabilizer incidents caused major changes in longitudinal trim characteristics. Once flights resumed with the third Skystreak, the issue of the effects of the stabilizer incidents was revisited in a more thorough investigation. The tests were made using shallow dives, pullouts, and windup turns at altitudes ranging from 37,000 to 27,000 feet, at Mach numbers between 0.60 and 0.89. The stabilizer incidences used during the research flights were 1.6°, 2.2°, 2.6°, 2.7°, 2.9°, and 3.3°. These tests were considerably more complete than those made during initial efforts with the first D-558-1.

In newspaper accounts of test pilots' experiences, the focus is more often on the drama and danger of the flights than on the test results. In NACA research memorandums, the text is dry and to the point. The results of the flights are depicted in charts and graphs and are often unclear to a lay reader. But sometimes, even dry text and charts make clear what has transpired. Regarding a dive to about Mach 0.89, "The data were obtained in a dive from about 37,000 feet with a stabilizer setting of 3.3°. At about 48 seconds, as the pilot attempted to pull out, the elevator angle and stick forces necessary to execute the maneuvers became excessive and the stabilizer had to be used to recover from the dive. The time history for this run was not extended beyond 48 seconds because the subsequent data were not satisfactory for analysis.... [I]t is evident from the figures that large changes in longitudinal trim occur at Mach numbers above about Mach 0.84."[45]

The pull-stick force needed to recover from the dive with the 3.3° stabilizer setting was about 80 pounds. More important, the recovery was only possible by also using the adjustable stabilizer. The conventional fixed horizontal

The third D-558-1 parked on the South Base ramp with three ground personnel. The Skystreak was one of two concepts for how best to gain data on transonic flight. It represented a traditional design, had straight wings, and was jet-powered, with a top speed just below Mach 1. It was funded in part by the Navy and built by Douglas to NACA specifications. In contrast, the Army Air Forces XS-1 was rocket-powered, with a top speed well above Mach 1. (NASA)

stabilizer and movable elevator, used since the early days of flight, were definitively shown to be obsolete for transonic and supersonic flight. The two-part design of the X-1 and D-558 was the origin of the all-moving tail fitted to the later model F-86 and subsequent high-performance aircraft and is still in use today. The report also noted, "The results indicate that large and rapid changes in elevator deflection and force were required for balance at Mach numbers above 0.84. At Mach numbers above about 0.84, a sharp decrease in the relative elevator-stabilizer effectiveness was shown and analysis indicated that a major part of the observed trim changes was explained by this decrease…. The increase in apparent stick-fixed stability parameter was attributed to a decrease of relative elevator effectiveness together with an increase of the stability of the airplane by a factor of 4 between Mach numbers of 0.75 and 0.89."[46]

Though the bulk of research undertaken with the D-558-1 was similar to that done with conventional aircraft to understand stability and control issues, another study using the Skystreak looked to the future, toward the dawning computer revolution. By the early 1950s, engineers realized that automatically stabilizing dynamic systems were necessary for future supersonic aircraft. To design such a system, however, engineers needed aircraft frequency-response data at high subsonic, transonic, and supersonic speeds. Acquiring these data involved the transfer functions of both the aircraft and the control systems.

The procedure used to collect the data was to make several stick-fixed 2° elevator pulses, each lasting 0.5 to 1.0 second. The aircraft was in stabilized 1-g flight at a speed between Mach 0.52 and 0.90 and altitudes of 30,000 to 37,000 feet. These pulses produced an initial aircraft oscillation of approximately ±½ g to ±1 g and a pitching velocity of ±0.1 radians per second. As with other tests, precision was central to ensuring that the data were valid. A restricting device was attached to the elevator control that returned it to approximately the original position following the pulses and also maintained the fixed elevator condition as the oscillation subsided. The other controls—ailerons, rudder, and stabilizers—were fixed during the maneuvers. The stabilizer incident was fixed throughout the tests at a nose-down angle of –2°. Another factor affecting the data was the twist of the elevator, which amounted to about 0.4°. To produce an average value, the elevator position was recorded at four positions along the external span of the fuselage. The four control positions were averaged, and this average was used as the input function.

When the flights were completed, Fourier transform (a mathematical process) was applied to the input and output functions, establishing the longitudinal frequency response of the aircraft as a function of Mach number. The report noted, "A comparison of the response data estimated from wind tunnel data with the experimental results showed good agreement. It was found that the maximum response amplitude was a minimum at a Mach number of 0.88. At lower Mach numbers (0.52 to 0.66) the effects of lift coefficient on frequency response are indicated."[47]

1952–1953: The Skystreak's Twilight Years

Much had changed at the High-Speed Flight Research Station since the D-558-1 had been delivered in the spring of 1947. New X-planes had been built, resulting in a heavy workload for the limited number of engineers, technicians, and computers at the remote site. The Skystreak was also showing its age. Following Butchart's second flight, it was grounded for maintenance work that involved repairing major fuel leaks and correcting engine-ignition problems. Work was completed in January 1952, but winter rains flooded Rogers Dry Lake, preventing flight operations. The research plan for the D-558-1 in early 1952 called for an investigation of vertical-tail loads. To support the tail-loads study, strain-gauge instrumentation was installed. Before this research activity could begin, however, or the strain gauges could even be calibrated, a study of lateral stability and aileron-roll effectiveness was undertaken with the D-558-1.

The D-558-1 resumed flight on June 25, 1952, with Crossfield as pilot, beginning the lateral-stability and aileron-effectiveness research flights. Crossfield made two flights before turning the project over to Butchart. The pilots made abrupt aileron rolls from Mach 0.4 to the Skystreak's limiting Mach number at 10,000 feet, 25,000 feet, and 35,000 feet. Results showed that aileron effectiveness dropped rapidly above Mach 0.88. Butchart made a total of five flights between July 17 and August 12, 1952. He later recalled the cramped Skystreak's cockpit. During takeoff on July 17, 1952, he reached for the landing gear handle but could not squeeze his hand between the control yoke column and the emergency oxygen bailout bottle strapped to his left leg. It took Butchart three tries to get the gear retracted.[48]

Horizontal stabilizer issues continued to plague the program. During a postflight inspection, the horizontal stabilizer mountings were found to be loose. High-Speed Flight Research Station engineers judged this to be due to wear over a long period of time, rather than to one-time damage resulting from a severe maneuver. The horizontal stabilizers were originally fitted to the first D-558-1, and about 100 flights already had been made with them. They were then sent to Langley to be instrumented. Once this was completed, the stabilizers were returned to the High-Speed Flight Research Station and reinstalled on the third Skystreak. By the time the loose mountings were discovered, 41 more flights had been made with the stabilizers. The risk posed by the loose mountings was considerable. The horizontal stabilizer was known to vibrate during buffeting, and during a Mach 0.90 dive, the vibration became quite pronounced. High-Speed Flight Research Station engineers decided to repair the vertical-load links and the pins that attached the links to the horizontal stabilizer.

Repairing the horizontal stabilizers first required removing their skins. Once this was done, the strain gauges were inspected and found to need extensive repairs; they would have to undergo a complete recalibration. The strain gauges were critical for measurements of vertical-tail load as the stabilizers were mounted directly on the tail.

The engineers estimated that repairs to the horizontal stabilizers and recalibrations of the tail-load gauges would take 3 months. This resulted in a management decision to omit the vertical-tail-load research from future D-558-1 activities. Managers at NACA Headquarters learned of the decision and sent a letter to Hartley Soulé at Langley seeking his input on the advisability of abandoning the tail-loads study. A letter was also sent to the High-Speed Flight Research Station asking for information on the circumstances of the decision.[49]

Donald Bellman, an engineer at the High-Speed Flight Research Station, wrote the reply to NACA Headquarters. He noted that the 3-month delay needed to make the repairs and complete the recalibration "eliminated the possibility of starting the vertical tail load program in the 1952 flying season. Prospective work of greater importance precluded the program from the 1953 flying season, so the program was abandoned."[50]

Research with the D-558-1 did not resume until January 29, 1953. Dynamic-stability measurements were the goals of the new flights. These would be accomplished by making elevator and rudder pulses at transonic speeds at 25,000- and 35,000-foot altitudes. Although some dynamic-stability data that had been collected in earlier missions focused on lateral stability, about two-thirds of the elevator pulse data and nearly all the rudder pulses had yet to be collected. Butchart made five dynamic-stability flights, the last on March 27.

As before, a new pilot now joined the project. He was John B. "Jack" McKay, a Navy F6F Hellcat pilot during World War II. After the war, he attended Virginia Polytechnic Institute and graduated in 1950 with a bachelor's degree in aeronautical engineering. McKay joined the NACA in January 1951, initially working at Langley for a brief period as an engineer before transferring to the High-Speed Flight Research Station. His assignment on the D-558-1 was to provide dynamic-stability "fill-in" data.

McKay made his pilot checkout on March 27, 1953. This was followed on April 1 and 2 by the two fill-in flights. At the time of his assignment, these flights were supposed to mark the end of research with the D-558-1. But High-Speed Flight Research Station managers had approved a new research project designed to investigate the effects of tip tanks on the Skystreak's buffet characteristics, so McKay also piloted these flights.

The first tip-tank flight, made on May 7, 1953, was aborted because a fuel-vent failure caused a leak in the left tank. The second flight, on May 12, was no more successful. The data recorder had not been turned on, so McKay came home with no data. Despite McKay's shaky start on the project, the next four flights, on May 13, May 20, June 2, and June 3, 1953, were successful. Crossfield made the 78th and final NACA research flight in the third D-558-1, an investigation of low-speed stability and control in coordinated turns, on June 10, 1953. With his landing, the Skystreak passed into history.[51]

An Assessment

The Skystreak's importance in the exploration of the supersonic frontier was, as the two opening quotations indicate, conflicted. This was due to many factors. The first was the aircraft's limitations. John Stack did not want a supersonic airplane, but one that could fly at high-transonic speeds and provide the data that existing wind tunnels could not. The NACA's large wind tunnels, then the best in the world, began to choke at the speeds at which compressibility

The third D-558-1 Skystreak parked outside an NACA hangar at Edwards South Base in 1949. The aircraft was painted overall white to make photo tracking easier against the dark blue desert sky. The original dark red paint was intended to be highly visible but actually made the Skystreak difficult to spot. (NASA)

problems were appearing with aircraft. Makeshift efforts designed to get around this stumbling block, such as wing flow and rocket-boosted models, had limitations, so building research aircraft remained the only option.

In a broader context, the D-558-1's limitations reflected the NACA's cautious approach to the sonic frontier. The agency's approach in 1944–46 was characterized by a focus on research conducted through small steps rather than bold leaps and through incremental improvements in aircraft technology rather than wholesale revolutionary breakthroughs. Much of the NACA's war work was in drag reduction for existing production aircraft and was focused on small increases in performance. The surprisingly ambivalent response to Robert T. Jones's paper on swept wings (until confirmed by evidence of Nazi wartime work) was another reflection of this mentality; it continued with the NACA's proposed X-planes research plan, which called for numerous flights with several different aircraft stretching over a long period, with supersonic flight achieved only at the very end—a program plan that led to the AAF ramming through its accelerated XS-1 assault.

The Douglas engineers designing the D-558-1 were driven by the NACA's recommendations for a simple first-generation transonic research aircraft, but also by the Navy's (and their own) interest in possibly using the aircraft to at least contribute to an operational naval fighter. The Skystreak represented a conservative design for a land-based jet aircraft, but a radical one for a naval fighter, in the age of straight-deck carriers more suited to straight-wing slow-approach-speed aircraft than to the "hotter" swept-wing jets. It is important to note that the advent of the swept wing did eventually result in pressures to build a swept-wing derivative of the D-558-1, which led to the Mach 2–breaking D-558-2 Skyrocket, first flown in February 1948. Compared to this pointed, streamlined (indeed elegant) design, the "original" D-558-1, with its cylindrical constant-diameter fuselage and straight wings and tail surfaces, looked archaic rather than futuristic.

Despite all of this, the Skystreak was a remarkably productive aircraft. During the D-558-1 research flights, a wide range of activities was undertaken. The tests included high-Mach-number dives; research on the effects of tip tanks and on aileron effectiveness; directional-stability rudder kicks and side slips made to collect stability data; measurements of pressure distribution and lift pressure; and checks of vortex generators, buffeting and tail loads, longitudinal stability, and dynamic and lateral stability in the transonic range.[52]

The significance of the Skystreak's accomplishments lies not in the tests themselves, many of which were the standard tests used on prototype and production aircraft, but rather in the database assembled across the range of speeds at which they were flown. This made the D-558-1 important. In this context, at least, it did not matter that the Skystreak lacked swept wings or rocket power.

The capabilities and limitations of the D-558-1 and the XS-1 (renamed the X-1 in June 1948) resulted in a division of research methodology. Because the Skystreak could cruise for (relatively) prolonged periods at transonic speeds, it was used for such research, freeing the shorter-duration XS-1 for use in collecting data at supersonic speeds. The XS-1 was ill-suited to undertake sustained flights at transonic speeds because of the rocket engine's ravenous fuel consumption, which left it with, at most, 2½ minutes of powered flight time.

Paradoxically, the D-558-1's contributions were also more limited for the same reason. The X-1s and swept-wing D-558-2 continued to be successfully used for research activities into the late 1950s. The lower performance of the D-558-1 meant its useful lifespan was shorter; Soulé's December 19, 1952, letter to NACA Headquarters regarding the cancellation of the vertical-tail-loading studies with the Skystreak noted, "It should be understood that the abandonment of the proposed D-558-1 vertical-tail-load flight tests does not mean the abandonment of the study of vertical-tail loads at Edwards. Vertical-tail load data are being obtained during flights of the X-5 and D-558-2 airplanes, *and it is believed that the resulting information will be of more interest than such information on the D-558-1 airplane.*"[53] (Emphasis added.)

The clear implication was that the D-558-1 was nearing the end of its usefulness and that the faster, rocket-powered Skyrocket had more to offer than the jet-powered Skystreak.

Over time, as memories of the debates that attended the development of the XS-1 and D-558-1 faded, the myth that their separate roles had been intentional from the start developed in the research community. This mythology held that the two airplanes were deliberately planned to undertake the two disparate sets of research activities. While not true, and while later aircraft such as the F-86 were soon made available to the NACA for high-speed research, it is certainly true that the availability of the Skystreak as a complementary test system to the flashier XS-1 benefited postwar aeronautical research. As John Becker noted, "It was the D-558-1's and not the advanced service aircraft that were used for extensive flight research at high subsonic speeds by [the] NACA, complementing coverage of the higher transonic speeds by the X-1s. It is quite understandable how some NACA managers by hindsight can see a logic in the way those two vehicles were used that did not really exist when they were promoted in 1944 and 1945."[54]

For NACA researchers, pilots, and engineers, the Skystreak also provided initial experience with the new demands of research aircraft operations, but at a terrible price. The death of "Tick" Lilly (whose portrait hangs in Dryden Flight Research Center to this day) in the second D-558-1 crash highlighted design flaws in the aircraft, as well as in the approach taken to the project. These oversights included the fact that the engine lacked the latest upgrades and modifications, as well as the vulnerability of the control cables, fuel lines, and other components to damage. Acting on the recommendations of the accident board in the wake of Lilly's crash, the Douglas X-3, Northrop X-4, and Bell X-5 research airplanes also received modifications, benefiting them greatly.[55]

There was a final accomplishment of the X-1 and D-558-1 programs that is often overlooked. The research aircraft were built in part because the existing wind tunnels choked between Mach 0.80 and low supersonic speeds. Researchers saw research aircraft as being a substitute for wind tunnel testing as drop bodies, rocket-boosted models, and the wing flow technique had been. From 1947 to the early 1950s, the D-558-1 and the X-1 represented the only tools available for collecting transonic data. The irony was that the construction of the research aircraft generated pressures forcing wind tunnel researchers to seek ways to fix the choking problem.

Overcoming the wind tunnel limitations required several steps. The first was reducing the size of the model to just one-tenth of 1 percent of the tunnel throat area. Choking still occurred, but its onset was delayed from Mach 0.80 to Mach 0.95. Langley researchers realized that in order to take advantage of

The third D-558-1 in flight with scattered clouds in the distance and the desert below. The Skystreak did not have the impact that the XS-1 had on aviation technology, but it did contribute to the understanding of transonic flight. (NASA)

the small-model technique, the support-structures' designs would have to be changed, as their surface area was now much larger than that of the models.

They developed the technique of attaching the model to a long rod, called a "sting," which was placed farther downstream in the tunnel. A specially contoured insert on the tunnel's wall was also added ahead of the sting. The two features both corrected the blockage of the tunnel and created a more uniform airflow. Langley researchers used an early version of the sting/liner beginning in the spring of 1946 for wind tunnel testing of the XS-1 and D-558-1 designs at speeds as high as Mach 0.92.

Langley engineer Ray H. Wright made the next significant breakthrough. He proposed putting lengthwise slots in the throat of a wind tunnel test section, originally to eliminate the effects of wall interference. This technique evolved into using the slots to reduce the choking at high transonic speeds, a practice to which Italian aerodynamicist Antonio Ferri and the German inventor of the swept wing, Adolf Busemann, both expatriate theoreticians working at Langley in the postwar years, objected to at a September 1947 meeting with John Stack. They argued that though the slots would reduce the choking, at Mach 1 the data were unlikely to be valid.

Stack was not overly concerned about the small remaining gap. His response to Ferri and Busemann's objections was to say that if the slotted tunnel worked at Mach 0.995 and Mach 1.005, the gap in the middle was meaningless. It took several more years before the slotted tunnel was an operational reality. The initial modifications to Langley's 8-Foot High Speed Tunnel (HST) exceeded Mach 1 in late 1948, but the airflow was "rough and uneven." The slots had to be carefully shaped to achieve smooth transonic airflow. On October 6, 1950, transonic research operations in the 8-Foot HST began. The 16-Foot HST also began operation with a slotted throat 3 months later. The significance of the achievement was recognized in 1951 when Stack and his associates were awarded the Collier Trophy for the development of the slotted tunnel, indirectly another accomplishment attributable to the onset of the postwar X-series aircraft.[56]

Endnotes

1. Opening quotations are from Hallion, *Supersonic Flight*, p. 141, and Becker, *The High-Speed Frontier*, p. 96.
2. During its development and service life, the Douglas Skystreak was variously referred to as the "D-558-I" and the "D-558-1." The latter usage is more prevalent in Douglas, Navy, and NACA documentation, and, accordingly, this work uses D-558-1 for consistency.
3. See Edward H. Heinemann and Rosario Rausa, *Ed Heinemann: Combat Aircraft Designer* (Annapolis, MD: Naval Institute Press, 1980), pp. 141–150.
4. Tuncer Cebeci, *Legacy of a Gentle Genius: The Life of A.M.O. Smith* (Long Beach, CA: Horizons Publishing, Inc., 1999), p. 28.
5. Hallion, *Supersonic Flight*, pp. 69, 71–73.
6. Edward H. Heinemann, "The Development of the Navy-Douglas Model D-558 Research Project" (El Segundo, CA: Douglas Aircraft Company, November 17, 1947), pp. 3–7.
7. Heinemann, "The Development of the Navy-Douglas Model D-558 Research Project," p. 7; Curtis Peebles, ed., *The Spoken Word: Recollections of Dryden History, The Early Years*, SP-2003-4530 (Washington, DC: NASA, 2003), pp. 84, 110. Scott Crossfield, who flew the D-558-1 and -2, did not have a high opinion of their escape systems. He later noted in *The Spoken Word*, "This is the way to commit suicide to keep from getting killed. They never did have the development on them that they should have had, and they weren't any good anyway. If you could make a capsule that was good enough to live through the emergency, you might as well fly it and throw away the airplane." Stanley P. Butchart, who also flew the D-558-1 and -2, echoed Crossfield's comments. Butchart added, also in *The Spoken Word*, "When you stop to think of it, [at] the higher speeds, and you drop the nose off, you're going to get a very big negative g as you come out of there. So that restricts you as to how fast you can be going and still use that escape method." Just such a problem killed Air Force Captain Milburn Apt on September 27, 1956, when he attempted to escape from the first Bell X-2 following his flight to Mach 3.2.
8. "Supersonic Douglas Skystreak To Race Speed of Sound for Navy" (Douglas press release), pp. 1–2; Hallion, *Supersonic Flight*, pp. 74–75; Dryden Flight Research Center public movie Web page, *http://www.dfrc.nasa.gov/Gallery/Movie/D-558-1/index.html*, accessed February 11, 2010.

9. Heinemann, "The Development of the Navy-Douglas Model D-558 Research Project" (El Segundo, CA: Douglas Aircraft Company, November 17, 1947), pp. 2–3.

10. Ibid.

11. Dryden Flight Research Center public movie Web page, *http://www.dfrc.nasa.gov/Gallery/Movie/D-558-1/index.html*, accessed February 11, 2010; Hallion, *Supersonic Flight*, pp. 140, 145.

12. Hallion, *Supersonic Flight*, pp. 140–142; Douglas Aircraft Company, "Skystreak World's Speed Records," September 19, 1947; Becker, *The High-Speed Frontier*, p. 96. The D-558-1 record stood until an F-86A broke the record on September 15, 1948, reaching a speed of 671 mph. By then, F-86s were routinely exceeding Mach 1 in dives. The low-altitude speed run was originally designed for wood-and-fabric biplanes, so pilots could not artificially increase their speed by making a dive from high altitude before beginning each run. By the late 1940s, with jets flying at speeds in excess of 600 mph in the dense lower atmosphere, this approach was very dangerous. A small control error would cause the aircraft to hit the ground. Ironically, while Carl's average speed was higher, both he and Caldwell had matching Mach numbers of 0.828. This was because Mach number depended on altitude and air temperature. Caldwell's flights were made at a temperature of a little over 75 °F. Carl's flight, in contrast, was made at an air temperature of nearly 95 °F.

13. Walter C. Williams, "Limited Measurements of Static Longitudinal Stability in Flight of Douglas D-558-1 Airplane" (BuAero No. 37971), NACA RM L8E14 (June 24, 1948), p. 2. The date on an NACA Research Memorandum was when it was issued.

14. Hallion, *Supersonic Flight*, pp. 142–144; Richard P. Hallion and Michael Gorn, *On the Frontier: Experimental Flight at NASA Dryden* (Washington, DC: Smithsonian Books, 2003), p. 386.

15. Letter, Walter C. Williams to NACA, "Choice of Color for Research Aircraft at Edwards," December 3, 1951, reprinted in J.D. Hunley, *Toward Mach 2: The Douglas D-558 Program* (Washington, DC: NASA, 1999), pp. 116–117. The word "photographability" is used in the text. The D-558-1s eventually had pronounced differences in their finishes. The first Douglas D-558-1 ended its career with a white fuselage and lower wings, and the canopy, wing tanks, rudder, vertical-tail tip, horizontal stabilizers, elevators, ailerons, speed brakes, and (apparently) upper wing surfaces and landing gear doors were red. The NACA's third D-558-1 was all-white with the exception of the red rudder, elevators, and ailerons. The second D-558-1

had an NACA shield on its vertical tail. The third D-558-1 bore the NACA shield initially, then a yellow band with "NACA" in black and "NACA" on the upper right wing. Late in its service, a large black "X" was painted on both sides of its forward and aft fuselages for photo tracking.

16. Hallion, *Supersonic Flight*, pp. 224–225.
17. "NACA Aircraft Accident Investigation Report, Douglas D-558-1 Airplane" (BuNo 37971), Muroc Air Force Base, Muroc, CA, May 3, 1948, p. 2.
18. "NACA Aircraft Accident Investigation Report, Douglas D-558-1 Airplane" (BuNo 37971), Muroc Air Force Base, Muroc, CA, May 3, 1948. The D-558-1 was originally fitted with a bubble canopy for the Douglas flights. In videos of early flights, May, who was small in stature, can be seen wearing a silver crash helmet. When the V-shaped canopy replaced the original design, it was then too small to allow most pilots to wear a crash helmet. The accident report noted that the lack of a helmet and the shoulder straps would have made no difference in Lilly's crash. During the speed-record flights, Caldwell had worn a helmet. Carl was taller than Caldwell, however, and he could not close the canopy while wearing a crash helmet. Carl had to wear a World War II–type cloth helmet.
19. Walter C. Williams, "Limited Measurements of Static Longitudinal Stability in Flight of Douglas D-558-1 Airplane, BuAero No. 37971," NACA RM L8E14, (June 24, 1948).
20. Ibid., p. 4.
21. Williams, "Limited Measurements of Static Longitudinal Stability in Flight of Douglas D-558-1 Airplane," pp. 3–4, 10.
22. Walter C. Williams, "Flight Measurement of the Stability Characteristics of the D-558-1 Airplane (BuAero No. 37971) in Sideslips," NACA RM L8E14a (April 18, 1949), pp. 1–4.
23. Ibid., p. 4.
24. William H. Barlow and Howard C. Lilly, "Stability Results Obtained with Douglas D-558-1 Airplane (BuAero No. 37971) in Flights up to a Mach Number of 0.89," NACA RM L8K03 (April 22, 1949).
25. Ibid., p. 4.
26. Ibid., pp. 3–5.
27. Scott Libis, *Skystreak, Skyrocket, & Stiletto: Douglas High-Speed X-Planes* (North Branch, MN: Specialty Press, 2005), pp. 26–28. Credit for the later development of the winglet goes primarily to

the remarkable NACA-NASA aeronautical scientist Richard T. Whitcomb of the Langley Research Center.

28. Hallion, *Supersonic Flight*, pp. 146, 260.
29. Ibid., pp. 146–147.
30. Hallion and Gorn, *On the Frontier*, p. 387.
31. Jim Rogers Thompson, William S. Roden, and John M. Eggleston, "Flight Investigation of the Aileron Characteristics of the Douglas D-558-1 Airplane (BuAero No. 37972) at Mach Numbers Between 0.6 and 0.89," NACA RM L50D20 (May 26, 1950), p. 5.
32. Ibid. pp. 1–6.
33. Earl R. Keener and Mary Pierce, "Tabulated Pressure Coefficients and Aerodynamic Characteristics in Flight on the Wing of the Douglas D-558-1 Airplane for a 1g Stall, a Speed Run to a Mach Number of 0.90, and a Wind-Up Turn at a Mach Number of 0.86," NACA RM L50J10 (December 15, 1950).
34. Hallion, *Supersonic Flight*, pp. 147–148; Libis, *Skystreak, Skyrocket, & Stiletto*, p. 121.
35. Keener and Pierce, "Tabulated Pressure Coefficients and Aerodynamic Characteristics in Flight on the Wing of the Douglas D-558-1 Airplane for a 1g Stall, a Speed Run to a Mach Number of 0.90, and a Wind-Up Turn at a Mach Number of 0.86," p. 5.
36. De E. Beeler, Donald R. Bellman, and John H. Griffith, "Flight Determination of the Effects of Wing Vortex Generators on the Aerodynamic Characteristics of the Douglas D-558-1 Airplane," NACA Research Memorandum RM L51A23, August 14, 1951, p. 8.
37. Ibid., pp. 4–7; Hallion and Gorn, *On the Frontier*, pp. 386–387. Vortex generators were also tested on the final flight of NACA X-1 #2 on October 23, 1951. The rocket cut out after two ignition attempts, and the aircraft glided to a landing. The aircraft was subsequently grounded due to possible fatigue failure of the nitrogen spheres.
38. Ibid., p. 149; Hallion and Gorn, *On the Frontier*, pp. 386–387.
39. Peebles, ed., *Spoken Word*, pp. 52–53, 77.
40. Hallion, *Supersonic Flight*, pp. 149–150.
41. Ibid., p. 135; Hallion and Gorn, *On the Frontier*, p. 388.
42. Ibid., p. 151; Peebles, ed., *The Spoken Word: Recollections of Dryden History, The Early Years*, pp. 103–104.
43. Butchart served with another outstanding young naval airman who became a close friend—then-Ensign George H.W. Bush, later President of the United States.

44. Earl R. Keener, James R. Peel, and Julia B. Woodbridge, "Tabulated Pressure Coefficients and Aerodynamic Characteristics Measured in Flight on the Wing of the Douglas D-558-1 Airplane Throughout the Normal-Force Range at Mach Numbers of 0.67, 0.74, 0.78, and 0.82," NACA RM L50L12a (January 29, 1951), pp. 1, 4–5. One possible reason for the lack of analysis in the reports is the outbreak of the Korean War in June 1950. The straight-wing U.S. Air Force and Navy jet fighters were outclassed by the swept-wing Soviet MiG-15, which entered combat in November 1950, forcing immediate deployment of the swept-wing USAF F-86A.

45. Melvin Sadoff, William S. Roden, and John M. Eggleston, "Flight Investigation of the Longitudinal Stability and Control Characteristics of the Douglas D-558-1 Airplane (BuAero No. 37972) at Mach Numbers up to 0.89," NACA RM L51D18 (June 25, 1951), p. 4.

46. Ibid., pp. 1, 7, 16–18. The all-moving stabilizer on the F-86 gave U.S. pilots an advantage over the Soviet MiG-15 in air combat during the Korean War. An F-86 could dive away from an attacking MiG-15 and retain control despite reaching transonic and low supersonic speeds. This was because the MiG-15 still used fixed-stabilizer and movable elevators, making it unstable at transonic speeds and incapable of reaching Mach 1 under any flight conditions.

47. Ellwyn E. Angle and Euclid C. Holleman, "Longitudinal Frequency-Response Characteristics of the D-558-1 Airplane as Determined from Experimental Transient-Response Histories to a Mach Number of 0.90," NACA RM L51K28 (February 11, 1952), pp. 1, 4, 7–8.

48. Hallion, *Supersonic Flight*, pp. 150–151; Libis, *Skystreak, Skyrocket, & Stiletto*, p. 32.

49. Letter, Hartley A. Soulé to NACA Headquarters, "Request for Comments on Abandonment of D-558-1 Vertical-Tail Load Investigation," December 19, 1952.

50. Letter, Donald R. Bellman to NACA, "Looseness of Stabilizer Mountings for the D-558-1 Airplane," November 5, 1952; letter, Donald R. Bellman to NACA, "Reply to Request for Information on D-558-1 Vertical-Tail Load Investigation," January 12, 1953.

51. Hallion, *Supersonic Flight*, pp. 152–153; Libis, *Skystreak, Skyrocket, & Stiletto*, p. 122; Hallion and Gorn, *On the Frontier*, p. 388. The fates of the different research aircraft reflected their perceived importance. The X-1 #1, in which Yeager made the first supersonic flight, was given to the Smithsonian Institution after its retirement

in May 1950. It is currently on display at the National Air and Space Museum in Washington, DC. It shares the main entrance with the Wright Flyer, the *Spirit of St. Louis*, the X-15 #1, and the Apollo 11 Command Module. After Crossfield's last flight in the third D-558-1, it joined the first D-558-1 in dead storage at Edwards Air Force Base. Both aircraft were subsequently transferred. The first D-558-1 was sent to California State Polytechnic College in San Luis Obispo, CA, in 1957. It was transferred to the National Museum of Naval Aviation in 1964, where it was restored and remains today. The third D-558-1 was sent for display at the Marine Corps Air-Ground Museum at Quantico, VA. The aircraft was displayed outdoors and rapidly deteriorated. Fortunately, it was transferred to the Carolina Aviation Museum, restored, and put on display in 2001.

52. Libis, *Skystreak, Skyrocket, & Stiletto*, pp. 116–122.
53. Soulé, "Request for Comments on Abandonment of D-558-1 Vertical-Tail Load Investigation."
54. Becker, *The High-Speed Frontier*, p. 96.
55. Hallion, *Supersonic Flight*, pp. 152–153.
56. Hanson, *Engineer in Charge*, pp. 312–327; Becker, *The High-Speed Frontier*, pp. 98–114.

The second D-558-2, NACA 144, parked on the ramp at South Base. Modifications made to allow air launch included the removal of the jet engine and fuel tanks. Between the air launch and the increased rocket burn time, the craft's maximum speed was doubled. On November 20, 1953, this aircraft made the first Mach 2 flight. (NASA)

CHAPTER 3

Proving the Swept Wing:
The Douglas D-558-2 Skyrocket

*It was actual flight time that was the real education—five minutes in
the air with the experimental ship was worth ten hours of study on the ground,
and gradually I understood the magnitude of the horizon that lay out there,
unknown, waiting to be probed in the rocket ship.*
—William "Bill" Bridgeman[1]

Ed Heinemann and the Douglas design team had always envisioned that the
D-558 project would entail multiple aircraft configurations, consistent with
what the Navy's Bureau of Aeronautics envisioned coming from the program.
Originally, the Navy contract awarded to Douglas called for six D-558 phase 1
aircraft, with different combinations of side and nose inlets and straight wings
with three different airfoil sections. Phase 2 involved adding rocket boosters
and replacing the TG-180 jet engine with a smaller Westinghouse 24C turbojet
on three of the aircraft. Phase 3 originally called for a mockup of an operational
combat aircraft.[2]

This plan underwent a radical change due both to the capture of research
material from Germany, after the war, and to R.T. Jones's paper on swept
wings. In the early summer of 1945, John Stack suggested to Douglas that the
D-558-1 incorporate a 35° swept wing. However, it was not until after analysis of German documents brought back to America by the Naval Technical
Mission to Europe ("NavTechMisEu"), one of whose members was Douglas
engineer A.M.O. Smith, that the NACA, the Bureau of Aeronautics, and
Douglas agreed to examine a swept-wing derivation of the D-558 program
effort. The formal request by the Navy and the NACA for the new configuration came in mid-August 1945.

A practical consideration was the fact that the existing turbojet engines lacked
the thrust capacity to reach high transonic speeds. As a result, Douglas, the Navy,
and the NACA agreed from the program's outset that a rocket-powered research
aircraft would be needed to evaluate the full potential of swept wings at transonic and supersonic speeds. Fortunately, with the development of the Reaction

NACA 144 at South Base. The "Turbine Ex" is the exhaust for the turbopump, which fed fuel to the rocket engine. The "LOX Prime" was part of the liquid-oxygen vent/jettison system. The X's on the forward and aft fuselages were photo reference marks. South Base was built during World War II as a training field for B-24 and P-38 pilots. It was the home for the NACA contingent from 1946 to 1954, when it moved to the current facility. (NASA)

Motors, Inc., (RMI) 6000C4 engine—which the AAF designated the XLR-11, and the Navy the XLR-8—just such an engine existed that could be applied to the D-558. The swept-wing D-558 would take off and climb to test altitude using a Westinghouse 24C jet engine. The pilot would then employ the RMI rocket engine to accelerate into the high transonic and low supersonic regime. Once this was completed, the rocket would shut down, and the pilot would restart the jet engine for the descent to a powered landing. Two separate engines and fuel systems would have to fit within the fuselage. Douglas engineers found it impossible to squeeze both a rocket and a jet engine into the D-558-1's already-narrow fuselage, so they had to start from scratch in designing the D-558-2. The result was a much shapelier and elegant design, which became one of the iconic symbols of aeronautical progress in the postwar era.

The D-558 Phase 2 Design Process

Kermit E. Van Every was assigned the task of designing the new aircraft, and he faced a number of design requirements. Among these was the Navy managers' requirement that the swept-wing version should have the low-speed and relatively benign stall characteristics of the straight-wing D-558-1. Douglas engineers faced a difficult task in meeting this requirement, as swept wings were known to have poor low-speed and stall behavior. At the same time, they had to ensure that the aircraft would be stable at high speeds.

The D-558-1's cylindrical fuselage and nose inlet were abandoned in the new design. Instead, the new aircraft had an elongated fuselage; a flush windshield similar to that of the XS-1 enhanced the plane's sleek lines. Flush air inlets were located low on the sides of the forward fuselage. The fuselage diameter had to be increased, as compared with that of the D-558-1, for it contained the Westinghouse 24C jet engine and two tanks holding 250 gallons of jet fuel, the LR-11 rocket engine and tanks holding 195 gallons of water/alcohol fuel, 180 gallons of liquid oxygen (LOX), 11 gallons of 90-percent hydrogen peroxide to power the turbopump, and the helium used to pressurize the fuel system. The nose and main landing gear also retracted into the fuselage. Finally, the flight data instrumentation, totaling between 800 and 1,100 pounds, completed the payload.

The rocket engine was mounted at the rear of the fuselage. The jet engine was positioned in the middle, with the air-inlet ducts passing around the liquid-oxygen tank to reach the engine. The two tanks for the jet fuel were above the jet engine. The water/alcohol fuel tank was located above the jet engine's exhaust pipe, which was angled slightly downward and exited under the aft fuselage. Saying that the airplane was oddly arranged—to say nothing of the mix of power plants—would be an understatement. In fact, the NACA never had another such amalgamation.

The D-558-1's straight cylindrical fuselage cross section was retained for the D-558-2 at the wing-fuselage intersection, which gave it a measure of "area ruling" before the advent of the concept. Had the fuselage been an ogival body, like the X-1's, local airflow velocity at the wing-fuselage juncture would have increased, causing early shockwave formation and, therefore, an increase in transonic drag. Its wing had a 35° sweep and a span of 25 feet, representing a compromise between low- and high-speed requirements. This also resulted in a lower aspect ratio than the D-558-1's straight wings, further reducing drag. But it also complicated making the airplane safe to fly at low speed. Kermit Van Every blended a variety of elements to ensure that the D-558-2's swept wing was suitable. He selected a modest 35° sweep angle since this was already, by the beginning of the postwar era, a much-studied planform, tested by German wartime researchers, employed on the postwar Bell L-39 swept-wing test bed (a Navy-funded research program), and intended for the AAF's XP-86 (prototype for the F-86) and the planned Boeing XB-47 jet bomber. Van Every replaced the NACA 65 series airfoil used on the D-558-1 with a higher-lift NACA 63 series airfoil. The latter had better low-speed/stall characteristics yet did not sacrifice much in high-speed performance. Next, he increased the wing's area to

175 square feet compared to the D-558-1's 150.7 square feet. He gave the wing a "reverse taper" (from a 10-percent thickness-chord ratio at the root to a more lift-friendly 12-percent thickness-chord ratio at the tip). Finally, he added flaps, wing fences, and automatic Handley Page wing-leading-edge slats to improve its low-speed behavior. The slats could either operate automatically or be locked open or closed. As with its predecessor, the D-558-2's horizontal stabilizers were thinner than the wings, could be moved independently of the elevators for high-speed control, and were positioned high on the vertical tail to remain out of the wing wake. Van Every increased the stabilizer's critical Mach number further by giving it a sharper 40° sweep, rather than the 35° sweep of the wings.[3]

First Flights

Douglas rolled out the first D-558-2 Skyrocket (BuNo 37973) on November 10, 1947, less than a month after Yeager's Mach 1 flight. The aircraft was not complete, however, as the LR-8 rocket engine had not yet been installed because the turbopump needed to supply it with propellants was not yet ready.[4] In its place, a cone-shaped fairing was added for the initial flights. Once the ceremonies were finished, ground tests of the aircraft began. The turbojet engine underwent test runs on November 21. The aircraft had a flush canopy (like the XS-1) that added to its racy looks but afforded its pilot minimal forward visibility during approach and landing. Consequently, by December this had been replaced with a standard raised canopy with a V-shaped windshield. This provided much better visibility for the pilot even if it did spoil the aircraft's sleek lines. Once these final details were complete, the D-558-2 was loaded on a flatbed truck and wrapped in tarps to conceal its shape. The convoy left for Muroc on December 10, 1947.

After arriving at Muroc, the aircraft underwent further checkouts and the instrumentation was installed, which took the rest of December. The pilot selected for the early flights of the first D-558-2 was John F. Martin, a Douglas test pilot since 1940 who had a background as a United Airlines pilot. He had served as test pilot on the A-20, A-26, and C-54.

Initial taxi tests were made on January 5 and February 2, 1948, clearing the way for the first flight on February 4. Problems were experienced on the first flight; the already-anemic Westinghouse J34 engine was sluggish during startup and acceleration. Things did not improve much when the takeoff roll across the lakebed took *15,000 feet*, and, once aloft, Martin discovered the airplane suffered from a persistent "Dutch roll" lateral-directional (roll-yaw) oscillation, an early indication that Douglas needed to increase the height (and hence area) of the vertical fin, which it subsequently did, by 18 inches.[5]

A D-558-2 jet and JATO rocket take off in 1949. Because the LR-8 rocket engine was not initially fitted, the program had to make do with this interim propulsion system to carry out research with the aircraft. The takeoff roll was long, hindering maximum performance. Modifications were subsequently made to allow the D-558-2 to be air-launched from a B-29. (NASA)

To correct the long takeoff roll, Douglas engineers prudently decided to attach two jet-assisted-takeoff (JATO) solid rocket boosters to the aircraft for an added boost. The first JATO-boosted flight was made on July 13, 1948. The rockets were fired midway through the roll and jettisoned after takeoff. This shortened the takeoff run to 8,210 feet, a little over half the distance required with the jet alone. As a result, the use of JATO rockets became standard for the jet-powered, ground-takeoff flights; they not only shortened the takeoff roll, but they also conserved fuel and improved safety. Various combinations of two, three, or four rockets were tested, with four rockets deemed best. Martin's last D-558-2 flight was on August 25, 1948. Skystreak veteran Gene May now took over the Douglas test duties, making his first flight in the airplane on September 16, 1948. May began an extensive flight-test effort that lasted more than a year.[6]

By this time, the second D-558-2 (BuNo 37974), intended for the NACA, had been delivered to Muroc, and May made a pair of dive demonstration flights on November 2 and 7, 1948, after which the aircraft was formally turned over to the NACA on December 1, 1948. Like the first Skyrocket, the second D-558-2 also lacked the LR-8 rocket engine when it was delivered because the planned turbopump to feed it was still unavailable. In spite of this, the NACA accepted the aircraft since initial flights were to be made for general stability and control and air-load measurements at Mach 0.85, both of which could be done with the jet engine alone. Once the LR-8 engine was available, the second Skyrocket would be returned to Douglas and the rocket installed.

Engine problems and the installation and calibration of instrumentation lasted through the winter and spring of 1949, delaying the start of research operations. NACA research pilot Robert Champine made the first NACA flight on May 24 for pilot familiarization, instrumentation checkout, and general handling characteristics. Champine made two more research flights in June for data on stability, control, and wing bending, as well as for wing twist measurements. During the second flight, the cockpit camera caught fire, filling the cockpit with smoke. Two airspeed calibration flights were made in July, followed by a lateral-control-exploration flight in August.[7]

The dynamic-lateral-stability data collected in the first two NACA Skyrocket flights were analyzed. Test pilots made sudden control inputs, and the onboard instrumentation evaluated aircraft response. One test involved "a lateral oscillation of the airplane resulting from abrupt deflection and release of the rudder." The research memorandum noted, "This maneuver was made at a Mach number of 0.63 and an altitude of 12,000 feet with the airplane in the clean condition. The data show the oscillation is slow to damp out especially at small amplitudes where the oscillation is practically of constant amplitude. The period of the oscillation is 1.6 seconds."[8]

A second test maneuver made was a lateral oscillation while in the landing condition (gear and flaps down). The memorandum noted, "This oscillation was again induced by abrupt deflection and release of the rudder. In the landing condition, the airplane performs a constant-amplitude oscillation with a period of approximately 2.7 seconds."[9]

A more complicated test maneuver measured the D-558-2's behavior during part of the landing approach. The report described the events as follows: "During the first part of this time history, between 30 and 44 seconds, the pilot did not attempt to stop the oscillation by use of the ailerons or rudder and the airplane performed a constant-amplitude oscillation. From 44 seconds to 60 seconds the pilot used the ailerons and was able to damp the oscillation. Even though the pilot can damp the oscillation, the oscillation is objectionable particularly during landing approaches and landings because the controls must be moved almost constantly. The rough-air handling qualities of the airplane would probably be particularly objectionable."[10]

The conclusion of the memorandum was that the D-558-2 showed differing dynamic-lateral-stability characteristics, depending on the situation. In a "clean" condition (flaps and landing gear up, slats locked), the airplane's lateral oscillations were lightly damped, particularly when they were of small amplitudes. With the D-558-2 in a landing condition, however, the airplane had neutral oscillatory stability, which was indicated by the airplane undergoing a

The NACA 144 undergoing wing-strain-gauge calibration in a hangar. Sandbags were piled on the upper wing to simulate aerodynamic forces. Strain-gauge readings were compared to calculated forces to determine any errors. These were used by the "computers" who reduced onboard data after a flight. The number of engineers required for the calibrations was impressive. (NASA)

constant-amplitude oscillation. The pilot could damp this oscillation, but doing so required vigorous control inputs, activity that was considered objectionable by the pilot, as it required almost continuous control-surface movements. These, in turn, rendered the D-558-2's handling poor in less than ideal conditions, such as turbulence.

This was not the only handling problem the D-558-2 would experience. A bigger issue soon came to light.

Pitch-Up: The Insidious Threat

The seventh NACA flight, with Champine as the pilot, came on August 8, 1949. The plan involved making a 4-g turn at Mach 0.6. Without warning, the Skyrocket's nose pitched up with an acceleration of 6 g's during the turn. Champine countered with full-down elevator, and the aircraft recovered. As a precaution, he immediately landed. What he had experienced was the first proof that a swept-wing aircraft would pitch up during a hard turn. Tests made using models had hinted at the possibility that longitudinal instability would occur, resulting in the nose's pitching up, but what the models had not indicated was the severity of the problem.[11]

The source of the pitch-up problem was a combination of several factors. A. Scott Crossfield, an NACA research pilot who made 62 D-558-2 flights, described the sequence: "The air we fly in doesn't like high sweep angles. It doesn't like severe taper ratios. And it doesn't like low aspect ratios. And the D-558-2 had a little bit or a lot of every one of these. And it was classic in what it did as a swept wing.... The tips of the [D-558-2] wings tended to stall before the roots of the wings. And if that's aft of the center of gravity, the airplane wants to pitch-up."[12]

Pitch-up posed a number of risks, not least of which was loss of control. In a turning dogfight, a swept-wing fighter experiencing a pitch-up could be overstressed by g forces; the sudden loss of airspeed resulting from a pitch-up could make an aircraft vulnerable to an enemy fighter's attack or could cause it to enter a spin and be unable to recover. Pitch-up posed risks in day-to-day operations. A swept-wing aircraft maneuvering during a landing approach might pitch up, stall, and have insufficient altitude and airspeed to recover before crashing. In an extreme case, structural failure could occur. With swept-wing F-86s entering service and a new generation of swept-wing fighters and bombers in development, understanding pitch-up assumed critical and urgent importance.

The NACA research effort with the second D-558-2 now focused on the pitch-up issue. Joining the project was another NACA research pilot, John Griffith. After Griffith's checkout flight on September 12, 1949, he and Champine split flying duties. Griffith experienced an inadvertent pitch-up on his November 1, 1949, flight. The sequence was similar to one Champine had experienced on a flight made nearly 3 months before. Griffith made a 4-g turn at Mach 0.6, and the aircraft became longitudinally unstable, triggering a pitch-up. Griffith attempted to fly beyond the instability; the D-558-2's angle of attack increased, and the aircraft yawed and rocked, then snap-rolled, turning completely upside down. Griffith recovered, confirmed that the Skyrocket had not been damaged, and continued the flight.[13]

Champine later described the experience of a D-558-2 pitch-up: "If you pulled up and got 4 or 5 gs, it would suddenly stall in such a manner that the lift distribution on the wing would cause it to pitch-up violently. It would go to extremely high angles of attack, between 45 and 60 degrees, and then it would start to roll violently, so the aircraft became completely and totally out of control—just spinning around in the sky. Once you fell into it you had no way of controlling it."[14]

Griffith's pitch-up experience was analyzed in a 1951 NACA research memorandum as follows:

> [T]he pilot attempted to fly the airplane in the normal-force-coefficient range where the airplane was unstable (times between 11 and 14 sec). After the airplane pitched up, the airplane first performed an unsteady rolling motion. The pilot used the rudder in attempting to control this rolling motion and caused the airplane to perform a 360° snaproll. The data indicate that very large angles of sideslip were reached during the snaproll. No sideslip-angle measurements were obtained during the maneuver, but integration of the yawing velocity indicates that sideslip angles on the order of 30° to 35° were approached. A maximum lateral acceleration of about 1.1g occurred during the snaproll. This lateral acceleration corresponds to a side force on the airplane of about 10,800 pounds. The distribution of side force on the airplane between the fuselage and vertical tail is not known, but it is likely that the load on the vertical tail, during the oscillatory yawed flight, approached the vertical tail design limit of 8,700 pounds. The maximum rolling velocity which occurred during the snaproll is not known as the 2.6-radian-per-second range of the rolling-velocity recorder was exceeded, but it is likely that the maximum rolling velocity was on the order of 3.5 to 4.0 radians per second. In recovering from the snap-roll the airplane again reached a negative normal acceleration of 3.0g.
>
> The pilot reported and the recording instruments showed that airplane buffeting occurred at normal accelerations slightly less than the acceleration at which the airplane became unstable. This buffeting served as a warning of the approach of instability. If the elevator is moved down when the airplane buffeting occurs, the response of the airplane is good and the instability can be avoided. In the pilot's opinion the airplane is unflyable in accelerated flight in the lift-coefficient range in which it is unstable. If the pitch-up resulting from the instability is not checked by moving the elevator down as soon as it is noticed by the pilot, the angle of attack increases very rapidly and violent rolling and yawing motions occur when the high angles of attack are reached.[15]

Between May 1949 and January 1950, 21 NACA research flights had been made with the second D-558-2. The bulk of these were for longitudinal- and lateral-stability, lateral-control, and stall data. The results of these flights were summarized in a series of NACA research memorandums.[16] Beyond describing the pitch-up characteristics of the D-558-2, one of the reports also gave a preliminary assessment of the D-558-2's longitudinal-stability and control characteristics based on these flights. It noted the following:

> With the slats locked and the flaps up, the airplane was longitudinally unstable at normal-force coefficients greater than approximately 0.8 in steady flight at low speeds and in maneuvering flight at Mach numbers up to at least 0.65. No data were obtained at high normal-force coefficients at Mach numbers greater than about 0.65 because of the power limitations of the airplane with only the jet engine installed. The instability proved objective to the pilots, particularly in accelerated flight because of the tendency for the airplane to pitch to high angles of attack very rapidly and because violent rolling and yawing motions sometimes occurred when the high angles of attack were reached. The instability probably resulted from a large increase in the rate of change of effective downwash at the tail with increase in angle of attack at moderate and high angles of attack.
>
> With the flaps down and the slats locked the longitudinal stability characteristics in steady flight at low speeds were very similar to the characteristics with the flaps up and the slats locked except that the instability occurred at a higher normal-force coefficient.
>
> The degree of instability present with the slats unlocked and the flaps up or down was much less than with the slats locked and the pilots had only minor objections to the longitudinal characteristics of the airplane.
>
> In steady flight in the Mach number range from 0.50 to 0.87 the airplane is stable longitudinally and no abrupt trim changes occurred up to the highest Mach number reached, 0.87. The data indicate that only a slight reduction in the relative elevator-stabilizer effectiveness occurred in going from a Mach number of about 0.55 to 0.85.[17]

Into the Supersonic: The Skyrocket Turns to Air Launch

With the initial jet-powered NACA research flights completed, the second D-558-2 was returned to Douglas for modifications. The shortcomings of the ground takeoffs, even with JATO rockets, were now apparent. Bridgeman later described the experience of a JATO takeoff in the Skyrocket:

A mile of runway is eaten up and she hasn't hit 100 [mph]. Up to 80, now 90, there it is, 100. Hit the first two JATOs. A second, and a kick in the fanny, and another kick as the remaining JATOs fire off. She's up to 180, roaring down the lakebed. This is the time; pull her nose up…this is no F-80! Without her rockets, climbing on jet alone, I can feel that she is far underpowered; she handles like a truck, heavy and large. I've got hold of something new all right.[18]

Clearly, something as simple as a blown tire from overheating during the long takeoff runs could spell disaster. Something had to be done, and the simplest solution was modifying the D-558-2s for air launching from a Boeing B-29 mother ship.

Though the first and second D-558-2s had been delivered without the LR-8 rocket engine, the third (BuNo 37975) was equipped with the rocket power plant (as well as its J34 turbojet) from the start. Gene May made the first flights in the third D-558-2 beginning on January 8, 1949. On June 24, 1949, May flew this aircraft through the speed of sound, noting later that the "flight got glassy smooth, placid, quite the smoothest flying I had ever known."[19]

But despite this, the D-558-2's performance was still disappointing, a byproduct of having both the Westinghouse 24C turbojet and LR-8 rocket engine. Given the large amount of kerosene needed for the J34 turbojet for the climb to altitude and descent to landing, the D-558-2 had insufficient rocket propellant—the diluted alcohol/water fuel and liquid-oxygen oxidizer—to permit the Skyrocket to penetrate far into the supersonic regime. An NACA study showed that a jet-only ground takeoff was limited to a top speed of Mach 0.9. Using the LR-8 for an added boost during ground takeoff resulted in a limiting top speed of Mach 0.95. NACA engineers concluded that the small increase in speed was not justified by the added risk of an LR-8 rocket ground takeoff. Following the fourth Douglas flight, on March 27, 1949, May had noted, "[The] ultimate performance of the aircraft will never be achieved with the limited supply of rocket fuel."[20]

Air launch enabled getting the most out of the aircraft by eliminating the need for using the scarce rocket propellants to help kick the Skyrocket off the ground. Better still was turning the Skyrocket into an all-rocket boost-glider like the Bell X-1. Douglas engineers calculated that by removing the jet engine and adding more fuel for the rocket (using the space previously taken up by the jet engine and its inlets and exhaust system), an air launch would produce a top speed of Mach 1.46 to 1.6, dramatically increasing the Skyrocket's value as a research tool. The NACA's chief of research, Hugh L. Dryden, supported the Douglas proposal, suggesting the company modify the second aircraft to an all-rocket/air-launch configuration at the same time the LR-8 rocket was installed. The third could be modified at the same time and used by Douglas in an air-launch demonstration before it was turned over to the NACA.

Dryden sent a letter to the Navy on September 1, 1949, strongly recommending the modifications. Navy managers agreed, and, on November 25, 1949, the Navy Bureau of Aeronautics issued a contract change ordering the second and third D-558-2 aircraft to be modified to an air-launch configuration and a B-29 modified as the mother ship, which, by the Navy's nomenclature system, was designated a P2B-1S Superfortress. (The B-29 already modified for the XS-1 could not be used to drop the Skyrocket, as the sweptback wings and tail surfaces of the D-558-2 necessitated a completely different geometric set of modifications to the bomb bay.)

The third D-558-2 would retain the J34 jet engine and inlets, the LR-8 rocket engine, and the existing fuel system. The only modifications would be the addition of retractable launch hooks. The aircraft was trucked back to the Douglas plant in El Segundo. Bridgeman made the first air launch of a D-558-2 on September 8, 1950, using only the turbojet. Five more air launches followed, the last two using both jet and rocket power. Bridgeman described his experiences on his November 27, 1950, flight:

> Ten…nine…eight…seven…. My hand is on the data switch… six…five. There. One hand on the wheel, one wrapped around the throttle. Four…three…two…one…drop!
>
> From out of the dark, protective belly of the [B-]29 the world bursts over me in bright light. She's free. I'm away from the mother ship clean and free. It works…. Rapidly I click on the four rocket tubes…. She heads out, still losing altitude but trimmed nose-up…. I check the rocket pressures. In the green…. I pull it up and begin the climb…. Too much…. I drop the nose a fraction. Too far. Up again; it is now a matter of calculation and feel…. I push her nose over for the speed run. She accelerates rapidly in the thin sky-meadow of the higher altitude.
>
> The buffet! Okay, that's .91. But she doesn't stop; she still buffets although we are through into .92, the other side, where she smooths out always. The buffeting continues… .93, .94…. I search the instrument panel and there's the answer—the turbine out temperature is overboard by 500[°]. At once I jerk the throttle to idle, but it is not fast enough; the engine gives up. She flames out, loses thrust, and pitches over, throwing me in the harness and against the panel…. At once, in rapid succession, the rocket tubes fail. The altitude is too much for the jet engine. When she

pitched forward she unported the rocket fuel, starving off the tubes—all in a matter of ten seconds.[21]

With the completion of the company's acceptance flights, the aircraft was turned over to the NACA on December 15, 1950, and given the designation NACA 145. Scott Crossfield became the project pilot. He made pilot-familiarization and instrumentation check flights on December 22 and 27, 1950. These were jet-only flights, as were the initial two research flights in March and April 1951. Crossfield made the first NACA jet-rocket flight on May 17, but he shut down the jet engine during the flight because of combustion instability. Joining the project at this point was NACA pilot Walter P. Jones, who made his first Skyrocket flight on July 20, 1951. Early activity in the series focused on lateral and longitudinal stability evaluated via aileron rolls and elevator pulses, as well as accelerated turns and pitch maneuvers.

Longitudinal-stability characteristics were determined with the aircraft in a clean condition and in turning flight at Mach numbers between 0.5 and 0.96, at altitudes between 19,000 and 36,000 feet. The Skyrocket was stable up to moderate values of normal-force coefficients. At higher coefficients, however, a constant elevator deflection triggered a rapid pitching of the aircraft. At the start of the pitch-up, the stick force lightened and the pilot reversed the elevator control in an attempt to stop the pitch-up. This was unsuccessful, and both the angle of attack and normal-force coefficient increased until a recovery was made.

In an effort to control the pitch-up, an outboard wing fence was added to both wings. Jones made the first flight on October 18, 1951, with the wing fences, at Mach 0.7. A second flight was made on November 9 at Mach 0.95. The pitch-up flights were halted until the following summer.[22]

The all-rocket second D-558-2 required more extensive changes before it returned to the air. It was sent back to the Douglas plant in El Segundo in early 1950 and disassembled. The two jet fuel tanks were removed, and, in their place, a liquid-oxygen tank and an alcohol/water tank were added. This almost doubled the fuel supply to 345 gallons of liquid oxygen and 378 gallons of alcohol/water. The jet engine was removed, and its exhaust in the lower aft fuselage was faired over. Air inlets were also removed and flush panels added. The LR-8 rocket engine and its turbopump were mounted in the aft fuselage. The result was an aircraft optimized for high-speed/high-altitude research flights.[23]

On November 8, 1950, the second D-558-2 was loaded under the P2B-1S mother ship and flown back to what was now Edwards Air Force Base after Muroc had been renamed. As with the third D-558-2, Bridgeman would make the initial flights with the second one before it was turned over to the NACA for research work. This proved difficult. Several attempts were aborted

A jet-powered D-558-2 parked on the ramp at South Base in 1949. The jet intakes are located low on the forward fuselage, and the exhaust is on the underside of the rear fuselage. The aircraft has been fitted with wing fences, and the wing slats are extended. The original NACA shield appears on the vertical tail but was subsequently replaced by a yellow band with a winged NACA insignia. (NASA)

shortly before launch. At one point, a sign appeared on the hangar wall: "Old Skyrockets Never Die—They Just Jettison Away." Bridgeman later said, "An experimental test pilot has to be right on the edge, at the peak of his performance; and the delay was sapping this capacity."[24] Finally, on January 26, 1951, the Douglas team's luck seemed about to change. Then, as the countdown reached less than a minute to launch, Bridgeman saw that a rocket pressure gauge was dropping. Bridgeman radioed the P2B-1S's pilot, George Jansen: "No drop. This is an abort," and began shutting down the systems. Bridgeman was startled to hear Jansen begin the 10-second countdown. Bridgeman radioed: "Don't drop me, George!" but Jansen had his thumb on the microphone key and could not hear Bridgeman's calls.

Bridgeman frantically pushed the circuit breakers back into place and centered the control stick, hoping he had not missed anything. When the launch count reached zero, the Skyrocket separated; once clear of the bomber, Bridgeman fired the four rockets in rapid sequence. They ignited despite the pressure readings, and the Skyrocket accelerated upward.

By now, 35 seconds had passed since he had been dropped, and Bridgeman made his first radio call: "George, I *told* you not to drop me!" Colonel Frank "Pete" Everest, the Air Force chase pilot, replied, "You got keen friends,

Bridgeman." Everest added, "He's accelerating away from me in a climb. Looks like he's doing all right…all four rockets appear to have lit off." Because of the higher speed, the elevators were ineffective and Bridgeman had to use the movable stabilizers for pitch control. The peak speed reached was Mach 1.28 in a slight dive.[25]

To prevent a repetition, a green light was rigged up in the P2B-1S cockpit to indicate that the D-558-2 was ready for launch, to be triggered by the research pilot in the test vehicle when he was ready in case there was another sticky microphone. The launch countdown was also shortened. It was not until April 5, 1951, that the second Douglas flight was made, reaching a peak speed of Mach 1.36 at 46,500 feet. Bridgeman again experienced severe lateral oscillations, forcing him to shut off all four chambers of the engine before burnout. The fix for the oscillations was to add a rudder lock, which prevented it from moving at speeds above Mach 1. The all-rocket D-558-2 had been proven airworthy and had proven that an air launch was feasible. The Navy, Douglas, and Bridgeman now began a series of maximum-speed and -altitude flights.

Bridgeman began the speed buildup on May 18, 1951. After launch, he climbed to about 55,000 feet and made a –0.8-g pushover to begin the speed run. He reached a maximum speed of Mach 1.72 at 62,000 feet before the engine shut down. This was followed on June 11 with a flight that reached Mach 1.79. Bridgeman was now the fastest man on Earth. Both these flights exceeded the most optimistic performance estimates made by Douglas for an all-rocket/air-launched Skyrocket.

The Douglas engineers decided to try for even faster speeds. Doing this, however, required that a lower 0.25-g pushover be made. The flight was scheduled for June 23. Bridgeman was successfully launched; he ignited the rocket and began the climb. Reaching 60,000 feet, he made the 0.25-g pushover and accelerated in a shallow dive. When the aircraft reached Mach 1.5 it began rolling violently, throwing Bridgeman from side to side as the wings rocked back and forth as much as 70° in less than a second. Bridgeman's attempts to bring the aircraft back under control actually aggravated the problem, and, as a last resort, he shut the engine down.

But instead of calming, the rocking motion increased. Bridgeman pulled back on the control wheel and made a 4-g pullout. Now headed toward the safety of the lakebed and accompanied by the F-86 chase plane, he made a successful landing. NACA engineers determined that the aircraft had reached a top speed of Mach 1.85 at 63,000 feet. This represented a new speed record for a rocket-powered aircraft and was well beyond what both the NACA and the Navy had originally envisioned as the upper-end of D-558-2 performance.

But NACA managers were troubled by the continuation of the Douglas flight test project. The all-rocket aircraft had been proven airworthy, and NACA

An in-flight photo of a Skyrocket descending toward the lakebed with an F-86 chase plane following behind. Chase planes were key elements in undertaking research flights safely. The chase pilot provides an external set of eyes to warn of problems and calls out the research airplane's altitude above the lakebed. (NASA)

researchers did not view record flights favorably. Speed and altitude records set during research flights were not significant. When setting records became the reason for a flight, airplanes crashed and pilots died. Research aircraft, their view held, were for use in collecting data for future aircraft development, and it was time—even beyond time—for the agency to have received the aircraft back for its own extensive research. Ultimately, the Navy agreed, but only after signing off on two more Douglas flights.

The first of these came on August 7, 1951, as a maximum-speed flight. To avoid the instability experienced on previous flights, the initial pushover load factor was 0.8 g. Bridgeman then reduced this to 0.6 g. The aircraft became left-wing-heavy, however, and his attempt to correct this with the ailerons was unsuccessful, so he raised the loading back to 0.8 g, which restored lateral stability. Bridgeman then reduced it to 0.6 g until the rocket engine shut down. When the data reduction was complete, engineers found that the Skyrocket had reached Mach 1.87, with a possible error of ±0.05, at a pressure altitude of 67,300 feet. The maximum airspeed was calculated to be 1,243 mph ± 33 mph. Bridgeman believed the aircraft capable of even higher speeds, stating, "[M]agic Mach 2 is attainable if lateral control can be maintained."[26]

Bridgeman's final Skyrocket flight was on August 15, a maximum-altitude flight. Charles Pettingall, chief aerodynamicist in the Douglas testing division, calculated the flightpath this time. It was designed to exceed the 72,395-foot altitude record set by the U.S. Army Air Corps–National Geographic Society *Explorer II* piloted balloon flight in 1935. After launch, Bridgeman ignited the rocket and reached a peak speed of Mach 1.35, slower than the maximum speeds attained in earlier launches. Passing through 63,000 feet, the D-558-2 began rolling to the left. Even with full opposite aileron input, the airplane was slow to recover. The rocket engine shut down, and the aircraft coasted upward under its own momentum. Bridgeman described the view from an altitude no other human had reached: "Out of the tiny window slits there is the earth, whipped clean of civilization, a vast relief map with papier-mâché mountains and mirrored lakes and seas. The desert is not the same desert I have seen for two years. The coastline is sharply drawn with little vacant bays and inlets, a lacy edge to the big brown pieces of earth."[27]

When calibration corrections were made to the air pressure data, results indicated that the Skyrocket had reached a pressure altitude of 77,500 feet ± 500 feet. But the radar data had to be corrected for errors in the radar slant range and elevation angle, as well as for such factors as beacon delay, atmospheric refraction, and Earth's curvature. Once done, the Skyrocket's altitude above sea level was shown to have been 79,500 feet ± 65 feet. Bridgeman was now both the fastest and highest-flying man on Earth.[28]

Beyond setting the new speed and altitude records, the Douglas demonstration flights significantly increased knowledge of the D-558-2 flying qualities and handling. On one of the first supersonic flights, an uncontrollable lateral oscillation occurred, forcing the pilot to abandon the speed run to Mach 1.4. The magnitude of the oscillations was inversely related to the angle of attack: the lower the angle of attack, the more violent the oscillations. At higher speeds, such as on the Mach 1.85 flight, a different problem appeared. If the pilot made the pushover to begin the speed runs at too low a g-force, severe oscillations were triggered.[29]

The all-rocket second D-558-2 was turned over to the NACA on August 31, 1951, and given the designation NACA 144. Research flights with both of the Skyrockets could now begin.[30]

The First NACA Supersonic Skyrocket Research Flights

There were two different Skyrocket configurations in NACA hands: the second D-558-2/NACA 144, with its all-rocket configuration, and the third D-558-2/ NACA 145, with a jet-rocket propulsion system. This dictated that each plane

The D-558-2 was not only used for aerodynamic research, but also for the collection of operationally oriented data. The third Skyrocket, NACA 145, in which the jet/rocket propulsion system was retained, was fitted with pylons and simulated bombs to test their effects. (NASA)

would be used for different types of research. Once the Douglas speed- and altitude-record flights had been completed, NACA engineers decided to explore the second Skyrocket's operational limitations, with Crossfield as pilot. He had his first pilot check flight in the new aircraft on September 28, 1951, during which he experienced rough engine operation but still reached Mach 1.2.

He made three more flights in October and November. The first two flights provided data on longitudinal and lateral stability and control, loads, and aileron effectiveness at low supersonic speeds (Mach 1.28 and Mach 1.11). The final flight, on November 16, 1951, saw Crossfield reach a speed of Mach 1.65 at 60,000 feet. The winter rains closed the lakebed until the spring of 1952.

In contrast, the third Skyrocket, with its dual jet-rocket propulsion system, had a much more limited performance capability and thus was more suitable for transonic research, exploring such issues as swept-wing pitch-up. Once the lakebed dried out, these flights resumed on June 19, 1952, with Crossfield and Jones as project pilots.[31] The initial flights were made to test aircraft response with an inboard and outboard fence on each wing. The first flight, by Crossfield, reached a speed of Mach 0.7. Subsequent flights were made at Mach 0.96. Four flights were made in this configuration, with one aborted due to a failed cockpit heater. The last flight in the series, on August 14, was made with the inboard wing fence removed.[32]

A 1951 photo showing one of a number of wing-fence configurations tested to counter the pitch-up caused by swept wings. The inboard fence is mounted on top of the wing, and the outboard fence extends around the wing leading edge. (NASA)

High-Speed Flight Research Station engineers Jack Fischel and Jack Nugent summarized the effectiveness of the wing fences in a research memorandum. The tests were made with the Skyrocket in a clean configuration in turning flight at speeds of Mach 0.5 to 0.96, at altitudes between 19,000 and 36,000 feet. The flights were made both with the original wing configuration and with the addition of an outboard fence on each wing since wind tunnel testing had indicated that this fence would alleviate the pitch-up problem.

Fischel and Nugent found the flight results less clear-cut than wind tunnel data had suggested they would be. They concluded: "The addition of wing fences appeared to provide only a slight improvement over the original configuration, inasmuch as the pitch-up occurred at only slightly higher values of normal-force coefficient for the modified airplane configuration."[33]

Their analysis also included the pilots' impressions, which were quite blunt:

> In the pilots' opinion, the airplane is uncontrollable for a range of normal acceleration of about 1 g and 1½ g above the value at which the reported change in stability occurs; this behavior is very objectionable. At low speeds, if the pilot does not check the pitch-up by use of the elevator as soon as it is noticed, the angle

of attack increases rapidly and violent rolling and yawing motions are experienced at large values of [angle of attack]. At high speeds the pitch-up appeared to be more severe and more abrupt.

Throughout the speed range covered, the occurrence of a reduction in stick-free stability, almost simultaneously with the reduction in stick-fixed stability, tended to accentuate the pitch-up to the pilot. The pilot felt that even with improved control, as would result from an all-movable tail, flight above the stability boundary would not be sufficiently steady for gunnery or other precise maneuvering."[34]

For the next series of flights, engineers tested several different wing configurations. The goal was to find a means of preventing instability and pitch-ups during accelerated longitudinal maneuvers at speeds of up to Mach 1 and altitudes of 10,000 and 35,000 feet. The aircraft was flown with wing slats fully extended, both with and without inboard wing fences, and, finally, with the wing slats half extended and wing fences removed. Another change made, in order to improve the stick-force characteristics at moderate and large angles of attack, was to attach two bungee cords to the control column.

Crossfield made the initial flight on October 8, 1952, at a speed of Mach 0.97. During the flight, and while performing a turn at high speed, the Skyrocket pitched up 36° followed by the now-anticipated sharp roll-off and near loss of control. The final pitch-up research flight for the year was made on October 22, 1952, also by Crossfield. In this instance, the aircraft was configured without wing fences. During the flight, pitch-up occurred when the aircraft made turns.[35]

The results from the extensive series of tests were summed up in a 1954 research memorandum written by Fischel:

> Opening the wing slats to the fully extended position improved the stability characteristics of the airplane by alleviating pitch-up at Mach numbers of below approximately 0.8; however, at Mach numbers between 0.80 and 0.85 the severity of the pitch-up remained unaltered. At Mach numbers of about 0.98 and 1.00, maneuvers performed up to relatively high values of normal-force coefficient with slats fully extended exhibited no evidence of pitch-up; however, this effect has since been duplicated with the clean-wing configuration (no fences, slats retracted).
>
> Removing the wing fences from the airplane configuration with slats fully extended caused the reduction in stick-fixed stability to become slightly more pronounced, and generally,

to occur at approximately the same or slightly lower values of normal-force coefficient.

With wing slats half extended and no wing fences, the airplane exhibited instability characteristics and pitch-up similar to that exhibited by the airplane with slats retracted and with wing fences.

With slats fully extended and wing fences removed, use of a bungee in the control system to alleviate or eliminate the stick-free instability caused the airplane to appear more controllable to the pilot and caused the decrease in stick-fixed stability to become less apparent and less objectionable.[36]

Fischel also described the pilots' impressions of the aircraft's behaviors:

In general, the pilots' reports corroborated the data and conclusions reached for the maneuvers performed. With the slats fully extended at all Mach numbers below M ≈ 0.8, it is the pilot's opinion that the airplane stability did not deteriorate appreciably after the initial decay, and as a consequence control was regained more rapidly than in the original slats-retracted configuration. At M ≈ 0.98 (wing fences on) and M ≈ 1.0 (wing fences removed), the airplane appeared controllable up to the maximum value of [angle of attack] attained. In both fence configurations with the slats fully extended the stability change most apparent to the pilot was lightening of stick forces at moderate angles of attack. The pilots reported a stick-fixed stability change at moderate angles of attack which became somewhat more apparent when the inboard wing fences were removed from the slats fully extended configuration. The pilots thought that the airplane configuration with slats fully extended were [*sic*] a definite improvement over the airplane configurations flown with the slats retracted.

Because the soft bungee had little or no effect on the stick forces, the character of the stick-free and stick-fixed instability of the airplane appeared to the pilot to be about the same as when no bungee was used. In both instances, the lightening of the stick forces at moderate angles of attack tended to increase the control rate, which in turn would aggravate any pitching. With the stiff bungee, however, the character of the decay in stability appeared much improved, for now the stick-free stability was improved and the airplane appeared to have a lower pitch divergence rate than previously; thus, the change in stick-fixed stability was somewhat less apparent and less objectionable.

In the configuration with slats half extended, the pilot thought the airplane behavior was similar to that encountered with slats retracted, and the pitch-up encountered was equally uncontrollable. Although data obtained in this configuration were limited to two high-speed maneuvers, the pilot reported that pitch-up was also encountered in other maneuvers performed at lower speeds (down to M < 0.7), at lower values of normal acceleration as the Mach number was decreased.

…If the stick-fixed stability is made acceptable, the provision of a bob weight, bungee, or artificial feel system to supply more satisfactory stick-force characteristics would be desirable.[37]

When pitch-up flights resumed in February 1953, with Crossfield as the sole project pilot, a new wing modification had been made to the airplane.[38] Wind tunnel tests indicated that a chord increase on the outer 32 percent of the wing might eliminate the tendency to pitch up under high lift conditions at around Mach 1.2. During the winter of 1952–53, new outer wing panels were added, effectively giving the Skyrocket a "sawtooth" leading edge.

The first flight with the chord extensions was made on February 27, 1953, in a jet-only flight. Crossfield made windup turns and 1-g stalls. The maneuvers were halted when longitudinal or lateral instability occurred. Additional tests of the modified wing shape were made on April 8 and 10 at speeds between Mach 0.45 and Mach 1.0 and altitudes from 18,000 to 34,000 feet. Crossfield made windup turns, aileron rolls, sideslips, and 1-g stalls during the flights. The tests were repeated on the final flight of the series, on June 15, bringing the tests to a close.

Jack Fischel and Cyril D. Brunn subsequently wrote a research memorandum on the chord extensions. Their summery concluded:

Addition of wing chord-extensions had only a minor effect on the decay in stick-fixed stability (pitch-up) and stick-free stability experienced by the airplane at moderate angles of attack. The chord-extensions alleviated the pitch-up to a small degree, but the pilot still considered the airplane unsatisfactory for controlled accelerated flight in this region. However, at higher angles of attack, the airplane appeared to retrim and regain some stability….

The buffeting of the airplane was of such a nature that the increase in buffeting intensity induced by the chord-extensions became a major problem, in addition to the longitudinal instability problem.

A comparison of wind tunnel with flight data showed good agreement in the reduction of stability evident at moderate angles

One approach tested on the D-558-2 was that of a sawtooth chord extension on the outer leading edge designed to prevent spanwise airflow across the wing. (NASA)

of attack. The results indicate that an abrupt reduction of stability to a region of neutral or even slight stability could tend to cause pitch-up.[39]

Following the April 10, 1953, flight, the chord extensions were removed from the aircraft and the slats were reinstalled and locked in an open position. The pitch-up research flights resumed on June 15, using both the jet and rocket engines. Accelerated longitudinal-stability maneuvers began in earnest, and the aircraft showed decay in stability at all speeds except Mach 1. Following the flight, a stiff bungee was installed on the control stick. This change was tested on the June 25 jet-only flight and showed improvement, sufficient at least to make the Skyrocket controllable at high angles of attack. The reduction in stability was judged by Crossfield to be less objectionable. After this flight, the aircraft was restored to its basic configuration.

Crossfield made five more flights between September 9 and December 22, 1953, in the third D-558-2, with both the jet and rocket propulsion systems. These looked at lateral, longitudinal, and directional stability and control at transonic speeds (Mach 0.4 to Mach 1.08), as well as turns and stalls. Two of the flights suffered rocket malfunctions; on the September 22 flight only two rocket cylinders fired, and on the final flight the rockets failed to ignite altogether. This completed pitch-up flight testing. After that final attempt, the group terminated tests with that aircraft.

A summation of the different wing modifications applied to the Skyrocket was published in 1956. The research memorandum noted:

> None of the wing modifications had an appreciable effect on the decay in stick-fixed stability (pitch-up) exhibited by the airplane at moderate angles of attack, particularly over a Mach number range from about 0.8 to 0.95. All configurations were considered unsatisfactory and uncontrollable in the pitch-up region by the pilots. On the basis of these tests and other flight and tunnel investigations, it is felt the position of the horizontal tail on this airplane should be lowered appreciably to obtain substantial improvements in longitudinal handling qualities.
>
> Wing fences had no apparent effects on the buffeting characteristics with slats retracted; however, unlocking the wing slats raised the buffet boundary, below a Mach number of 0.70, above that for the retracted slats condition for the basic-wing, one-fence, and two-fence configurations. Wing chord-extensions lowered the buffet boundary, compared with unmodified airplane configuration, up to a Mach number of 0.80 and caused an increase in buffet intensity which was objectionable to the pilot. Moderate buffeting appeared to exist over most of the lower and moderate lift range with the slats fully extended; however, this configuration did alleviate some of the pitch-up divergent rate and appeared to the pilots to provide the greatest improvement in the longitudinal handling characteristics of the airplane.[40]
>
> None of the wing modifications had an appreciable effect on the trim-stability characteristics of the airplane and all configurations exhibited similar trends over the Mach number range. The airplane was stable at Mach numbers below about 0.82, and exhibited characteristic nose-down and nose-up trim changes between Mach numbers of about 0.87 and 1.03.[41]

Clearly, the various wing modifications failed to solve the pitch-up issue. For all the advantages of sweptback wings, pitch-up represented a major problem that required a solution. This was found not exclusively in modifying the wings, but rather in moving the location of the horizontal tail. The original placement of the horizontal stabilizer midway up on the D-558-2's vertical tail was to avoid the wing wake. This, however, placed the stabilizer in the downwash from the wings when the pilot pulled back on the stick, initiating a sharp pull-up maneuver that increased the aircraft's angle of attack relative to the airflow around it. The report continued:

> On the basis of wind-tunnel tests performed on a model of the D-558-2 airplane, as well as other wind-tunnel and flight investigations, it has been concluded that with the present tail configuration of the D-558-2 airplane, a real cure of the pitch-up is not feasible. Lowering the horizontal tail to approximately the height of the wing-chord plane extended would be required to obtain substantial improvement in airplane longitudinal handling qualities.[42]

The combined results of the D-558-2 research flights and wind tunnel testing altered subsequent aircraft designs. The first generation of jet fighters had horizontal stabilizers located at the base of the vertical fin. Later aircraft had their stabilizers located on the lower aft fuselage, even with or below the wing centerline. This cured the pitch-up issue, and it is why the low-placed horizontal tail is a standard feature of transonic and supersonic combat aircraft design.

Exploring Operational Limits, Lateral Stability, and Vertical-Tail Loads

At the same time that the third D-558-2, NACA 145, was making its pitch-up research flights, the all-rocket second D-558-2, NACA 144, was also flying research missions. After the latter had been turned over to the NACA, Crossfield had made a series of flights to explore its operational limits. Once these were completed, NACA researchers undertook a new effort focused on the aircraft's lateral stability and control at high Mach numbers. This had been the cause of the violent rolling motions experienced by Bridgeman during the Douglas contractor flights in 1951. Additionally, loads on the vertical tail were also to be recorded.

Flights in the new research effort began on June 13, 1952. The first of these reached a speed of Mach 1.36. Two more flights were made in June, reaching low supersonic speeds of Mach 1.05 and Mach 1.35. The July 10 flight reached Mach 1.68 at 55,000 feet, the peak speed for this initial test series. As with the other Skyrocket, the flights did not always go smoothly. The July 15 flight reached only Mach 1.05 because of an engine malfunction, and the August 13 flight was aborted after launch from the P2B-1S when a liquid-oxygen valve stuck in the open position. The aircraft did not return to flight until October 10, 1952. This flight measured longitudinal stability at speeds of up

The second D-558-2, NACA 144, parked on the ramp at South Base. Modifications made to allow air launch included the removal of the jet engine and fuel tanks. Between the air launch and the increased rocket burn time, the craft's maximum speed was doubled. On November 20, 1953, this aircraft made the first Mach 2 flight. (NASA)

The modified B-29 used to launch the Skyrockets had striking nose art. This included its nick-name, "Fertile Myrtle," and a scoreboard that tallied the number of launches made with each of the D-558-2s. Each of the launch aircraft was used for a single rocket plane, as modifications made to the mother ships' underside were specific to each aircraft type. Fertile Myrtle survived damage it sustained when the no. 4 propeller tore free. (NASA)

to Mach 1.65. The year's activities ended with a flight on October 23, and the research effort was then placed on hold until the following spring. The first flight of 1953, made on March 26 by Crossfield, brought the longitudinal-stability flights to a close.

The level of D-558-2 flight activity was lower than that of any new jet fighter undergoing testing at Edwards. This highlighted the difference between specialized flight research and production and acquisition-oriented test operations. Extensive effort went into planning for each research flight. Research aircraft also required extensive ground testing before a flight, including careful calibration of instrumentation. Once the flight was completed, malfunctions had to be identified, understood, and corrected before the next flight was attempted. Onboard systems had to be inspected and tested after the flight was completed. Finally, the data collected during the flight had to be reduced and then analyzed to assess results, detect any problems, and identify data points that would have to be repeated or would be used in preparing the next flight's plan.

The next phase in research activity with the second D-558-2 was a series of flights to collect data on supersonic lateral stability at low and moderate angles of attack, in both pushover and straight flight, at altitudes between 50,000 and 70,000 feet. Crossfield made six flights between April 2 and August 5, 1953. One of the flights, on June 18, was aborted after launch due to a rough running rocket engine. During the August 5 flight, Crossfield reached a speed of Mach 1.878, just below Bridgeman's maximum speed flight.[43]

The research memorandum noted:

> The first flights to Mach numbers near 1.8 were performed by climbing the airplane to altitudes of about 55,000 feet and push-ing over to nearly zero lift (angle of attack $\approx -2°$) with the rudder locked. During these flights, violent lateral oscillations occurred, with side-slip angles reaching $\pm 6°$ and roll angles reaching about $\pm 60°$.... It was decided that the low angle of attack, and conse-quent low inclination of the principal axis of inertia with respect to the flight path, may have aggravated the motion. A subsequent flight was made in which the pilot did not push over to low lift but maintained an angle of attack greater than $0°$. In this condi-tion, the lateral oscillation was much less pronounced. It should be noted that the two flights were made at different altitudes and at different constant angles of attack.[44]

The memorandum also noted the Skyrocket pilots' experiences:

> During one of the flights with the rudder locked, the pilot attempted to hold the ailerons fixed for a period of time in order to determine the lateral motion that would ensue…. The airplane tended to roll off at a fairly rapid rate until the roll angle reached about 90°, at which time the pilot stopped the motion with the ailerons. During another flight at a low angle of attack with the rudder locked…the lateral motion was of such a nature that the airplane rolled nearly 140° although the pilot was trying to control the airplane with the ailerons. At one time during the flight when the pilot felt the controls were ineffective in stopping the rolling motion…the pilot reversed the aileron control in order to make the airplane complete the roll to 360° in order to recover from the inverted attitude. This action was also ineffective as the airplane at the same time apparently began to recover of its own accord against the control motion supplied by the pilot. It is pertinent to point out here that this condition was not caused by a complete lack of aileron effectiveness. Unpublished flight data indicate that aileron effectiveness at these speeds is indeed low but that an appreciable amount still remains….
>
> The motions obtained during these two flights suggest the possibility that the control-fixed transient oscillation at high supersonic speeds at low angles of attack may be one in which the roll angles reach values in excess of 90°, whereas the transient sideslip angles remain at relatively low values. However, because of the difficulty of flying the airplane at these speeds and angles of attack, it has not been possible to check this hypothesis further in flight.[45]

The Road to Mach 2

Crossfield's flights were approaching twice the speed of sound. Though reaching Mach 2 was the next landmark in the quest for higher altitudes and faster speeds, it did not have the significance of breaking the sound barrier. Unlike the transition from transonic to supersonic flow, no fundamentally different aerodynamic phenomena appeared going from Mach 1.88 to Mach 2.0. The D-558-2 had been reaching speeds of about Mach 1.8 to 1.9 during both Bridgeman's and Crossfield's flights made between 1951 and 1953. But although a Mach 2 flight seemed to be only an incremental increase over earlier flights, it was, in fact, far more difficult, and, if nothing else, it had tremendous symbolic importance as the next important milestone on a path that, increasingly, many saw as eventually leading to flight into space.

Crossfield noted that "even at Mach 1.8 we were pressing [the Skyrocket] far beyond rational limits."[46] That the NACA team could even reach Mach 1.8 was due to experience gathered in earlier flights. Recalled Crossfield, "The plane was by now almost completely debugged."[47] The team had also learned the "many little tricks to save time and gain an edge on the unknown."[48] Even so, Crossfield said, "the best any ordinary team could hope for, with luck, was a speed of Mach 1.9."[49]

A second factor working against the prospect of a Mach 2 flight was the traditional NACA mindset. NACA flights were made to collect data, not set speed records. Crossfield's flights in the D-558-2 had exceeded the existing world speed record, but the NACA had not highlighted the achievement in any public announcements. The research memorandums on the flights were classified "Confidential" and were limited to distribution among the NACA, contractors, and the military. Most important, Hugh L. Dryden had told Crossfield not to attempt a Mach 2 flight.

But much larger issues were at hand than whether research for its own sake was justified. The cost of research activities was going up, and construction of new, more advanced facilities was required to explore new realms of flight. The NACA required political support for this, as money was short and the new Eisenhower administration, elected in November 1952, was skeptical about devoting scarce resources into research activities at a time when the Nation was at war in Korea and facing extremely serious global challenges in Europe and Asia.[50]

The NACA contributions were highly technical ones, easily appreciated by the science and engineering community but not so readily discerned by others outside those fields. What others *could* understand, however, was a new world airspeed record. Aviation had always been about flying faster, higher, and farther. In the 1930s, air races had been major spectator events. In both commercial activities and military aviation, better aircraft performance was equated with better aircraft. Additionally, aircraft technology continued to undergo rapid change in the early 1950s. In late 1953, the F-80 Shooting Star, the hottest American airplane in 1945, was being phased out of service; the F-86 Sabre was approaching old age; the supersonic F-100 Super Sabre was beginning production; and the Mach 2 F-104 was in advanced development.[51]

So Hugh Dryden gave Walt Williams approval for a single attempt at a Mach 2 flight. Exceeding Mach 2 in the Skyrocket would require careful planning and special preparations. Herman O. Ankenbruck, the project engineer,

Aft view of NACA 144. The four nozzles of the LR-8 rocket engine are visible. This engine was essentially the same one used in the X-1 series of aircraft. (NASA)

developed a flight plan that would offer the best chance of reaching the goal. Success would depend on Crossfield's ability to fly the plan, the thrust of the rocket engine, and the amount of fuel that could be carried.

None of this would prove easy. Lieutenant Colonel Marion Carl, a superb Marine test pilot, had made two attempts in the summer of 1953 to reach Mach 2 and fallen short both times. Crossfield noted that "the slightest over-pressure on the stick would cut the speed back drastically." Crossfield did have an advantage over Carl, however. The D-558-2 had been fitted with cone-like nozzle extensions following Carl's Mach 2 attempts, to increase thrust at high altitude. These allowed Crossfield to reach Mach 1.96 during an October 14, 1953, flight, on the sixth anniversary of the first supersonic flight by Chuck Yeager in the first XS-1.[52]

The nozzle extensions were critical to Crossfield's eventual success in reaching Mach 2. The reason literally came down to rocket science. High-pressure gas in the LR-8 combustion chambers expanded out the nozzles to produce an equal and opposite force, which accelerated the D-558-2. As the exhaust gas left the nozzles, it expanded and its pressure dropped. In an ideal expansion, exhaust pressure drops to that of the outside atmospheric pressure, but no lower. These conditions would achieve maximum thrust. But if the exhaust gas over-expanded, it created drag.

Because atmospheric pressure varied according to the altitude at which the D-558-2 was flying, the extended nozzle was shorter than the length needed for ideal expansion. The excess energy was lost, as the pressure was not fully recovered. If Crossfield were to reach Mach 2, however, he would have to fly at a higher altitude than that for which the rocket nozzles had originally been designed. Moreover, he would need to get every bit of thrust he could from the rocket. He needed the larger, extended nozzles to capture more of the ideal expansion of exhaust gas.[53]

This was not the only advantage that would be needed to reach Mach 2. The second D-558-2 underwent special preparation. To minimize drag, the ground crew sanded and polished the aircraft, and every panel seam was taped over. The two stainless-steel fuel-jettison tubes were replaced with aluminum tubes, which were bent into the rocket's exhaust. Once the rockets fired, the tubes were no longer needed and would burn off, reducing drag and weight by a small amount. But even with the reductions in drag and weight, a longer rocket burn time would also be needed. To enable this, the water/alcohol fuel would be cold-soaked in a refrigerator the night before the flight, increasing the amount that could be carried by 10 or 15 gallons. The liquid oxygen was also loaded into the aircraft the night before, cold-soaking the tank and airframe around it, which enabled the crew to add a little more oxidizer. Some of the liquid oxygen would boil off during ground preparations and

From left are Walter C. Williams, High-Speed Flight Research Station director; A. Scott Crossfield, D-558-2 pilot; and Joe Vensel, HSFRS official in charge of operations, in front of a D-558-2, circa 1953. (NASA)

the flight under the P2B-1S to the launch point, they knew; such was always the case. Just before the drop, the plane's liquid-oxygen tank would be topped off from a tank on the P2B-1S, replacing the lost oxidizer.

The attempt was scheduled for November 20, 1953. Crossfield was not in the best condition. He had a bad case of the flu but was determined to fly. With the Skyrocket's preflight preparations completed, the P2B-1S launch aircraft took off. Stanley Butchart piloted the P2B-1S and was in charge of a precise sequence of events. Each of the rocket planes had an individual launch area. The second D-558-2 (NACA 144) was typically launched over Lake Elizabeth. The jet-and-rocket-powered third D-558-2 was usually launched

The rocket-powered X-planes underwent regular engine test firings. The shock diamonds in the rocket exhaust are visible. Engineers monitoring the test are standing close to the D-558-2. In the early 1950s, ear protectors, blast shields, and similar safety measures were not required. The panels attached to the horizontal stabilizers were there to prevent any damage. (NASA)

west of Rosamond. The X-1s were mostly launched over Victorville, southeast of Edwards.

Butchart later described the Skyrocket launch procedures. After takeoff, he would head out over Big Bear Lake in the long, slow climb to launch altitude. With no control room then in use, the launch plane pilot directed the operation. The first step in the sequence came after about 20 to 30 minutes, when Butchart called for fire trucks to be deployed on the lakebed. This was followed a few minutes later by a call for the chase planes to take off and join up with the P2B-1S. When the launch plane reached 10,000 feet, Crossfield climbed into the D-558-2, closed the canopy, and began launch preparations. The maximum power of the P2B-1S engines was used for the climb, for which an hour to an hour and a half was allotted. This put a heavy strain on the engines. Once the launch altitude was reached, Butchart began the final 6-minute sequence before launch. He would then fly out for 2 minutes, make a turn lasting 2 minutes, and take the final 2 minutes to return to the launch point. The release would then be pulled.

On November 20, 1953, Crossfield was successfully launched from the P2B-1S, and he followed the flightpath Ankenbruck had calculated. Reaching 72,000 feet, he gently nosed over into a shallow dive, reaching the maximum Mach number at 62,000 feet. In doing so, Crossfield avoided too low a g-force on the aircraft, which had caused the uncontrolled rolls Bridgeman had experienced 2 years before. Following burnout, he made a sweeping approach to the lakebed for a deadstick landing, the usual chase plane trailing behind.

Flight data indicated that Crossfield had reached a speed of Mach 2.005 ± 0.02. Calculated in a standard atmosphere, the true airspeed was determined to be 1,327 miles per hour. However, weather balloon data indicated the air temperature was 22° lower than that of the standard atmosphere. With this correction, the D-558-2 had reached 1,291 miles per hour ± 17 miles per hour. This was the highest speed yet reached in the Skystreak, and no subsequent attempts were made to exceed Mach 2. Crossfield later recalled that it was decided that the extraordinary efforts needed to exceed Mach 2 would not be justified by the value of the data.[54]

After the brief interlude of the Mach 2 flight, research with the second D-558-2 resumed. For the next 3 years, engineers and pilots put the aircraft through a wide range of research activities. These included examinations of dynamic stability and control, structural temperature and loads, wing and tail pressure distribution, buffeting data, and vertical-tail loads.

Though Crossfield made most of those flights, he left the NACA High-Speed Flight Station in the late summer of 1955 to join North American

A D-558-2 being loaded into its launch aircraft. The B-29 was lifted up on jacks inside a hangar, the Skyrocket was rolled underneath, and the launch plane was then lowered. Executing the process inside a hangar eliminated problems posed by desert winds. (NASA)

Aviation as a technical adviser and eventually became a corporate test pilot on the X-15 program.[55] His replacements on the Skyrocket were NACA research pilots Joseph A. Walker and John B. "Jack" McKay. And while the D-558-2 research flights had been an ongoing NACA project since 1949, they were never routine. On McKay's pilot-familiarization flight, made on September 16, 1955, the landing gear failed to extend, and he had to use the emergency hydraulic system to lower the wheels.[56]

McKay also experienced a far more dangerous situation that nearly resulted in the loss of his own life, the second D-558-2, the P2B-1S launch aircraft, and the P2B-1S crew. On March 22, 1956, the P2B-1S had reached drop altitude when its number 4 engine abruptly failed. The flight engineer reported the problem to Butchart, who responded by feathering the propeller, that is, adjusting the pitch of the blades so that it would stop and present a minimal-drag profile to the airflow. The propeller slowed to a stop but then unfeathered and began spinning again. Butchart feathered the propeller again and again, but it continued to unfeather and spin back up. At this speed and altitude, the propeller was spinning so fast that centrifugal force was inevitably going to cause the blades to disintegrate. On his third try, Butchart was still unable to feather the propeller. (He later recalled that the airplane's manual warned that there was only enough hydraulic fluid for three in-flight feathering attempts.) At that point, McKay called out that he had a problem with the Skyrocket and directed the P2B-1S crew not to drop him.

But Butchart and P2B-1S copilot Neil Armstrong had no choice, as the propeller would soon disintegrate. They nosed the P2B-1S down, and Butchart pulled the emergency jettison handle. The D-558-2 separated; McKay jettisoned the fuel and glided to a lakebed landing. That aircraft was undamaged and McKay was not harmed.

Just 10 to 15 seconds after Butchart dropped the Skyrocket, the P2B-1S propeller disintegrated. A blade from the number 4 engine passed through the number 3 engine, destroying it, then sliced all the way through the fuselage, exiting to strike the number 2 engine. Had Butchart not released the D-558-2, the blade would have hit the Skyrocket, likely triggering an explosion that would have destroyed both planes and all aboard them. Shrapnel from the disintegrating propeller hub and blades severely damaged engine number 3 and severed the aileron cables to Butchart's yoke, leaving him with no control. Armstrong's aileron cables had only one or two remaining strands. The severed wires rendered the yoke difficult to move. Despite the loss of engines 3 and 4 and the damaged controls, Armstrong was able to retain control and limp home to land on the north lakebed. The P2B-1S was grounded for nearly 5 months of repairs.[57]

The second D-558-2 returned to flight on August 17, 1956, with McKay as pilot. This was the first of eight flights following the near tragedy. The final flight was on December 20, 1956, and it was the last flight by a Skyrocket. Today, the historic second D-558-2 is suspended in honor at the National Air and Space Museum of the Smithsonian Institution, Washington, DC.

Denouement: Skyrocket External Stores Research Flights

The rocket-powered X-planes were commonly viewed by the public as exotic aircraft being used to probe the boundaries of the unknown, traveling ever higher and faster. In reality, their role also included the collection of flight data on more mundane aspects of high-performance aircraft. While the second D-558-2 was flying at high Mach numbers, the third Skyrocket was testing the effects of "external stores," such as bombs and fuel tanks, on aircraft handling qualities at subsonic and transonic speeds. Fighter aircraft had long carried these items under their wings. These payloads increased drag and affected flight characteristics. As part of the development effort of operational fighters, extensive wind-tunnel testing had been done to verify the safety and aerodynamics of these fixtures. In contrast, little effort had been made to assess the effects of external stores on longitudinal and lateral handling.

To explore these effects, the third Skyrocket was used for a series of flight tests involving three different streamlined configurations: with an empty

A close-up of the pylon/bomb on NACA 145. Data collected on their effects was applied to operational Air Force and Navy strike aircraft. (NASA)

mid-semispan under-slung pylon on each wing; with a simulated 1,000-pound bomb shape attached to the pylon; and with a simulated 150-gallon fuel tank attached. The three were respectively referred to as the "pylon configuration," the "small store configuration," and the "large store configuration," all built by Douglas Aircraft Company.[58]

The aircraft was modified with the pylons in mid-May 1954 and made its first flight in the stores project on June 2, 1954, with Crossfield as pilot. The aircraft was in the pylon configuration for the test and used the jet engine only. Top speed was Mach 0.72. The flight was repeated on June 16, again using only the jet engine and also at Mach 0.72, but with the small store configuration. The flight went smoothly, with no apparent complications.

The same was not true for the next flight, on July 8. Top speed was Mach 1, using both the jet and rocket engines. The small store configuration resulted in a decrease in transonic performance and an increase in buffeting. These problems caused the stores project to temporarily be put on hold, resuming on October 8. The first flight made once research resumed used the large store configuration's simulated 150-gallon fuel tank. As on the initial flights, the jet engine only was used for this mission, and speed was limited to Mach 0.74.

The way was now cleared for testing the large store configuration at higher speeds. Crossfield reported no adverse effects but noted a rise in drag and heavier buffeting in longitudinal maneuvers. More serious, the data from the wing strain gauges indicated problems. The stores flights were again halted until Douglas engineers completed rechecking the strength of both the wings and pylon.

The stores flights resumed in December 1954 with McKay in the third D-558-2. These were made in the clean configuration, without the pylons or stores shapes, and with the jet engine only. Once this series was complete, however, another 4 months would pass before more stores flights would be made. Flights resumed again on April 27, 1955, using the pylon configuration and both the jet and rocket engines. Reaching a speed of Mach 1, McKay made sideslips, rolls, and elevator and rudder pulses to collect data on the Skyrocket's handling qualities, wing and pylon loading, and buffet levels.

Nearly a month later, on May 23, McKay repeated the maneuvers, this time with the large stores configuration. He noted that the simulated fuel tanks caused high buffet levels compared to those of the pylon configuration. June 1955 was a busy month, with five flights—two with the pylon configuration and three with the large stores configuration. Identical maneuvers were performed on all five.[59]

Data on the static longitudinal-stability and control characteristics were obtained during speed runs made at about 35,000 feet, along with windup turns between Mach 0.50 and 1.03 and altitudes ranging from 22,200 and 39,400 feet. Elevator pulses provided data on the aircraft's longitudinal-dynamic characteristics. These were made at Mach numbers between 0.49 and 0.75, at altitudes between 22,000 and 27,000 feet. Data were also collected on low-speed characteristics during 1-g stalls with the slats both locked and unlocked and in the landing configuration with the slats unlocked and flaps and gear down.

The D-558-2's static lateral- and directional-stability characteristics were determined through incremental increases in constant flightpath sideslips, abrupt aileron rolls, and trim runs at Mach numbers of 0.44 to 1.04 and altitudes of 22,000 to 36,000 feet. Lateral damping characteristics were derived from rudder pulses made at Mach numbers between 0.50 and 0.87, at 20,000 and 32,000 feet. Both the longitudinal and lateral pulses were abrupt inputs, with the pilot attempting to return and hold the controls at the trim position while the oscillation damped out.[60]

Following the series of flights in June, tests were halted and did not resume until August 30. As with previous flights, these were made with large store

The Skyrocket following a landing on the lakebed. Ground support personnel would remove the film used to record the flight data and prepare the aircraft to be towed back to the hangar. The dress code at the High-Speed Flight Research Station was relaxed but ran the gamut from suits and ties to work clothes, short-sleeve shirts, baseball caps and sun hats, and Hawaiian shirts. Crossfield was the pilot for the flight. (NASA)

configurations, and, though the maneuvers performed were the same, the outcome was different. McKay landed nose high, and the underside of the aft fuselage was damaged when it scraped on the lakebed. The aircraft was grounded for 2 months for repairs.

Butchart flew the next mission with the D-558-2 on November 2, and McKay made the next three flights on November 8 and 17 and December 8, 1955. As with all the flights since May, the large store configuration was used and the same maneuvers were performed. This brought the stores research project to a close. Two flights remained, however. The Skyrocket was stripped of the pylons and restored to the original clean configuration. This took place during the winter months, while the lakebed was typically closed to flight anyway. Once the work was completed, the two additional flights would be made to collect wing-load data. The lateral, directional, and longitudinal data from the two clean flights would identify the effects caused by the stores.

The first of these, on February 1, 1956, was successful, reaching a speed of Mach 1. The final flight, planned for Mach 0.9, was attempted on February 3. However, a turbopump overspeed aborted the flight. Because the flight data were needed to complete the analysis of the stores data, a final flight of the third D-558-2 was added. It did not take place until August 28, 1956, more than 6 months after the initial attempt. This time the flight was successful, reaching Mach 0.96. The aircraft was permanently grounded, and the stores tests ended.

The results of the external stores tests were summarized in a research memorandum issued in October 1957:

> The results presented herein are somewhat limited—particularly in regard to the dynamic characteristics of the airplane—because only a few flights were obtained with each external-store configuration. Sufficient data were obtained, however, to establish trends of the effects of the stores on the stability and control characteristics of the airplane at subsonic and transonic speeds. Since most of the tests were performed in the large-stores configuration and only small differences were noted in the data for the various configurations, most of the data presented here are for the large-store configuration.
>
> The incremental lift and drag effects for the large-store configuration…indicate the appreciable increment of drag produced by the stores, especially at M > 0.9. In addition, the pilots commented that they detected an increased penalty in airplane performance with an increase in size of the stores investigated, particularly at transonic speeds.[61]

The report's concluding remarks noted:

> The results of a flight investigation, from a Mach number of approximately 0.45 to a Mach number of approximately 1.05, of the Douglas D-558-2 research airplane equipped with several configurations of external stores have indicated that the smaller mid-semispan store installations generally had a small or negligible effect on the handling qualities of the airplane. With the large-store configuration, the trends exhibited in the longitudinal and lateral trim, stall approach, dynamic and static stability and control, and buffeting characteristics were generally the same as for the clean airplane; however, significant changes in the magnitude of the parameters measured were sometimes apparent, particularly at the higher speeds.
>
> The large-store configuration effected: a decrease in the subsonic static longitudinal stability; an improvement in the lateral damping characteristics at subsonic speed; an appraisable left-wing drop at a Mach number greater than 0.9; an appreciable decrease in lift-curve slope between a Mach number of about 0.85 and 0.96; a slight decrease in the level of lift for the onset of buffeting at all subsonic speeds; and an appreciable increase in apparent dihedral parameter $d\delta_a / d\beta$ particularly at a Mach number greater than 0.94. The side force parameter $C_{Y\beta}$ increased and the aileron control parameter $(pb / 2V) / \delta_a$ decreased with an increase in the size of the store.[62]

Originally, this was not to be the end of the stores testing. A second series of tests, at supersonic speeds, was planned. The aircraft to be used for these flights was to have been the first D-558-2, used in the Douglas test flights. As the others were, NACA 143 (as it was designated) had been transferred by the Navy to the NACA in August 1951. It spent the following 3 years in storage at Edwards. NACA managers decided in 1954 to have it modified to an all-rocket/air-launched configuration. (The same as the second D-558-2.) The Skyrocket was returned to Edwards on November 15, 1955, and checkout began. It was not until the fall of 1956 that preparations with NACA 143 were complete. McKay made the modified aircraft's first flight on September 17, 1956. And though the flight was successful, time had run out. The NACA canceled the planned supersonic stores test project. As a result, this was the first and only flight NACA 143 would ever make following modifications. The third Skyrocket had made its final flight in August 1956. The second D-558-2 would continue to fly until December 1956 before being grounded. This brought the 8-year Skyrocket project to a close.[63]

The NACA's focus was shifting, and despite the sad irony of the end of the Skyrocket project after many productive years, a new set of challenges was on the horizon. Flights with the X-15 were due to begin in 3 years. The goals of the X-15 program were not simply to fly slightly faster, but to triple both the speeds and altitudes reached with the D-558-2. The X-15 would not just reach Mach 6 and fly to the edge of Earth's atmosphere. It would enter space.

An Assessment

Although the D-558-1 Skystreak's achievements in the development of high-speed flight were mixed, the importance of the D-558-2's accomplishments was clear. Ironically, like its jet-powered predecessor, the D-558-2's original performance was designed only for Mach 0.9 to 0.95 due to having to make a ground takeoff. Had the Skyrocket not been modified for air launch, its accomplishments would have been minimal and would have probably been seen as a major disappointment.

NACA researchers had opposed air-launching the XS-1, arguing it should be capable of normal takeoff and landing from Langley's runway. By the time the Douglas test flights on the Skyrocket were starting, however, the advantages of air-launching research aircraft had been made clear. Converting the second and third Skyrockets to an air-launched configuration greatly expanded their performance envelope and, as a result, their research value. Another consequence of the decision to use an air launch was that the second and third Skyrockets ultimately were assigned different research roles. The earlier objections of the Langley researchers were forgotten.

Removal of the second D-558-2's jet engine allowed the aircraft to carry a larger rocket fuel supply, doubling its maximum speed. It repeatedly flew at speeds of Mach 1.8 to 1.9. This allowed testing of the swept wings to speeds higher than could be reached with operational service aircraft. The third D-558-2 retained the jet/rocket configuration, which reduced its top speed. Work with this aircraft focused on transonic and low-supersonic research, with top speeds ranging from Mach 0.72 to 1.04. As with the XS-1 and D-558-1, this provided a complementary research capability.

An interrelated series of factors in the D-558-2 wing design contributed to one of its major accomplishments. The idea that swept wings could reduce the detrimental effects of transonic and supersonic flight was new. The means of ground-testing the Skyrocket's wing design were limited by wind tunnel choking, which referred to the inability of wind tunnels to provide reliable data at

Aft upper view of NACA 144 at South Base. Though a variety of methods were tried in attempts to reduce or eliminate pitch-up, their effects were limited. The solution was to place the horizontal stabilizer low on the fuselage, where it would not be affected by airflow from the wings. (NASA)

high transonic and supersonic speeds. Finally, the D-558-2 wing design focused on good low-speed/stall characteristics without loss of high-speed performance. Thanks to Van Every's careful design, the result was a wing with good low-speed handling, low drag, and excellent transonic and supersonic characteristics.

The Skyrocket wing's susceptibility to pitch-up, coupled with its comprehensive instrumentation package, ironically rendered the aircraft ideal for research on the problem. To find solutions, various configurations of wing fences, slats, leading-edge chord extensions, and bungee cords were developed in wind tunnel tests. These tests looked at ways of reducing the flow of air that caused the separation of flow at the tips. Separation triggered both the pitch-up and the tip stalls, which were then exacerbated by the swept-wing configuration. Crossfield described the test procedures: "The technique would be to go up there and pull g at a fairly constant rate, trying to maintain as constant an air speed as possible. And incidentally, there was something we really re-learned with these kinds of wings. And that is that the old C_{MCl} was a bunch of garbage as far as this goes. We had to go back to the C_{Ma} because C_L was dropping so fast that it looked like the airplane was going stable—when really it was going quite unstable at the time. And it would pitch."[64]

Pitch-up was the most significant stability problem plaguing the D-558-2, but it was not the only one. The aircraft was originally designed for transonic and low-supersonic speeds due to the ground takeoff profile. When Bridgeman made the early air launches, he experienced severe oscillations and directional divergence from straight and level flight. This became known as "supersonic yaw," and it had not been expected as other high-speed phenomena such as dynamic and static instability had been. Crossfield said later, "Bill Bridgeman found that by manipulating the G, you could control the rate of this divergence, and give yourself time to get in very soft controls to hold it on almost a knife edge.... And we managed to take the airplane out substantially beyond its expected design speed."[65] Originally built to fly

The D-558-2 and other X-planes existed expressly for the collection of flight data. Shown here on a D-558-2 wing are some of the instruments used to record measurements of the forces and moments acting on the aircraft. (NASA)

Mach 0.9 after a ground takeoff, the second D-558-2 ultimately broke Mach 2.

The Skyrocket also served as a training ground for the engineers and pilots who later worked on the X-15 rocket plane in the 1960s. Crossfield made a total of 87 rocket-powered flights in the X-1 and D-558-2, along with another 12 D-558-2 jet-only flights, all of these between 1951 and 1956. He subsequently made another 14 X-15 flights (1 glide flight and 13 powered flights) as the North American Aviation contractor pilot. This made him the most experienced rocket-plane pilot in the Nation. Jack McKay was the second-most experienced rocket pilot, with 46 flights in the X-1B, X-1E, and D-558-2. He subsequently made another 29 X-15 flights. Joe Walker made 26 flights in the X-1, X-1A, X-1E, and D-558-2 (3 glide flights and 23 powered), which he followed with 25 X-15 flights. Additionally, McKay and Walker qualified for astronaut wings, as they exceeded an altitude of 50 statute miles in the X-15.

Another measure of the Skyrocket's success was that all three aircraft survived the unknowns of research work. In contrast, of the six X-1 aircraft completed, only three—two of the first X-1s (the NACA aircraft, the second XS-1, was rebuilt as the X-1E) and the X-1B—survived. The third X-1, X-1A, and X-1D were all lost in explosions caused by the use of so-called "Ulmer" leather gaskets in the liquid-oxygen tanks. Both of the X-2 aircraft were lost, the first in a gasket explosion during a captive flight, the second when its pilot lost control during a Mach 3 flight.[66]

In the end, however, it was the data that counted. The Skyrocket research activities covered a wide range of fields: aircraft control and stability at speeds approaching Mach 2, measurements of structural temperature and loads, wing and tail pressure distribution, buffeting data, vertical-tail loads, possible solutions to pitch-up, and data on the effects of external stores. Though it was overshadowed by both the X-1 and the X-15, the D-558-2 played a major role in exploring the unknowns of supersonic flight during the critical years between the late 1940s and the mid-1950s.

Endnotes

1. Opening quotation from William Bridgeman and Jacqueline Hazard, *The Lonely Sky* (New York: Henry Holt and Company, Inc., 1955), p. 154.
2. Hallion, *Supersonic Flight*, pp. 68–69, 75–76.
3. Ibid., pp. 76–79.
4. The turbopump delay was, of course, why the first two XS-1s had been completed with high-pressure blow-down nitrogen fuel and oxidizer-feed systems. The turbopump issue thus prevented both the X-1 and the D-558-2 from achieving their greatest possible performance, which, in both cases, was approximately Mach 2 and more than 70,000 feet.
5. The change is very noticeable when comparing photos taken during the initial versus the later Douglas flights.
6. Hallion, *Supersonic Flight*, pp. 157–159; Libis, *Skystreak, Skyrocket, & Stiletto*, pp. 48–53, 123–126. According to legend, John Martin became the first D-558-2 project pilot due to the Douglas test pilots' being reluctant to fly the aircraft. After discussion, the story goes, the Douglas test pilots all decided to submit very high bids that they knew the company would turn down. Martin was away delivering an aircraft and did not know about the plan. Martin submitted a reasonable bid and "won" the job.
7. Sigurd A. Sjoberg, "Preliminary Measurements of the Dynamic Lateral Stability Characteristics of the Douglas D-558-2 (BuAero No. 37974) Airplane," NACA RM L9G18 (August 18, 1949), p. 2; Hallion, *Supersonic Flight*, p. 159; Libis, *Skystreak, Skyrocket, & Stiletto*, p. 128.
8. Sjoberg, "Preliminary Measurements of the Dynamic Lateral Stability Characteristics of the Douglas D-558-2 (BuAero No. 37974) Airplane," pp. 2–3.
9. Ibid., p. 3.
10. Ibid., p. 3.
11. Hallion, *Supersonic Flight*, p. 159.
12. J.D. Hunley, ed., *Toward Mach 2: The Douglas D-558 Program* (Washington: DC: NASA SP-2003-4531, 1999), p. 48.
13. Peebles, ed., *The Spoken Word: Recollections of Dryden History, The Early Years*, pp. 50–51; Hallion, *Supersonic Flight*, pp. 159–160.

14. Michael H. Gorn, *Expanding the Envelope Flight Research at NACA and NASA* (Lexington, KY: The University Press of Kentucky, 2001), p. 220.

15. S.A. Sjoberg, James R. Peele, and John H. Griffith, "Static Longitudinal Stability and Control Characteristics at Mach Numbers up to 0.87," NACA RM L50K13 (January 17, 1951), p. 11.

16. Those seeking more information on the results of early flights with the D-558-2 can refer to these NACA research memorandums: S.A. Sjoberg, "Static Lateral and Directional Stability Characteristics as Measured in Sideslips at Mach Numbers up to 0.87," NACA RM 50C14 (May 19, 1950); J.V. Wilmerding, W.H. Stillwell, and S.A. Sjoberg, "Lateral Control Characteristics as Measured in Abrupt Aileron Rolls at Mach Numbers up to 0.86," NACA RM L50E17 (July 20, 1950); John P. Mayer and George M. Valentine, "Measurements of the Buffet Boundary and Peak Airplane Normal-Force Coefficients at Mach Numbers up to 0.90," NACA RM L50E31 (August 28, 1950); W.H. Stillwell, J.V. Wilmerding, and R.A. Champine, "Low-Speed Stalling and Lift Characteristics," NACA RM L50G10 (September 5, 1950); John P. Mayer, George M. Valentine, and Beverly J. Swanson, "Measurements of Wing Loads at Mach Numbers up to 0.87," NACA RM L50H16 (December 26, 1950); John P. Mayer and George M. Valentine, "Measurements of the Distribution of the Aerodynamic Loads Among the Wings, Fuselage, and Horizontal Tail at Mach Numbers up to 0.87," NACA RM L50J13 (January 19, 1951); and W.H. Stillwell and J.V. Wilmerding, "Dynamic Lateral Stability," NACA RM L51C23 (June 18, 1951).

17. S.A. Sjoberg, James R. Peele, and John H. Griffith, "Static Longitudinal Stability and Control Characteristics at Mach Numbers up to 0.87," NACA RM L50K13 (January 17, 1951), pp. 5, 11, 13–14.

18. Bridgeman and Hazard, *The Lonely Sky*, p. 145.

19. Hallion, *Supersonic Flight*, p. 160.

20. Libis, *Skystreak, Skyrocket, & Stiletto*, p. 133

21. Hallion, *Supersonic Flight*, pp. 226–231.

22. Ibid., pp. 162–163.

23. Ibid.

24. Bridgeman and Hazard, *The Lonely Sky*, p. 248.

25. Ibid., pp. 257–261; Hallion, *Supersonic Flight*, p. 231.

26. Libis, *Skystreak, Skyrocket, & Stiletto*, p. 130.

27. Hallion, *Supersonic Flight*, pp. 165–167; Bridgeman and Hazard, *The Lonely Sky*, pp. 304–305; Libis, *Skystreak, Skyrocket, & Stiletto*, p. 130; Theodore E. Dahlen, "Maximum Altitude and Maximum Mach Number Obtained with the Modified Douglas D-558-2 Research Airplane During Demonstrations Flights," NACA RM L53B24 (April 20, 1953), pp. 4–5.

28. Dahlen, "Maximum Altitude and Maximum Mach Number D-558-2," p. 4.

29. Herman O. Ankenbruck and Theodore E. Dahlen, "Some Measurements of Flying Qualities of a Douglas D-558-2 Research Airplane During Flights to Supersonic Speeds," NACA RM L53A06 (March 10, 1953), pp. 2, 8–9.

30. Letter, Chief, Bureau of Aeronautics, "Transfer of Aircraft to the NACA under Public Law 266 of the 81st Congress," December 27, 1950; letter, Chief of Naval Operations, "Transfer of Aircraft to the NACA under Public Law 266 of the 81st Congress," January 5, 1951. These letters covered the transfer of the two D-558-1s, the three D-558-2s, the ex-B-29–now–P2B-1S launch aircraft, and spare parts to the NACA.

31. Rogers Dry Lake is often flooded by winter rains, turning it into an actual lake.

32. Hallion, *Supersonic Flight*, pp. 175, 184–185, 232, 237.

33. Jack Fischel and Jack Nugent, "Flight Determination of the Longitudinal Stability in Accelerated Maneuvers at Transonic Speeds for the Douglas D-558-2 Research Aircraft Including the Effects of an Outboard Wing Fence," NACA RM L53A16 (March 13, 1953), pp. 1, 5–8.

34. Ibid.

35. Hallion, *Supersonic Flight*, pp. 175, 184–185, 232, 237.

36. Jack Fischel, "Effects of Wing Slats and Inboard Fences on the Longitudinal Stability Characteristics of the Douglas D-558-2 Research Airplane in Accelerated Maneuvers at Subsonic and Transonic Speeds," NACA RM L53L16 (February 8, 1954), pp. 13–14.

37. Ibid., pp. 13–14.

38. This period also saw the High-Speed Flight Research Station pilot's office undergo a number of changes. Robert Champine transferred back to Langley, and John Griffith took a job with Chance Vought in Texas. Walter P. Jones left for a job as a test pilot with Northrop in August 1952, during the pitch-up tests. Jones was killed in the crash of a YF-89D prototype on October 20, 1953. Crossfield made nearly all the Skyrocket flights for the next 2 years.

39. Jack Fischel and Cyril D. Brunn, "Longitudinal Stability Characteristics in Accelerated Maneuvers at Subsonic and Transonic Speeds of the Douglas D-558-2 Research Airplane Equipped with a Leading Edge Wing Chord-Extension," NACA RM H54H16 (October 27, 1954), pp. 1–2.

40. Jack Fischel and Donald Reisert, "Effects of Several Wing Modifications on the Subsonic and Transonic Longitudinal Handling Qualities of the Douglas D-558-2 Research Airplane," NACA RM H56C30 (June 5, 1956), p. 12.

41. Ibid., p. 13.

42. Ibid., p. 7.

43. Libis, *Skystreak, Skyrocket, & Stiletto*, p. 75.

44. Herman O. Ankenbruck and Chester H. Wolowicz, "Lateral Motions Encountered with the Douglas D-558-2 All-Rocket Research Airplane During Exploratory Flights to a Mach Number of 2.0," NACA RM H54I27 (December 17, 1954), p. 7.

45. Ibid., pp. 8–9.

46. A. Scott Crossfield and Clay Blair, Jr., *Always Another Dawn: The Story of a Rocket Test Pilot* (New York: Arno Press, 1972), pp. 171–172.

47. Ibid., p. 160.

48. Ibid., p. 172.

49. Ibid.

50. Ibid.

51. Marcelle Size Knaack, *Post–World War II Fighters* (Washington, DC: Office of Air Force History, 1986), pp. 10, 60–64, 114, 175–176.

52. Crossfield and Blair, *Always Another Dawn*, pp. 160–161.

53. E-mail, Albion H. Bowers to Curtis Peebles, "Rocket Science," July 14, 2010. In possession of the author.

54. Hunley, ed., *Toward Mach 2: The Douglas D-558 Program*, pp. 54–56; Cyril D. Brunn and Wendell H. Stillwell, "Mach Number Measurements and Calibrations During Flights at High Speeds and at High Altitudes Including Data for the D-558-2 Research Airplane," NACA RM H55J18 (March 12, 1956), p. 15. Crossfield was not the only person who was not in the best condition that morning. Jack Moise, a B-29 launch panel operator, was sprayed with highly concentrated hydrogen peroxide during preflight preparations. A mechanic named Kinkaid hosed him down with water, and both were taken to the flight-line dispensary. Moise suffered several minor chemical burns on his face, which cleared up within a few days. Crossfield saw Kinkaid sitting on a

bench, wearing wet clothing. When Crossfield asked if he was cold, Kinkaid replied that he was warm. Crossfield realized Kinkaid was also soaked in hydrogen peroxide and could catch fire. Crossfield ripped off the clothing and found that chemical burns had bleached Kinkaid's arms and legs white.

55. Crossfield's departure roughly coincided with another change in the NACA's High Desert test team: the High-Speed Flight Research Station dropped "Research" from its name in 1954, becoming simply the High-Speed Flight Station.

56. Hallion and Gorn, *On the Frontier*, p. 392.

57. Peebles, ed., *The Spoken Word: Recollections of Dryden History, The Early Years*, pp. 121–123.

58. Jack Fischel, Robert W. Darville, and Donald Reisert, "Effects of Wing-Mounted External Stores on the Longitudinal and Lateral Handling Qualities of the Douglas D-558-2 Research Airplane," NACA RM H57H12 (October 28, 1957), pp. 1–2.

59. Hallion, *Supersonic Flight*, p. 240. Those seeking detailed information on the results of later D-558-2 research missions can refer to these NACA research memorandums: Jack Nugent, "Lift and Drag Characteristics of the Douglas D-558-2 Research Airplane Obtained in Exploratory Flights to a Mach Number of 2.0," NACA RM L54F03 (August 4, 1954); Wendell H. Stillwell, "Results of Measurements Made During the Approach and Landing of Seven High-Speed Research Airplanes," NACA RM H54K24 (February 4, 1955); Gareth H. Jordan and Earl R. Keener, "Flight-Determined Pressure Distribution over a Section of the 35° Swept Wing of the Douglas D-558-2 Research Airplane at Mach Numbers up to 2.0," NACA RM H55A03 (March 25, 1955); and Glenn H. Robinson, George E. Cothren, Jr., and Chris Pembo, "Wing Load Measurements at Supersonic Speeds of the Douglas D-558-2 Research Airplane," NACA RM H54L27 (March 30, 1955).

60. Fischel, Darville, and Reisert, "Effects of Wing-Mounted External Stores on the Longitudinal and Lateral Handling Qualities of the Douglas D-558-2 Research Airplane," pp. 2–3, 6. The apparent dihedral parameter $d\delta_a / d\beta$ is defined as the "rate of change of aileron deflection with sideslip angle." The side force parameter $C_{Y\beta}$ is defined as the "rate of change of lateral force coefficient with angle of sideslip." The aileron control parameter $(pb/2V)/\delta_a$ is defined as the "variation of wing-tip helix angle with total aileron deflection" and is measured in radians/degrees.

61. Ibid., p. 4.

62. Ibid., p. 13.
63. Hallion, *Supersonic Flight*, p. 230. Once retired, the three D-558-2s were put on display. The first D-558-2, used by Douglas and later modified to an all-rocket configuration, is at the Planes of Fame Museum in Chino, CA. The second D-558-2 (all-rocket configuration) is in the Smithsonian Institution National Air and Space Museum in Washington, DC. The third D-558-2 (jet-and-rocket configuration) is mounted outdoors on a pole at Antelope Valley College in Lancaster, CA.
64. J.D. Hunley, ed., *Toward Mach 2: The Douglas D-558 Program*, pp. 48–49. C_{MCl} is the static stability in pitch of an aircraft. C_M is the pitching-moment coefficient. C_{Ma} is the partial derivative of the pitching-moment coefficient with respect to the angle of attack.
65. Ibid., p. 54.
66. For details, see Hallion, *Supersonic Flight*, pp. 169–172, 175–177, 189–191.

Mockup of the X-3 at the Douglas factory. The X-3 was the sleekest of the early X-planes but delivered the most disappointing performance. (USAF)

CHAPTER 4

Unfulfilled Promise, Serendipitous Success: The Douglas X-3 Stiletto

Boy, it's hard to keep your speed and altitude in this thing.
—William "Bill" Bridgeman[1]

An ambitious jet-powered research aircraft meant to cruise at Mach 2, the twin-engine Douglas X-3 Stiletto was the sleekest and most radical-appearing of the early X-planes. Like the D-558-1, the Stiletto's accomplishments were mixed. The X-3 never achieved its intended design speed but did furnish critical data on a new stability and control peril spawned by the design requirements of supersonic flight. The X-3's failure to attain Mach 2 stemmed largely from the failure of Westinghouse, its engine manufacturer, to successfully develop its Westinghouse J46 turbojet. As a consequence, the X-3 had to employ smaller and far less powerful Westinghouse J34 engines, inhibiting its potential performance and making a mockery of its sleek supersonic shape.

The X-3 had its origins in December 1943, when the Army Air Forces requested that the Douglas Aircraft Company study the feasibility of an aircraft capable of sustained speeds in excess of Mach 1. This was a bold request, as many (as discussed previously) considered the "sound barrier" as presenting an insurmountable challenge. A team of Douglas engineers working for Frank N. Fleming took on the challenge, submitting a proposal in January 1945, and the AAF responded by issuing Douglas a contract in June 1945 for the design of a supersonic jet-powered research aircraft capable of attaining Mach 2 at 30,000 feet and having a flight endurance of 30 minutes. The project was designated MX-656, the plane to be known as the XS-3 (later simply X-3).[2] As with the X-1 and D-558 aircraft, initial flights with the X-3 would be made by the contractor to demonstrate that the aircraft could meet the basic performance requirements. The Air Force would then conduct an abbreviated performance evaluation up to the X-3's maximum design speed and altitude. Finally, NACA pilots would make a long-term series of research flights to extract the maximum amount of data on aerodynamics, stability and control, handling qualities, and other aspects of the aircraft.

Designing the Stiletto

Douglas Aircraft's Frank N. Fleming was named project engineer on the X-3 and faced a demanding task. The design had to be a conventional one capable of operating without special launch and handling equipment, taking off and landing under its own power using standard landing gear, and flying its entire speed range without external assistance, and it would be required to demonstrate flying and handling qualities like those of modern high-speed aircraft. Finally, it would have to have conservative thrust margins, fly for a reasonable amount of time at supersonic speeds, perform satisfactorily at transonic speeds, and withstand aerodynamic heating.[3]

Thanks largely to the visual power of the V-2 missile and Douglas's shapely Skyrocket, the popular image of a supersonic aircraft in the late 1940s was one featuring an elongated, needle-shaped fuselage with highly swept wings and tail surfaces. Actually making such airplanes was extremely challenging. The basic requirement would call for the engines' thrust capacity to be greater than the airplane's drag up to the Mach 2 design goal. If the thrust and drag curves intersected below this speed, the X-3 would not perform as required. The engines would need to have a frontal area that was as small as possible yet still capable of producing the necessary amount of thrust. In the late 1940s, this meant turbojet engines fitted with afterburners.

To minimize drag, the engines had to be enclosed within a fuselage likewise having the minimum possible frontal area. But jet engines typically had a considerable amount of external equipment attached to their cylindrical casings. This necessarily increased frontal area. Designers also determined that in order for the X-3 to achieve its performance goals, two engines would be needed, both for safety and to improve thrust-to-drag ratio. The two engines represented the greatest mass of the aircraft, so the center of lift would need to be near the engines. This meant the wing spar had to be under the engines, which would further enlarge the fuselage. The X-3's main landing gear, like that of the D-558-2, also had to be housed in the fuselage. And as with the wings, the main landing gear had to be near the center of the greatest mass, reinforcing yet again the fact that the fuselage would have to be made bigger.

Auxiliary equipment also had to be included. Air had to be supplied to the engines. Protruding air inlets were added to the fuselage, and diffusers of the proper length and expansion ratio connected these to the engines. The two turbojet engines and afterburners generated considerable heat. Countering this effect required having ducting sufficient for carrying a large volume of cool air, the source of which was the boundary layer bled off ahead of the air intake scoops. Air passed through ducts between the two engines. To make room for the ducts, the two engines were spread apart. Shrouds and insulation were required to direct the cooling air and keep the aircraft structure at proper temperatures. Still more space would be needed to allow for thermal expansion, structural deformation, vibration, and manufacturing tolerances. A tunnel was added on top of the fuselage to contain the flight control cables, hydraulic lines, tank vents, wiring, instrumentation tubing, and other items.

An overhead photo of the completed X-3. The aircraft had a very long fuselage and a short wingspan. The fuselage was tightly packed with the two engines, fuel tanks, landing gear, and other systems required. (USAF)

These changes resulted in an increase in the X-3's frontal area and thus the amount of drag. The ratio of the engine area as a percentage of total fuselage frontal area had been 93 percent in the minimal fuselage design. With all the added equipment, the ratio of engine area to total fuselage frontal area dropped to 33 percent for the two-engine design.

The next design issue was the selection of a wing planform combining the optimum values of high-speed drag, stability, weight, maximum lift, structural strength, and minimum drag for a given amount of lift. The X-3's wings would need both a high critical Mach number and the ability to cope with the effects of compressibility over the full speed range up to Mach 2. The design that emerged was a slightly swept low-aspect-ratio wing that was very thin and had a sharp-wedge airfoil shape and leading and trailing-edge flaps.

Beyond wind tunnel tests of the proposed wing shape, a series of free-flight rocket launches were made by the NACA to compare the coefficient of drag for various wing shapes. These shapes included the X-1 (high-aspect-ratio, straight wings), D-558-2 (low-aspect-ratio, swept wings), X-2 (high-aspect-ratio, swept wings), and X-3 (low-aspect-ratio, swept wings). All the wings had identical areas and fuselage bodies, so the lone variable was wing drag due to compressibility. Of the four wing shapes, the X-3s had the lowest drag coefficient over the range of Mach 0.9 to Mach 1.7. The highest-drag wing was the X-1's. Although the main fuselage and wing designs were complete, the X-3 still lacked a cockpit, fins, rudder or horizontal control surfaces, fuel tanks, or accommodations for an instrument payload.

Early rocket-powered model flights and drop tests had indicated that drag on an optimum ogival body was reduced when the shape had a high fineness ratio (the body's length divided by its diameter). The optimum ratio for a subsonic aircraft was 3:1, versus 14:1 for a supersonic aircraft. With the frontal area established, it was clear that the X-3's fuselage length would need to be extended to minimize supersonic drag. This was accomplished by adding a long nose that held the pilot, data instrumentation, controls, radio, and other equipment.

The next step was the addition of tail surfaces. There were long-established relationships between the positions of the tail surfaces and the wing, relationships shaped by structural and aerodynamic factors. In the early X-3 design studies, the tail area was increased and moved downward and forward relative to the wing. This also allowed the tailpipes and supporting structure to be extended to support the tail. The flaw in this design was added weight, but engineers reduced the weight by keeping the tailpipe short. Additionally, experience held that to maximize the tail surfaces' stability and control effectiveness, they should be located as far back as practical. As a result, a tail boom was used on the final X-3 design, the Model 499D. The X-3's horizontal stabilizer also had an all-moving, one-piece design, rather than the two-part movable stabilizer and elevator used on the X-1, D-558-1, and D-558-2. The X-3 marked the first application of an all-moving "slab" tail to an American supersonic aircraft. Testing in Langley's 7-by-10-foot High-Speed Wind Tunnel resulted in Douglas's enlarging the horizontal tail by 40 percent.

The X-3 design was fitted with an air conditioning system installed between the air intakes; additional flight data equipment placed below the wing; and the hydraulic units, fire extinguishers, electrical components, and other items fixed in various nooks and crannies. Finally, fuel tanks were fitted into the remaining fuselage volume. A fuel tank holding 500 gallons of kerosene was located in the lower fuselage, below the diffusers, and another 170-gallon fuel tank was added to the aft fuselage, under the engine exhaust. The final 330-gallon fuel tank was located in the tail boom, above the jet engines. Douglas engineers estimated this would enable a 3-hour flight at high-subsonic speeds or 10 minutes at Mach 2. To protect the fuel tanks and control cables in the event of an engine compressor or turbine wheel failure, armor plating was installed in critical locations. This was similar to the modifications made to the D-558-1.[4]

Reaching a sustained speed of Mach 2 required considerable thrust. Consequently, the X-3 had a pair of Westinghouse J46 axial-flow jet engines. These were derivations of the firm's earlier J34 engine, but with a greatly redesigned turbine and compressor section. Though the J34 jet could produce a maximum thrust of 3,000 pounds, the J46's basic thrust was to be 4,200 pounds. Use of the afterburner raised this to 6,600 pounds. Douglas engineers estimated that the X-3 could reach Mach 2 at 35,000 feet using only 80.6 percent of the J46's anticipated maximum thrust. The top speed of the X-3 was limited not by engine thrust, but by structural heating of its largely 24S-T81 aluminum alloy airframe.[5]

The result was an aircraft that seemed as if it had flown in from the future. None of the other early X-planes had the X-3's look of raw power. The bullet shapes of the X-1 and D-558-2 looked conventional by comparison, while the cylindrical D-558-1 was old-fashioned. Not until the hypersonic X-43A a half century later was there another experimental aircraft that so embodied the concept of speed.

In Thrust, Not Enough

Because its designers drastically underestimated the challenges they would face creating several new high-performance engines, Westinghouse's efforts to build upon its combat-proven J34 experience failed miserably, crippling a number of aircraft programs, one of which was the X-3. "The history of the Westinghouse J34," RAND analyst Thomas A. Marschak wrote in 1964, "[gives] a rather clear impression of a 'classic' case of engine-airframe commitments being made in the face of great uncertainty about all engine magnitudes."[6] By June 1951, development of the J46 was a year behind schedule, and Westinghouse, in desperation, decided to spin off a lower-powered variant of the J46 that could be installed in the X-3, with the higher-performance J46 variant installed later. But a year later, by August 1952, the problems had grown worse, and even the lower-powered engine was now 14 months behind schedule and not expected to be ready until 1955, 11 years after the X-3 program had begun.[7]

Douglas managers had already considered using the less-powerful J34-WE-17 engines as an interim measure pending the availability of the more powerful J46. These could produce 4,850 pounds of thrust with afterburner and had dimensions similar to those envisioned for the more powerful J46, minimizing the difficulties created by the switch. The assumption was that initial flights would be made with these J34 engines. Then, once the J46 engines were ready, they would be installed in the pair of X-3s being built. It was a reasonable strategy, and one followed subsequently for other programs, such as the North

American X-15 (which used two RMI XLR-11 interim engines until the more powerful Thiokol XLR-99 was ready) and the Lockheed A-12 Oxcart program (which employed two Pratt & Whitney J75 engines until its more powerful P&W J58s were available).

But now, the J46 was not only behind schedule, it was growing too large to permit two to fit within the X-3, forcing Douglas to turn to an alternative: the earlier J34. The transonic thrust-to-drag ratio of the X-3 with the interim J34-WE-17 engines was much lower than that calculated for the J46 engine. Various means of boosting the J34's thrust were examined. NACA engineers at the High-Speed Flight Station went even further and considered modifying the X-3 to an all-rocket/air-launched configuration.[8]

This, however, would have involved removing the fuel tanks, air inlets, and jet engines and replacing the latter with a pair of Reaction Motors 6000C4 four-chamber rocket engines. The eight rocket cylinders would also have to be fitted with nozzle extensions, resulting in exhaust expansion to the ambient air pressure at 50,000 feet. The amount of propellant to be carried, based on the assumed consumption rate, was approximately equal to the available volume of the jet engine compartment.

A second prohibitive issue was the choice of a launch aircraft for use with an all-rocket/air-launched configuration. The candidates were the Douglas C-74 and C-124 transports and the B-36, B-52, and YB-60 bombers. The C-74 and C-124 were swiftly eliminated because their maximum launch speed was slower than the X-3's anticipated stall speed. (As well, the C-124 was also too small to carry the X-3). The B-36 could carry and launch the X-3 but was unavailable because the Air Force required all available examples of this huge 6- (and later 10-) engine bomber for its global strategic nuclear bombing mission. The B-52's wheelbase was too short to allow the X-3 to be mounted beneath the fuselage (air-launch advocates did not yet conceive of attaching the X-3 to a launch shackle under the wing, as with the later North American X-15). The only possibility was the YB-60, a jet-powered version of the B-36 that met the performance requirements. Ultimately, however, both the acquisition of a launch aircraft and the necessary modifications to the X-3 were deemed too costly, ending any prospects for the program's future entirely.[9]

The failure to produce the J46 engine in time and in a size to be incorporated on the aircraft crippled the X-3 program. The X-3's best speed in level flight with the J34-WE-17 engines was a meager Mach 0.96. If it entered a dive, its smooth high-fineness-ratio fuselage and low transonic drag ensured that it rapidly accelerated into the supersonic, to Mach 1.2—but the pilot then had to pull out, and its speed would swiftly drop back to the "other side" of the sonic divide. Although hopes lingered for a time that a rocket-powered/air-launched conversion might be approved, the NACA Research

A view of the X-3 from the rear. The fuselage was painted white but the wings, horizontal stabilizer, jet exhaust, and parts of the tail boom were left in bare metal. (NASA)

Aircraft Projects Panel rejected both options as too expensive and unjustified. The panel reasoned that "other aircraft are coming along which operate in the same speed range as that for which the X-3 was intended," a reference to the Mach 2 Lockheed F-104, which, ironically, benefited greatly from the X-3's development experience.[10] By this time, the first X-3 was nearly ready for delivery to Edwards Air Force Base; the second airframe was only partially completed. The Air Force ended construction of the nearly complete vehicle and transferred the unfinished airframe to the NACA for spare-parts support.

The X-3 research aircraft had been intended for the exploration of the unknowns of sustained Mach 2 flight, such as aerodynamic heating, intake scoop and air duct flow characteristics, and high-speed stability and control. But the failure to produce a J46 that could fit in the airplane effectively transformed the X-3 into a low-speed test bed for aircraft having low-aspect-ratio wings joined to high-fineness-ratio fuselages, nothing more.[11]

The completed X-3 was delivered to Edwards on September 11, 1952, and final checkout by Douglas engineers began in preparation for high-speed taxi tests. This involved making engine test runs, replacing failed components, and installing NACA instrumentation. The instruments recorded airspeed and altitude; normal and transverse acceleration; roll, pitch, and yaw angular velocity; angle of attack and sideslip; control column, control wheel, and rudder pedal positions; stabilizer, aileron, and rudder positions and control forces; and leading and trailing-edge flap positions.[12]

The X-3 high-speed taxi tests began on September 30, 1952. William Bridgeman, having made the air-launched high-speed/high-altitude flights in the second D-558-2 the previous summer for Douglas, now conducted the manufacturer acceptance flights with the X-3. A series of problems were encountered in early tests, including a failure of the afterburner hydraulic actuator; a primary engine control system malfunction; a malfunction of the drag chute, which was jettisoned immediately after deployment on several runs; the loss of all tread on the nosewheel; and problems with the main landing gear brakes and tires. By the sixth taxi test, made on October 14, the problems had been largely resolved. The following day, Bridgeman lifted the X-3 off the lakebed and remained airborne for about a mile and a half. The way had now been cleared for the first flight, scheduled for October 20.

The eighth and final taxi test was made to check the X-3's longitudinal control with hydraulic power off. Bridgeman found the resulting control forces were very high, and the dead spot around neutral made control difficult. Despite this, the first flight went ahead. The weekly status report noted:

> Flight No. 1 was made on 10-20-52 right after taxi test No. 8. Loss of some power on the right-hand engine and loss of the right-hand hydraulic pump output was caused by a malfunction of the right-hand fire shut-off control. Longitudinal pitching of the airplane was excessive. Duration of the flight was nineteen minutes.[13]

Troubleshooting of the problems took nearly 2 weeks, and the second flight was made on October 31, 1952. Again, as the progress report noted, "[During t]he longitudinal control sensitivity oscillations in which fairly large attitude changes occurred, a buffet-like shutter was felt in the airplane. Flight duration was 13 minutes."[14]

A considerable amount of troubleshooting, repairs, testing, and modification had to be undertaken. The resulting delays were made worse when a new nozzle actuator on the right engine afterburner failed twice. Then in mid-November 1952, an inch of rain fell, closing the lakebed. The initial estimate was that the lakebed would be closed for 3 weeks. But coupled with

Normally, aircraft were taxied or towed to the runway. The X-3's tires had to withstand very high takeoff and landing speeds. To avoid tire damage, a special vehicle was built to carry the aircraft out to the lakebed. Here it is seen on the back ramp behind Hangar 4802, at the new NACA facility at Edwards (still in use more than a half-century later). (NASA)

the weather, continuing repair work on the X-3 delayed the third flight until late April 1953.

The X-3 was ready, but delays persisted. The first attempt was made on April 21, 1953. As with the first flight, a taxi run was made to check out the aircraft. This was followed by the attempt at the third flight. The taxi test resulted in a loss of tread from all three tires. The tires were replaced, but by the time the work was finished, wind conditions had changed, and the flight was postponed. The tire failures were later traced to the high takeoff speeds. Underpowered engines and small wings meant the X-3 had to reach 260 knots before it could take off. Existing tire technology and materials were incapable of withstanding the stresses this produced.

A second try came on April 23, but high-altitude turbulence forced another cancellation. The following day, Bridgeman attempted to take off, but just before leaving the ground he felt the aircraft vibrating, so he aborted the takeoff. An inspection showed that the nose tire's tread and most of the main tires' treads were missing. Again, the high-speed takeoff had resulted in tire failure. Engineers concluded that the loss of tread had caused the main tires to be unbalanced, resulting in the vibration.[15]

Flight 3 was rescheduled for April 27, 1953, but rain fell the night before, closing the lakebed for a day and a half. Bridgeman successfully made a 34-minute flight on April 30. Among changes that had been made to the X-3 in the months since its last flight was an increase of the elevator power-valve linkage ratio to 5:1, which resulted in some improvement in longitudinal control. However, the aircraft had been fitted with a "load feel control" that allowed the control setting to be changed either automatically or manually. The weekly report noted, "But it was still very difficult, if not impossible, to avoid over-controlling with the load feel control operating automatically. Manual increase of the load feel gradient to its maximum value improved control considerably at the speeds encountered during the flight.... With the exception of longitudinal control, airplane and engine operation was satisfactory."[16]

A subsequent report expanded on the handling problems:

> During the climb following take-off on Flight No. 3, while the control system was still on automatic load feel, longitudinal oscillations periodically appeared. These oscillations were similar to those encountered on Flight No. 2 following afterburner shutdown.... It is apparent that at oscillation frequencies as low as ½ cps [cycles per second], the time lag between aircraft normal acceleration response and pilot's elevator force makes it difficult for the pilot to control these longitudinal oscillations.[17]

Again, extensive work and checkout were required before the fourth flight could be made on June 5. This one lacked most of the problems of earlier flights. The X-3 Weekly Status Report for the week ending on June 5, 1953, stated, "Flight no. 4 was made on 6-5-53. A maximum indicated airspeed of 525 knots was reached. Airplane and control stability was good."[18]

X-3 Flight 5 was made on June 11, 1953, and reached an altitude of 25,000 feet. In a level flight run at this altitude, a maximum observed Mach number of 0.943 was reached. The X-3's control and stability appeared satisfactory.[19]

Flight number 6 was made on June 25. The report for the week ending on June 27, 1953, noted:

> The airplane climbed to 34,000 feet and a level run was made at approximately 33,000 feet. The maximum observed Mach No. during the run was approximately .94. An accelerated turn at a load factor of 2.0 was made at approximately 30,000 feet and an observed Mach No. between .93 and .90. At approximately 28,000 feet, a pushover at a load factor between 0.2 and 0.5 was made at an observed Mach No. of approximately .94. A lateral and directional stability check made during the pushover indicated no reduction in damping at the reduced load factor. During the recovery from the pushover, a maximum observed Mach No. of 1.018 was reached....[20]

This cleared the way for supersonic dive flights. The NACA X-3 weekly report noted:

> Flight No. 7 was made on 7-15-53. The airplane climbed to 36,000 feet from which a dive at an angle of approximately 15° was started. During the dive, a rudder pulse was made at an observed Mach No. of .96, an aileron pulse was made at an observed Mach No. of 1.05 and an elevator pulse was made at an observed Mach No. of 1.09. Immediately following the elevator pulse, a +2.5g pullout was made and the minimum observed altitude reached was 23,790 feet. A maximum Mach No. of M=1.10 was reached at 26,150 feet during the dive. All pulses during the dive were satisfactory.[21]

Bridgeman commented after the flight in "Douglas Flight Report No. 7":

> In the initial part of the dive, the rudder was pulsed. The damping of the lateral-directional oscillations was slow and, because of the necessity of waiting for the damping before increasing the dive angle, the requested twenty degree attitude was never reached.[22]

The first attempt to make flight 8 on July 21 was aborted during the takeoff roll when the nose wheel again lost tread. The flight was successfully made on July 22. Bridgeman climbed to about 36,160 feet, accelerated in level flight to Mach 0.89, and pushed over into a 25° dive angle. During the dive, Bridgeman made rudder and elevator pulses and reached Mach 1.19 before pulling out of the dive. The X-3 pitched around the lateral axis several times. Bridgeman commented, "This was mostly pilot induced [while] coping with the tender longitudinal control." Low-speed stability and control tests were made before landing.[23]

Bridgeman made the X-3's fastest flight on July 27, 1953. The weekly report stated:

> A dive was made from 36,440 feet to 19,320 feet at a maximum dive angle of approximately 30°. A maximum observed Mach No. of 1.21 was attained during the dive and a maximum load factor of 6.7 was reached during the pullout. Low-speed stability and control was investigated during three approaches to stall and two stalls using "military" power with the leading edge flaps full down. In each stall, the airplane rolled to the right.[24]

Despite the successful supersonic flight, it was now clear that the X-3 was a disappointment in terms of performance. Even in a steep dive, its top speed was little different from that of an F-86. Bridgeman continued to make X-3 flights, with his 25th and final flight coming on December 1, 1953, but most were in the low-supersonic speed range. Nevertheless, given the X-3's lack of thrust and stability, the flights were never routine. On Bridgeman's 23rd flight, on October 21, he made a rolling pullout from a dive. Both afterburners were already shut down due to high temperatures in the tail area. Bridgeman felt severe vibrations, and the right engine switched to emergency mode, its revolutions dropped, and the outlet temperature increased. He was unable to restart the engine and had to use the left engine's afterburner just to stay aloft. He was able to make a lakebed landing on one engine without damaging the even more severely underpowered aircraft, which itself constituted a tremendous tribute to his extraordinary abilities as an experimental test pilot.[25]

A postflight report noted the scale of the engine malfunction:

> The failure was due to the root failure of one blade in the second-stage turbine and shearing at approximately the mid-span of an adjoining blade. It is the opinion of the engine manufacturer's representative that the whole blade was ejected downstream through the engine and the afterburner and subsequently lost to the free stream but that the half-blade segment or a fragment of it traveled forward, finally becoming wedged between the first-stage turbine and the first-stage stator vanes. Further, it is his opinion that the half-blade segment being wedged between the turbine wheel and the nozzle vanes was responsible for the failure of 10 doweled bolts which allowed all of the first-stage nozzle vanes to fall to the bottom of the nozzle, from where they were recovered.[26]

A replacement engine was installed in the X-3, and Bridgeman made contractor flights 24 and 25, completing Douglas's obligations to the customer. On December 8, 1953, Douglas turned the X-3 over to the Air Force.

Launching the Air Force–NACA Program

Originally, the Air Force had planned to conduct an extensive evaluation of the aircraft. But the X-3's disappointing performance caused Air Force testers to drastically scale back their planned evaluation, particularly as the service had major flight-testing responsibilities reflecting its participation in—and lessons learned from—the Korean War, which had ended the previous July.

Charles E. Yeager beside the X-3, in which he made three flights. The aircraft was designed to reach Mach 2, but the jet engines that powered it were never capable of delivering the required amount of thrust. As a result, the X-3 barely exceeded Mach 1 in a dive. The aircraft's design, with its mass concentrated in the fuselage and small, razor-blade-like wings, made it susceptible to inertial coupling. Ironically, data collected on this phenomenon constituted the project's most important results. (USAF)

Accordingly, Lieutenant Colonel Frank K. Everest and Major Charles E. "Chuck" Yeager each made only three flights in the X-3, then washed their hands of the project. Although these were made by Air Force pilots, they were listed as NACA flights 1 through 6 because NACA instrumentation was aboard the X-3, enabling the taking of flight research data. Everest made his first flight on December 23, 1953, with Yeager following on December 29. The flights included windup turns, stalls, level runs, dives, and rudder pulses. The top speed reached during NACA flights 1 and 2 was Mach 1.09. NACA flights 3 through 6 were made between July 2 and July 29, 1954. Like the two initial flights, these were primarily for evaluating handling qualities and performance. Strain gauges were also checked out, and measurements were made of wing-pressure as well as of wing, tail, and landing gear loads.[27]

Colonel Everest later recounted his experiences with the X-3, which he called "one of the most difficult airplanes I have ever flown":

> Distinct control problems resulted from its combination of very long fuselage and extra-short wings. Longitudinal control was sensitive and the airplane pitched up and down on the slightest provocation…. The wings had both leading and trailing edge flaps to give it added lift during take-off and landing. In fact, leading edge flaps were required after take-off until the airplane had attained an air speed close to 350 knots. I found this out on my first flight, when I retracted them at 300 knots and at the same time began a turn back toward the base. The X-3 immediately began to buffet and stall because the wings could not support the weight, and I had to level out and continue flying straight ahead. I climb[ed] to about 37,000 feet, where I made some maneuvers, put the airplane in a dive and went supersonic…. After more maneuvers I returned to Edwards for my landing. At 5,000 feet I extended leading edge flaps and chopped the engines back to a low power setting. Then I turned into my downwind leg, and extended the trailing edge flaps and landing gear. As I did so I began sinking like a rock. At once I applied full power and pulled my gear up, and not until I was turning into my final approach did I again extend the gear.[28]

On a more detailed level, the stability and control data from the Douglas contractor flights and those made by Everest and Yeager were summarized in an NACA research memorandum:

> Longitudinal control deflection required to trim the airplane over the Mach number range was generally similar to that of other airplanes, characterized by a stable variation at Mach numbers below 0.92 and a slight nose-down trim change at Mach numbers above 1.07. Data obtained during turns and pull-ups indicated that throughout the Mach number range from 0.65 to 1.21, the apparent static longitudinal stability was positive at low lifts and increased by a factor of about 2½ as Mach number was increased from 0.9 to 1.2. The apparent stability exhibited a

gradual decrease as lift increased and mild pitch-ups occurred at Mach numbers above 0.95....

Difficulty was experienced in performing smooth longitudinal maneuvers. This condition appeared to result from the combination of control system, pilot, airplane, and their dynamic characteristics; however, additional tests are required to determine the primary cause of the lag and oscillations experienced. Unaccelerated stalls appeared stable in all configurations tested, except at large angles of attack in the landing configuration where some instability was evident. Roll-off tendencies, which became more severe as the speed was decreased, were apparent in all configurations. Data obtained during sideslips at Mach numbers from 0.84 to 0.98 showed the apparent directional stability to be positive and to increase with increase in Mach number. A smaller degree of apparent stability existed for smaller angles of sideslip than existed for larger angles.

Meager aileron effectiveness data obtained at Mach numbers of 0.89 to 0.98 indicate that the control effectiveness was generally linear with deflection and exhibited little change with increase in Mach number. Comparison of flight data with wind-tunnel and rocket-model tests showed similar trends and good quantitative agreement.[29]

With the completion of the six Air Force flights, the X-3 was turned over to the NACA for planned research flights. NACA pilot Joseph A. Walker was assigned as X-3 project pilot. After an engine inspection, instrument calibration, and maintenance work, Walker made his first X-3 flight (NACA flight 7) on August 23, 1954. During the flight, he made two windup turns, stalls in both clean and landing configurations, and a dive to Mach 1.05. After the flight, the vertical-tail strain gauges were calibrated. With both Walker and the X-3 checked out, the NACA research flights could begin.[30]

On September 3, Walker successfully made NACA flight 8, which involved speed runs, longitudinal maneuvers, and stalls. Data were collected at speeds between Mach 0.70 and 1.1. A second flight by Walker was planned but was canceled due to lakebed cross winds. Walker then completed NACA flights 9 and 10 on September 9. Despite the flight series' successful start, the basic unreliability of the X-3 continued to hamper progress. Two flights were planned for September 16. Walker took off and began to climb on NACA flight 11 but noticed that the right afterburner's fuel consumption was too high. This suggested a problem with the afterburner's fuel-flow control, and Walker cut the afterburners. Despite the failure, some useful data were salvaged from the

The X-3 parked on the ramp after ownership was transferred to the NACA. The Air Force markings were removed and NACA insignia added. Joe Walker, who also flew the X-1E, X-4, X-5, and X-15, among other aircraft, was the only NACA research pilot to fly the X-3. He made 20 flights and experienced its demanding flight characteristics. (NASA)

aborted flight. He performed 1-g stalls in a clean configuration with the leading edge flaps in the 10° and full-down 30° positions and landed on the lakebed without mishap. To correct the fuel-consumption problem, the ground crew had to replace the afterburner and repair the fuel-flow control.[31]

Walker made five NACA flights in late October, collecting data on stability and control; wing pressure distribution pattern; lift and drag; buffeting; and wing, horizontal stabilizer, and vertical-tail loading. Walker also made fixed-rudder aileron rolling maneuvers at Mach 0.9 and 1.05. On the plane's 10th NACA flight, on October 27, 1954, Joe Walker and the X-3 entered aviation safety's history book, and their milestone came nearly at the price of both plane and pilot.[32]

The Inertial Coupling Crisis

In June 1948, NACA Langley researcher William Hewitt Phillips published a technical note innocuously entitled "Effects of Steady Rolling on Longitudinal and Directional Stability."[33] It soon proved a remarkably prescient and important report, one of particular significance for the future design of practical high-speed aircraft.

In his introduction, Phillips set forth why studying the inertial characteristics of the new generation of high-speed airplanes—airplanes that had long fuselages and increasingly smaller wings—was important:

> When an airplane rolls around an axis…not aligned with its longitudinal axis, inertial forces are introduced which tend to swing the fuselage out of line with the flight path. These forces are ordinarily neglected when the usual theory of lateral stability of aircraft is used to calculate the motion of an airplane in a roll. This assumption is probably justified for the case of most conventional airplanes because inertial forces involved are small compared with aerodynamic forces on the airplane. Design trends of very high-speed aircraft, however, which include short wing spans, fuselages of high density, and flight at high altitude, all tend to increase the inertial forces due to rolling in comparison with the aerodynamic restoring forces provided by the longitudinal and directional stabilities. It is therefore desirable to investigate the effects of rolling on the longitudinal and directional stabilities of these aircraft.[34]

As a consequence of these phenomena, Phillips wrote, "The rolling motion introduces coupling between the longitudinal and lateral motion of the aircraft. An exact solution of this problem is very complicated because of the large number of degrees of freedom involved."[35]

At the same time Phillips was writing his paper, Fleming and the Douglas engineers were in the midst of designing the X-3. The Douglas aircraft had a fuselage 66.75 feet long containing two jet engines, fuel tanks, air conditioning, research instrumentation, ducts, control cables, landing gear, and a host of other systems. Yet its wingspan was just 22.69 feet. Douglas, in short, was building the airplane Phillips had imagined.[36]

Phillips's idea was still considered a theoretical one at the time of his writing, but there was already a crucial data point from the XS-1 program that applied. In the summer of 1947, during falling-body tests of the XS-1, a model of the rocket plane veered wildly off course and disappeared after having been dropped from a high-flying B-29. Postflight analysis of optical and telemetric records indicated that, as Phillips recalled, "some kind of gyroscopic effect" had taken place, causing the XS-1 to roll, pitch, and tumble, falling so far off its predicted trajectory that it was never found.[37] Out of this incident, Phillips began an analytical study that resulted in his

1948 technical note, which introduced the aeronautical world to the expression "inertial coupling."[38]

A hint of problems to come was mentioned briefly in a memorandum by Hartley Soulé about Douglas engineer Harold F. Kleckner's visit to Langley on September 5, 1951. Soulé's text read:

> Early computations of the lateral stability of the X-3 airplane at supersonic speeds indicate that the relation between rolling and yawing motions would be different from...past experience, primarily because of the high airplane length to wingspan ratio with the resulting large differences in the moment of inertia and rolling as compared with yaw and pitching. For this reason, *these characteristics have been the subject of concern* although it is not definitely known that the different characteristics would be undesirable.[39] (Emphasis added.)

Slightly less than a year later, in August 1952, technicians at the NACA's Pilotless Aircraft Research Division (PARD) located on Wallops Island, VA, fired a rocket-boosted model of an early short-fin D-558-2 model fitted with a small rocket thruster in its nose to induce combined rolling, pitching, and yawing motions typical of inertial coupling as the model decelerated below the speed of sound. After it fired, the D-558-2, as expected, "coupled" and experienced the combined roll, pitch, and yaw motions. But they did not dampen out. Rather, they grew in severity, and the D-558-2 model was completely out of control by the time it impacted in the Atlantic Ocean off the Virginia coast. As the XS-1 model had shown 6 years earlier, and the D-558-2 model confirmed, roll-coupling was a far from innocuous phenomenon.[40]

On December 12, 1953, during a Bell X-1A flight to Mach 2.44 (1,612 mph) at 74,200 feet, Air Force test pilot Major Chuck Yeager nearly perished when the speeding rocket plane violently coupled, tumbling over 50,000 feet before Yeager managed (in a feat of superlative airmanship unequaled in flight-testing history) to recover the airplane safely to level flight and return to Edwards.[41] Inertial coupling had struck a piloted aircraft and, had it not been for its extraordinary pilot, likely would have destroyed it. In any case, during his glide earthwards, Yeager confided to listeners that "if I'd had [an ejection] seat, you wouldn't still see me in this thing."[42] Because the X-1A was, like its XS-1 predecessor, thoroughly instrumented, the NACA was able to analyze the flight and the onset of the coupling departure in detail, issuing a thorough report on the episode.[43]

While NACA analysts pondered their experience with models and the X-1A, events were moving swiftly and ominously in the fast-paced world of

Another overhead shot of the X-3 on the back ramp. Unlike the D-558-I and D-558-II, the X-3 was fitted with a downward-firing ejection seat. The seat was lowered to allow the pilot to enter the cockpit then returned to its original position once he was seated. A similar design was used in the early F-104s, with poor results. (NASA)

fighter aircraft development. North American had designed a new jet fighter, the F-100A Super Sabre, for the supersonic era. Highly streamlined, with an afterburning J57 turbojet and a 45° swept wing, it first flew at the end of May 1953. Slightly over a year later, the Tactical Air Command activated its first F-100A fighter wing, at George AFB, Victorville, CA, just 35 miles southeast of Edwards, over the objections of Frank Everest and other Edwards test pilots, who thought the plane needed more study and possible modifications to increase its stability at supersonic speeds. Almost immediately, some pilots encountered disturbing, unsettling motions at high speed. On October 12, 1954, disaster struck. North American Aviation test pilot George "Wheaties" Welch took off from Palmdale, CA, in an F-100A, climbed high over Rosamond, dove to supersonic speed, and then began a rolling dive pullout. The F-100A abruptly yawed, rolled, and pitched out of control, disintegrating and killing its pilot. Inertial coupling had claimed its first, but not its last, victim.[44]

As accident investigators analyzed the wreckage of Welch's ill-fated F-100A, Joe Walker and the X-3 continued probing the behavior and performance of the sleek research jet. On October 27, Walker initiated an abrupt left roll at Mach 0.92 at an altitude of 30,000 feet. For 5 wild seconds, as the X-3 rolled, its nose pitched up and simultaneously yawed until its motions finally damped out. As NACA researchers Richard E. "Dick" Day and Jack Fischel of the High-Speed Flight Station dryly reported afterwards (describing the time history of the maneuver):

> While the ailerons are deflected for the aileron roll, a favorable sideslip angle is generated, together with a rather large increase in angle of attack. (The initial decrease in angle of attack is probably attributable to pilot stabilizer control input.) At time 3.8 seconds, even though the pilot is now applying 10° right aileron control, left rolling velocity increased and exceeded 5 radians/sec accompanied by violent pitching and sideslipping motions. During this uncontrollable phase of the maneuver, an angle of attack of 20° and left sideslip angle of 16° were encountered. It might be of interest to note that the onset of the violent maneuver coincided with the attainment of the angle of attack ($\alpha = 80$) at which unpublished flight data indicates the occurrence of reduction of longitudinal stability. Also, the angle of attack of 8° corresponds to the angle of attack at which a reduction in the measured wing lift slope occurs; therefore large wing loads were not experienced at the maximum angles of attack. After the primary rolling motion has subsided at t = 5 seconds, the large lateral and longitudinal motions damp fairly well.[45]

Walker's next foray with inertial coupling—during another left roll at Mach 1.05—was far more violent, and even the dry language of aeronautical engineering cannot mask the danger and drama attending his encounter:

> During this maneuver the favorable sideslip builds up rapidly with roll velocity and peaks at 21° at the time the airplane ceases rolling left. This large sideslip angle results in about 2g transverse acceleration. Near the time at which maximum sideslip occurs (t ≈ 4.0 sec) a large divergence in pitch develops in the negative direction which attains about –6.7g. The pilot applied control to stop this pitch-down and immediately reduced the control deflection, but was unable to avoid obtaining 7g when the airplane pitched up. Maximum wing loads measured during the maneuver did not approach or exceed the design limit load; however, the fuselage load obtained from airplane weight and acceleration, and horizontal tail loads, and wing load showed maximum values of

63,000 pounds. These maximum values approximated the limit design total load of the fuselage. The measured horizontal tail loads were near limit design load. The maximum measured vertical tail loads reached approximately 50 percent of the limit load at sideslip angles of 21°. It may be noted that a reduction in vertical tail load with sideslip was experienced at sideslip angles about 8°. In this maneuver…when the rolling stopped, the airplane motions quickly damped.[46]

Fortunately, the plane was at such a high pitch angle that the wing was effectively robbed of lift, thus not exceeding its limit loads. But the fuselage, as noted above, had reached, though not exceeded, its limit load. Following this flight, the X-3 was grounded for an extensive structural inspection, not flying again for 11 months.

In the wake of both the F-100A crash and the near loss of the X-3, Scott Crossfield was assigned to fly inertial coupling research missions in an F-100A delivered to the High-Speed Flight Station for research. Crossfield made a total of 45 flights to probe the phenomenon. During one flight, the forces were so severe that Crossfield suffered a cracked vertebra in his neck.[47]

In the research memorandum detailing the X-3's inertial coupling incidents, there is a description of an F-100 flight, this one made at 30,000 feet and Mach 0.70, initiated by an abrupt left aileron roll:

> As peak aileron deflection is attained, there is a steady development of left (adverse) sideslip and a progressive decrease in angle of attack. Between t = 3 seconds and t = 4 seconds, the divergence rates are accelerated considerably and negative angles of attack greater than 16° (−4.4 g) and the left sideslip angles as large as 26° were reached in the more violent stages of this maneuver. Maximum vertical tail loads of 5,500 pounds were measured at a sideslip angle of 26°.[48]

Day and Fischel summed up the results of the X-3 and F-100 inertial coupling tests by noting that "[t]he behavior of the two airplanes in the aileron rolls is similar in that large cross-coupling effects are evidenced. The airplanes are loaded primarily along the fuselage, particularly in the case of [the X-3], so that considerable inertial coupling is expected."[49]

In addition to analyzing the data from the X-3 and Crossfield's F-100 flights, a new tool was used for the first time in the inertial coupling investigation: the first computer flight simulations. Analog computers were programmed by Richard E. Day to simulate the inertial conditions that led to the incidents.

In an interview, Day commented on the value of Phillips's theoretical paper on inertial coupling:

> It was almost essential. It was great, because nobody had any idea what had happened…. So once the F-100 and X-3 got into roll coupling, somebody either at Edwards or back at Langley said Bill Phillips had written a theoretical report on this. So Walt Williams sent Hubert Drake and Joe Weil back to Langley to talk with Phillips.[50]

The inertial coupling problem with the F-100 was solved by making the vertical tail taller and increasing the wingspan by 2 feet. The grounding order was partially lifted in February 1955. Subsequently, automatic dampers and stability augmentation systems were added to supersonic aircraft control systems to prevent the inertial coupling from occurring. Even so, until the advent of advanced stability augmentation and electronic flight controls, the challenge of inertial coupling imposed serious handling-quality limitations on new high-performance aircraft such as the McDonnell F-101 Voodoo and the Lockheed F-104 Starfighter. The legacy of the inertial coupling crisis could be found in the proliferation of ventral fins and large vertical fins on advanced fighters (and eventually twin vertical fins, beginning with the MiG-25 and the Grumman F-14A Tomcat, which are now found on many, though not all, of the world's high-performance supersonic military aircraft).[51]

The X-3 did not fly again until September 20, 1955, and when it did, it marked the beginning of the final phase of the aircraft's useful life. Walker continued as project pilot. Research goals included collecting data on static longitudinal stability and control, wing and tail loads, and pressure distribution, but NACA researchers were careful not to probe further into the inertial coupling arena. Six more flights were made in October of 1955 focusing on directional stability and control and tail loads. The October 12 flight was marred by the inadvertent deployment of the drag chute in flight, although the plane landed safely.

The X-3 made its next flight on December 13, 1955, but the flight was cut short when a pressure probe broke off and damaged an engine. The aircraft was grounded for repairs until the following spring. It next took to the air on April 6, 1956, for pressure-distribution measurements. That day, there was an in-flight abort when Walker smelled smoke in the cockpit and landed quickly. The problem was traced to an electrical failure of test instrumentation in the nose. The damage was limited to charred wiring, and the airplane was again repaired. The final flight of the project was made May 23, 1956, to collect lateral control data. With the research flights complete, the aircraft was retired and sent to the Air Force Museum, where, even today, it impresses visitors with its sleekness and purity of line.[52]

An Assessment

Before the X-3 flew, researchers already realized that the ambitious goals set for the aircraft would never be met, not through the fault of its manufacturer or its creators, but because of the regrettable failure of its engine manufacturer to deliver suitable engines. Thus, the desired data on aerodynamic heating, inlet duct and scoop airflow, stability and control of high-fineness-ratio fuselages, and aerodynamics of low-thickness-chord-ratio wings at Mach 2—the *raison d'être* of the program—were never collected.[53]

The X-3 was difficult to fly—John McTigue, a former High-Speed Flight Station engineer, recalled that following one landing, Joe Walker had climbed out of the aircraft and thrown his helmet to the lakebed in apparent frustration with the plane—though this reflected as much the unknowns and challenges of control system design in the early supersonic era as it did any inherent flaw in the system itself. Specifically, the system suffered from control lag, a flawed automatic load feel system, longitudinal oscillations that were difficult to control, and poor damping of oscillations. In light of these control system shortcomings, a question arises. If the J46 jet engines *had* been available or the pair of LR-8 rocket engines had been fitted, could the pilot have even controlled the aircraft at Mach 2? Inertial coupling came close to destroying the X-3 at just over Mach 1, nearly destroyed the X-1A at Mach 2.44, and did destroy the Bell X-2 at Mach 3. At Mach 2, the loads on the X-3 would have been much higher; it is reasonable to wonder how long the airplane would have remained intact at that speed at the first hint of roll coupling.

The relative "research worth" of the X-3 compared with that of the three Douglas D-558-2 research aircraft can also be measured by the number of flights made with each aircraft. The single X-3 accumulated only 52 flights, and the three D-558-2s made 313 flights in total.[54]

Given all this, the X-3 might be easily dismissed as an outright failure—underpowered, exhibiting poor control characteristics, and unable to meet performance or research goals. Yet the X-3 provided critical data on inertial coupling, a goal never planned and one involving an aircraft design issue no one knew existed. Its contribution was a happy accident. The D-558-2's swept-wing design had inadvertently allowed the testing of methods for preventing pitch-up. In the same way, Douglas's efforts to build a Mach 2 aircraft resulted in a design that concentrated mass in the fuselage. Entirely by accident, this resulted in production of an aircraft susceptible to inertial coupling. This, in

The transport vehicle on the lakebed with the X-3. Once at the takeoff point, the X-3 was rolled off the trailer and prepared for flight. (NASA)

turn, facilitated the discovery of an as yet unknown problem with high-speed aircraft. Since modern jet fighters would be built to resemble the F-100 in their concentration of mass in the fuselage, with swept, low-aspect wings, the X-3's contributions were invaluable to virtually every new fighter coming off the drawing boards.

The best illustration of this is seen in the iconic 1950s fighter, the Lockheed F-104, to whose design the X-3 contributed immediately. Both aircraft had thin, short, razorbladelike wings and heavy fuselages. The development of the F-104 overlapped with the X-3 research flights, and the Air Force insisted that Douglas provide Lockheed with the X-3 plans. The F-104 was designed as a lightweight air-superiority fighter capable of reaching high altitudes and engaging Soviet fighters. The initial contract for two XF-104 aircraft was signed on March 11, 1953, and the first XF-104 flight was made on February 28, 1954. The speed with which the XF-104 went from drawing board to flying aircraft was due to the X-3's development, which proved the aerodynamic validity of the low-aspect-ratio wing, performance predictions, and other details.

A RAND study of the F-104's development underscored this assessment, observing:

> The F-104 history illustrates that research and development in one program can have a great carry-over value in another. Lockheed's success in building and flying a prototype less than a year after

go-ahead would very probably not been possible without the knowledge derived from the Douglas X-3 program. Although the value of this experimental effort in the F-104 could hardly have been anticipated when Air Force money was advanced to finance the program, nevertheless the value to the Air Force of the X-3 program extended far beyond the immediate results achieved with it.[55]

The F-104 was used by the U.S. Air Force and by allied air forces in West Germany, Canada, Belgium, the Netherlands, Italy, and Japan. More than 1,400 F-104s of all variants were built by Lockheed and under license. The low-aspect-ratio wing design was incorporated into other fighter designs as well, including the Northrop F-5, which saw service in 15 air forces, including those of South Vietnam, Greece, Iran, South Korea, the Philippines, Nationalist China, Turkey, Norway, and Libya.[56] In its own way, this, too, represented a legacy of the X-3.

Endnotes

1. Opening quotation from the pilot transcript of the X-3's second flight, October 31, 1952, DFRC archives.
2. The AAF development contract was W33-038-ac-10413, dated 30 June 1945, and the aircraft received project designation MX-656. For the detailed development history of this airplane, see Richard P. Hallion, "Serendipity at Santa Monica: The Story of the Douglas X-3," *Air Enthusiast Quarterly* 4 (October 1977): 129–136.
3. Douglas Aircraft Company, "Model X-3 Mock-Up Conference Airplane Descriptions and Illustrations," December 6, 1948, p. 7.
4. Ibid., pp. 8, 13–14, 38, 42–43; Frank N. Fleming, "Evolution of the Configuration of the X-3 Supersonic Research Aircraft" (Santa Monica, CA: Douglas Aircraft Company, August 1, 1949), pp. 1, 4–18.
5. Douglas Aircraft Company, "Model X-3 Mock-Up Conference Airplane Descriptions and Illustrations," pp. 8–10.
6. Thomas A. Marschak, *The Role of Project Histories in the Study of R&D*, Report P-2850 (Santa Monica: The RAND Corporation, January 1964), p. 43.
7. Marschak, *Role of Project Histories*, p. 44; see also James St. Peter, *The History of Gas Turbine Development in the United States…A Tradition of Excellence* (Atlanta, GA: International Gas Turbine Institute of The American Society of Mechanical Engineers, 1999), pp. 139–140. Nor was the X-3 the J46's only "victim": it helped limit the Navy's Vought F7U-3 Cutlass, rendered the entire first production run of McDonnell F3H-1 Demons both dangerous and useless, led to the abandonment of the Lockheed XF-90, nearly crippled the Navy's F3D-2 Skyknight, and forced Vought to lay off over 2,500 production workers, resulting in widespread criticism of Westinghouse. Though the company ostensibly remained in the jet engine business for another decade, it dropped out of the first rank of engine manufacturers and never matched the success it had enjoyed with its J34, an excellent design. The tragedy is that the X-3 appeared too early to employ a magnificent small afterburning turbojet, the General Electric J85 (the power plant for the later Northrop F-5/T-38 family). At half the weight and smaller even than the J34, the J85 had substantially higher performance. With it, the X-3 could clearly have reached Mach 2—but the J85 was not ready for flight testing until almost the end of the decade.
8. Hallion, "Serendipity at Santa Monica," pp. 131–132.

9. Memorandum for Chief of Research, "Proposed Modifications of X-3 Airplane to Rocket Power and Air Launch," October 24, 1952.

10. Hallion, "Serendipity From Santa Monica," p. 132; for the F-104 benefit, see Marschak, *Role of Project Histories*, pp. 85–86, which notes, "Lockheed's task was made substantially easier by the availability of information, particularly wind-tunnel data, gathered in the course of the Douglas X-3 program [whose experience] had a carry-over value for the F-104 program." Richard P. Hallion recalls a conversation with Melvin B. Zisfein, Deputy Director of the National Air and Space Museum, who recalled seeing X-3 wind tunnel reports handed to Lockheed staff for reference as they worked on the F-104's design.

11. Hallion, "Serendipity at Santa Monica," pp. 132, 136.

12. Richard E. Day and Jack Fischel, "Stability and Control Characteristics Obtained During Demonstration of the Douglas X-3 Research Airplane," NACA RM H55E16 (July 21, 1955), p. 6.

13. NACA HSFRS, "X-3 Status Report for Period 14 September to 18 October 1952," DFRC Archives. Unless otherwise noted, all NACA status reports are located in the DFRC archives.

14. NACA HSFRS, "X-3 Status Report for Week Ending 25 October 1952."

15. NACA HSFRS, "X-3 Weekly Status Report for Week Ending 1 November 1953"; "X-3 Weekly Status Report for Week Ending 15 November 1953"; "X-3 Weekly Status Report Week Ending 25 April 1953."

16. NACA HSFRS, "X-3 Weekly Status Report Week Ending 2 May 1953."

17. NACA HSFRS, "X-3 Weekly Status Report Week Ending 20 June 1953," p. 1.

18. NACA HSFRS, "X-3 Weekly Status Report Week Ending 5 June 1953," p. 1.

19. NACA HSFRS, "X-3 Weekly Status Report Week Ending 13 June 1953," p. 1.

20. NACA HSFRS, "X-3 Weekly Status Report Week Ending 27 June 1953," p. 1.

21. NACA HSFRS, "X-3 Weekly Status Report Week Ending 18 July 1953."

22. Douglas Aircraft Company, Flight Test Division, "Flight Report No. 7," 1953, DFRC Archives.

23. NACA HSFRS, "X-3 Weekly Status Report Week Ending 25 July 1953"; Douglas Aircraft Company, Flight Test Division, "Flight Report No. 8 (1953)."

24. NACA HSFRS, "X-3 Weekly Status Report Week Ending 1 August 1953."

25. Douglas Aircraft Company Testing Division, "Flight Report No. 23," 1953, DFRC Archives.

26. Memorandum for Research Airplane Projects Leader, "Progress Report for the X-3 Research Airplane for the Period November 1 to November 30, 1953"; "Bridgeman," *http://www.astronautix.com/astros/brigeman.htm*, accessed October 6, 2010.

27. Memorandum for Research Airplane Projects Leader, "Progress Report for the X-3 Research Airplane for the Period July 1 to July 31, 1954."

28. Lt. Col. Frank K. Everest, as told to John Guenther, *The Fastest Man Alive* (New York: E.P. Dutton, 1958), pp. 158–160.

29. Day and Fischel, "Stability and Control Characteristics Obtained During Demonstrations of the Douglas X-3 Research Airplane," pp. 1–2.

30. Memorandum for Research Airplane Projects Director, "Progress Report for the X-3 Research Airplane for the Period August 1 to August 31, 1954."

31. Memorandum for Research Airplane Projects Director, "Progress Report for the X-3 Research Airplane for the Period September 1 to September 30, 1954."

32. Memorandum for Research Airplane Projects Director, "Progress Report for the X-3 Research Airplane for the Period October 1 to October 31, 1954."

33. NACA Technical Note 1627. For this remarkable aeronautical scientist, see W. Hewitt Phillips, *Journey in Aeronautical Research: A Career at NASA Langley Research Center* (Washington, DC: NASA, 1998).

34. William H. Phillips, "Effects of Steady Rolling on Longitudinal and Directional Stability," NACA Technical Note No. 1627, June 1948, pp. 1–2.

35. Ibid.

36. Fleming, "Evolution of the Configuration of the X-3 Supersonic Research Aircraft," pp. 10, 20–23; High-Speed Flight Station, "Flight Experience with Two High-Speed Airplanes Having Violent Lateral-Longitudinal Coupling in Aileron Rolls," NACA RM H55A13 (February 4, 1955), pp. 7–8.

37. Quoted in Richard P. Hallion, "Sweep and Swing: Reshaping the Wing for the Jet and Rocket Age," in Richard P. Hallion, ed., *NASA's Contributions to Aeronautics*, vol. 1: *Aerodynamics, Structures, Propulsion, Controls* (Washington, DC: NASA SP-2010-570-Vol 1. 2010), p. 38.

38. As well, the more descriptive "roll coupling" was used.

39. Memorandum for Chief of Research, "X-3 Airplane Visit of Harold F. Kleckner of the Douglas Company to Langley on October 18, 1951," p. 2.

40. Hallion, "Sweep and Swing," pp. 39–40; James H. Parks, "Experimental Evidence of Sustained Coupled Longitudinal and Lateral Oscillations from a Rocket-Propelled Model of a 35° Swept Wing Airplane Configuration," NACA RM L54D15 (May 28, 1954).

41. Hallion, *Supersonic Flight*, pp. 180–182.

42. Yeager transcript and pilot report, 23 December 1953, and J.L. Powell, "X-1A Airplane Contract W33-038-ac-20062, Flight Test Progress Report No. 15, Period from 9 December through 20 December 1953," Bell Aircraft Corporation Report No. 58-980-019 (February 3, 1954), in AFFTC History Office archives.

43. Hubert M. Drake and Wendell H. Stillwell, "Behavior of the Bell X-1A Research Airplane During Exploratory Flights at Mach Numbers Near 2.0 and at Extreme Altitudes," NACA RM H55G25 (September 1, 1955).

44. Everest and Guenther, *The Fastest Man Alive*, pp. 19–22; Bill Gunston, *Early Supersonic Fighters of the West* (New York: Charles Scribner's Sons, 1975), pp. 146–154; Knaack, *Post–World War II*, pp. 115–116.

45. NACA High-Speed Flight Station (HSFS), "Flight Experience with Two High-Speed Airplanes Having Violent Lateral-Longitudinal Coupling in Aileron Rolls," NACA RM H55A13 (February 4, 1955), p. 4.

46. Ibid.

47. Crossfield and Blair, *Always Another Dawn*, pp. 198, 199.

48. HSFS, "Flight Experience with Two High-Speed Airplanes," p. 5.

49. Ibid.

50. Peebles, ed., *The Spoken Word*, pp. 68–69.

51. Ibid.

52. Hallion, "Serendipity at Santa Monica," p. 136; Hallion and Gorn, *On the Frontier*, p. 398. More information on the X-3 research results can be found in the following NACA research memorandums: Harriet J. Stephenson, "Flight Measurements of

Horizontal-Tail Loads on the Douglas X-3 Research Airplane," NACA RM H56A23 (April 18, 1956); William L. Marcy, Harriet J. Stephenson, and Thomas V. Cooney, "Analysis of the Vertical-Tail Loads Measured During a Flight Investigation at Transonic Speeds of the Douglas X-3 Airplane," NACA RM H56H08 (November 9, 1956); Jack Fischel, Euclid C. Holleman, and Robert A. Tremant, "Flight Investigation of the Transonic Longitudinal and Lateral Handling Qualities of the Douglas X-3 Research Airplane," NACA RM H57I05 (December 5, 1957); William L. Marcy, "High-Speed Loads Measured on the Douglas X-3 Research Airplane," NACA RM H57L08 (February 24, 1958); and Earl R. Keener, Norman J. McLeod, and Norman V. Taillon, "Effect of Leading-Edge-Flap Deflections on the Wing Loads, Load Distribution, and Flap Hinge Moments of the Douglas X-3 Research Airplane at Transonic Speeds," NACA RM H58D29 (July 15, 1958).

53. Hallion, "Serendipity at Santa Monica," p. 136.
54. "D-588 II Skyrocket," *http://www.globalsecurity.org/military/systems/ aircraft/d-588-ii.htm*, accessed May 24, 2010; John McTigue interview notes, March 9, 2010.
55. Marschak, *Role of Project Histories*, pp. 85–86; Knaack, *Post–World War II Fighters*, pp. 175–176; Hallion and Gorn, *On the Frontier*, pp. 57–58.
56. Knaack, *Post–World War II Fighters*, pp. 185–187, 288–289.

The X-4 Bantam, the second X-4 flown by the NACA between 1950 and 1953, after restoration at the National Museum of the Air Force. The semi-tailless swept-wing design was influenced by Northrop's work on flying-wing aircraft, the belief that a lack of horizontal stabilizers would prevent transonic handling problems, and the Me-163B Komet rocket-powered fighter developed by Nazi Germany. (USAF)

CHAPTER 5

Versatile Minimalist:
The Northrop X-4 Bantam

We did a lot of things with the X-4 that
weren't only involved in its being a tailless airplane.
—A. Scott Crossfield[1]

The tiny Northrop X-4 Bantam, one of the smallest piloted jet aircraft ever built and flown, represented the confluence of several technological threads. First was aviation pioneer and industrialist John Knudsen "Jack" Northrop's longstanding interest in flying-wing aircraft, dating to the late 1920s. By the early postwar years, his dream had culminated in the graceful and futuristic multiengine Northrop XB-35 and YB-49 flying wing bombers, the former piston-powered and the latter a pure turbojet, undergoing flight testing at Muroc. Another thread was the transonic revolution itself: studies by both the Army Air Forces and the NACA indicated that a semi-tailless aircraft with swept wings and a vertical tail, devoid of horizontal stabilizer and elevators, might avoid the buffeting and controllability problems afflicting conventional "tailed" aircraft (a byproduct of the deleterious interaction between the turbulent flow streaming behind a wing and the tail surfaces located at the rear of the aircraft). Instead, to compensate for the lack of conventional elevators for pitch control, combined elevator and aileron control surfaces (called elevons) were built into the wing. Operating symmetrically (both up or both down), they controlled pitch, like elevators; operating differentially (one up, the other down), they controlled roll, like ailerons.

Tailless aircraft (pure flying wings with no tail surfaces whatsoever) and semi-tailless aircraft (ones having only a vertical tail) had a long heritage dating to the pre–World War I era, and while (by the late 1940s) never securing a dominant position among widely accepted aircraft configurations, they nevertheless had undergone significant technical evolution, rendering them increasingly practicable.[2] The advent of the swept-wing semi-tailless Messerschmitt Me 163 Komet rocket-propelled interceptor had added to their allure. In an era when 400-mph propeller-driven fighters climbing at 4,000 feet per minute were considered remarkable, the 600-mph Komet—climbing to 30,000 feet in little over 2 minutes and then streaking through Allied bomber formations so rapidly that bomber gunners could not bring their weapons to bear—was fantastic. At first glance, to a postwar world entranced by German wartime aerodynamic and design accomplishments, the Me 163 seemed to point the way to future flight. What was missed was that the Me 163 had demonstrated extremely dangerous transonic handling qualities, as a result of its highly deficient high-speed stability and control, and that this had severely limited its military effectiveness. Coupled with other weaknesses, including an unreliable, unstable, and highly dangerous propulsion system and limited endurance, these deficiencies as a group ensured that the Me 163 remained more a curiosity than a serious threat.[3]

Fascination with the semi- or completely tailless configuration had spawned some remarkable concepts for a variety of military and civil aircraft. In Britain, this had led to the de Havilland DH 108 Swallow, a transonic swept-wing research aircraft intended to function as a technology demonstrator for the proposed DH 106 jet airliner.[4] Inspired by the Me 163 and launched in late July 1945, the Swallow took the fuselage and turbojet engine installation of the de Havilland DH 100 Vampire jet fighter and joined it to a graceful swept wing, with an equally graceful vertical fin installed on the aft fuselage. The DH 108 had a more sharply swept wing compared to the Me 163's gentler sweep. Flight testing of the first of three DH 108s began in May 1946, with the aircraft flown by Geoffrey de Havilland, Jr., son of the firm's founder. The first Swallow (TG 283) was reserved for low-speed trials, but the second (TG 306) was a high-speed machine. It achieved Mach 0.895 at 34,000 feet on its fourth flight. During its early trials, it experienced a "short period" longitudinal pitching oscillation at higher Mach numbers that was poorly damped. On September 27, 1946, as young de Havilland practiced for a world airspeed record attempt, TG 306 violently pitched at Mach 0.875 at only 7,500 feet (an altitude that imposed very high structural loadings on the aircraft), breaking up and killing him instantly. Though a third DH 108 Swallow (VW 120) eventually did exceed the speed of sound during a high-speed dive from 45,000 feet to 23,500 feet on September 6, 1948 (becoming the first British-designed jet airplane to exceed the sound barrier), it entailed another wild ride. At one point (as test pilot John Derry noted), the plane exhibited an "extremely rapid and completely unstable nose-down pitch" during which the VW 120 briefly went past the vertical, attaining –3 g's.[5] Derry, an unusually skilled and courageous airman (even by the standards of test pilots) managed to both exceed Mach 1 and then return safely to Earth. The Swallow had earned a more favorable place in aviation history, but it still clearly was a dangerous airplane, and, indeed, all three were eventually lost in uniformly fatal accidents.[6]

The first X-4 was used only for contractor demonstration flights, as it had a number of deficiencies. After the flights were completed, it was turned over to the NACA for spare parts. (USAF)

The X-4: Concept, Design, and Construction

On June 11, 1946, slightly over 3 months before Geoffrey de Havilland, Jr.'s fatal crash in the second DH 108, Northrop and Army Air Forces' representatives had signed a contract to build and flight-test two examples of a semi-tailless swept-wing aircraft. This marked the beginning of the XS-4 (later X-4) program, which was undertaken as Air Force research and development project MX-810. As with Britain's luckless Swallow, the inspiration for the Northrop design was largely that of the Me 163. Northrop constituted a natural contractor for the experimental airplane, as no other American company had such extensive experience and insight into the special challenges and problems of tailless and flying-wing aircraft. Unlike any of its X-series predecessors, the X-4 was specifically intended for subsonic testing.

Northrop entrusted design of the X-4 to a team led by chief project engineer Arthur Lusk. Assisting Lusk were aerodynamicist Irving Ashkenas; chief of structures A.M. Schwartz; and a team of specialists in weight and balance, wing construction, propulsion, hydraulics, landing gear, instrumentation, and avionics. Basic design work for the aircraft was completed at Northrop's Hawthorne, CA, plant by the fall of 1946, and the mockup was finished in mid-November. Results of the inspection of the mockup by Air Force and NACA engineers were generally favorable. The exception was one item found by NACA personnel, who noted that no space had been allotted for specialized research instrumentation. In response, the Air Force and Northrop (at the NACA's suggestion) reduced the fuselage fuel tank's size to provide the requisite room.[7]

The aircraft employed two Westinghouse J30-WE-7-9 nonafterburning turbojet engines, each producing just 1,600 pounds of thrust at sea level—the same propulsion package used earlier in an unsuccessful Northrop flying-wing fighter, the XP-79B, that had fatally crashed on its very first flight. Use of the low-thrust engines underscored that the airframe had to be both small and light; in its final configuration, a person could look into the cockpit without having to use a ladder. To minimize weight, the X-4's wings were made of magnesium and incorporated integral fuel tanks that, when combined to the tanks in the fuselage, carried 230 gallons of useable fuel, giving the little jet a 45-minute endurance.[8] In configuration, the X-4 resembled the British Swallow, but with a more angular and lower-aspect-ratio 200-square-foot wing. Its leading-edge sweep was 41.57°, it had an overall span of 26.83 feet (its fuselage length was 23.25 feet), and it had an aspect ratio of 3.6. For safety, the X-4 design team prudently incorporated hydraulically actuated split flaps on the wing's inner trailing edge. If the X-4 encountered dangerous transonic pitching, its pilot could actuate the flaps, which would immediately extend both above and below the wing, increasing its frontal area and generating such drag that the X-4 would rapidly decelerate to firmly subsonic velocities before it emulated the unfortunate DH 108 and pitched to destruction. Overall, the little X-4 had a maximum weight of 7,050 pounds.[9]

Northrop completed the first X-4 (AF serial number 46-676) in June 1948, and the aircraft underwent an engineering inspection with mixed results. Issues surfaced regarding the landing gear up-and-down locks, the fuel system, and the level of protection for control cables against engine failure or fire. Howard Lilly had been killed the previous month in the second D-558-1 when its engine disintegrated, causing inspectors to regard new aircraft more stringently. The required changes to install armor shielding for its flight control system and around the engines to prevent a disintegrating engine from puncturing the fuselage or wing tanks took 4 months to make. The first X-4 finally arrived at Muroc aboard a flatbed trailer on November 15, 1948. After taxi tests were completed, it was ready for its first flight.[10]

Early Flights

Northrop test pilot Charles Tucker flew the customary proving flights before the two X-4s were turned over to the Air Force and the NACA. The first Northrop flight was made on December 16, 1948. Instrumenting the aircraft promptly proved problematic due to the aircraft's small size and Northrop's structural and engine-temperature-measurement requirements. As a result, NACA stability and control instrumentation on the first flight was minimal. Standard NACA instrumentation recorded altitude, airspeed, angle of side-slip, right and left elevon position, and rudder position. The instrumentation transmitted some data to a ground station, where they were recorded for later analysis. (Monitoring in real time, however, was not possible.) Data taken included rates of normal acceleration, altitude, airspeed, right and left elevon position, and rudder position. The data were synchronized with a common time stamp.

During the first flight, Tucker took data during takeoff and landing and made in-flight records of the X-4's speed as it went from 250 to 275 miles per hour and back down to 225 miles per hour indicated air speed (IAS). A subsequent research memorandum on the flight noted:

> These data show that in the clean condition the airplane is slightly unstable as shown by an upward deflection of the control required for increasing speed. The pilot stated that it was impossible to trim the airplane in the clean condition. With gear down the airplane is stable for both center-of-gravity positions. There is an indication that there may be some instability at high normal-force coefficients with the gear down. However, the data at 145 miles per hour were obtained in the landing approach just before contact so there may be some effects of the proximity of the ground on these data. Although these data are rather sketchy, they indicate that the center of gravity should be moved forward.[11]

One issue that appeared on the first flight was the effectiveness of the rudder control. The X-4 originally was fitted with an electronically operated system with a four-speed actuator, an early example of applying electronic flight control (though not a computerized flight control) to an experimental airplane. The maximum rate of rudder movement was 25° per second. Available evidence indicates that this system was designed to serve as a yaw-damper stability-augmentation system. Controlling yaw excursions was far from an innocuous issue. Should too large a sideslip angle develop, the aircraft could stall and then enter a dangerous spin.

Flying-wing aircraft had inherently poor spin characteristics, the danger exacerbated by often violent longitudinal pitch changes that could result in structural failure. Several Northrop flying wings already had been lost in spins and pitching accidents, including an MX-324 glider, an N-9M subscale piloted demonstrator for the XB-35, an experimental XP-56 tailless propeller-driven fighter, and the sole XP-79B jet-powered flying-wing fighter. Then, on June 5,

1948, as Northrop readied the first X-4 for flight, came the dramatic loss of a test crew aboard an eight-engine Northrop YB-49, resulting in the renaming of Muroc as Edwards Air Force Base, after the ill-fated plane's copilot, Captain Glen Edwards. An investigation indicated that the YB-49 had stalled, entered a spinning dive, and then had broken up as the crew tried to recover. Thus, in the X-4, Northrop, the Air Force, and the NACA all had a compelling desire to ensure that yaw rates could be limited, thus reducing the risk of the little jet's entering an unrecoverable or otherwise destructive spin.[12]

For that reason, researchers noted with concern the apparent lag test pilot Charles Tucker reported in the X-4's rudder response:

> The pilot stated that the rudder control seemed to have considerable lag and the motion of the control was too slow…. [T]he rate of rudder motion was about 25° per second, which [shows that the] rate is considerably slower than the rate at which a pilot is able to move the rudder pedals. The electrical system which operates the rudder is arranged to give several rates of control movement corresponding to the rate at which the pilot moves the pedals. The rate of 25° per second is the maximum rate that is available to the pilot at the present. The flight records showed this rate was used in virtually all rudder applications indicating that motion to the pedals was applied at a rate of 25° per second or greater. During the first attempt for take-off, it was also indicated that this rate of rudder movement is too slow for maintaining directional control.
>
> The pilot reported excessive friction in the elevon control system[,] which is an irreversible hydraulic system with artificial feel for the pilot. He also reported that the aileron forces seemed very heavy relative to the elevator forces[,] which on occasion caused him to apply elevator control as well as aileron when attempting to move only the ailerons. Since the aileron forces are about normal it is believed that the pilot was given this impression by the excessively light elevator forces. Since the elevator-force system depends primarily upon elevator position, it could be expected that with a change in center-of-gravity location sufficient to provide adequate stick-fixed longitudinal stability, the aileron-elevator forces would be proportioned satisfactorily.
>
> Inspection of the sideslip records showed no evidence of snaking oscillation over the range of speeds covered.[13]

Changes were made to the X-4 that reflected the results of the first flight. Postflight analysis indicated that the aft position of the center of gravity was

Head-on view of the first X-4. The aircraft was the smallest of the early X-planes. The bubble canopy was different from the V-shaped windshields of most other research aircraft. Like the X-3, X-5, and XF-92A, the X-4 offered the advantage of an ejection seat. (NASA)

the cause of the poor longitudinal stability. Consequently, the airplane's center of gravity was shifted to 19.7 percent of the mean aerodynamic chord (MAC) from 22.4 percent of the MAC. To resolve the rudder issues, the theoretically more advanced electrically operated rudder actuator was removed and replaced with a much more reliable (and, somewhat counterintuitively, faster) mechanical cable and bell-crank system, akin to the rudder control in a model airplane. This doubled the rate of rudder travel to 50° per second. The control system friction and springs were also checked by mechanics to eliminate the excessive friction reported by the pilot. A check of engine vibrations during ground run-up was planned. The date of the second flight was dependent on lakebed conditions. In late January 1949, it was not expected that it would be usable for about 4 weeks.[14]

In fact, because of lingering water on the lakebed, the X-4's second flight was not made until April 27, 1949. Tucker collected data during stabilized speed runs at 170, 210, and 290 miles per hour IAS and at altitudes from 12,000 to 15,000 feet, but he had to terminate the flight prematurely because of fuel transfer difficulties.[15] The approach and landing data were also analyzed from the second flight; the results reflected both good and bad characteristics. Williams's postflight memorandum noted, "The airplane possesses adequate position stick-fixed longitudinal stability with the center of gravity at 19.7 percent mean aerodynamic chord as compared with the slight instability with the center of gravity at 22 percent mean aerodynamic chord."[16]

As for the approach and landing, Williams wrote,

> [T]he airplane possessed slight positive longitudinal stability with the landing gear down and flaps up as evidenced by the increase in upward elevon deflection as the speed was decreased. Approximately 14° of longitudinal control was used for landing[,] which left adequate control for lateral motions of the airplane. It should be pointed out, however, that this landing was made well above minimum speed without flaps. It should be noted that during the approach to landing, the small movements of the rudder caused a lateral oscillation that was slow to damp and even continued at small amplitudes with the rudder held fixed…. [The control was] held essentially fixed while the airplane oscillated in sideslip…. The lateral oscillation has a period of approximately 2 to 3 seconds and…the oscillation damps to half-amplitude in approximately 4 to 5 seconds.
>
> The pilot was satisfied with the longitudinal stability with the center of gravity at 19.7 percent mean aerodynamic chord. The rudder control was considered adequate. Although the pilot did not consider the poor damping of the lateral oscillation objectionable at the speeds for which data are presented herein, he encountered a poorly damped lateral oscillation at 290 miles per hour which he considered very objectionable.[17]

Clearly, the X-4 had stability and control issues, reflecting its close-coupled configuration, which virtually guaranteed poorly damped control response, low inherent stability, and a greater than usual susceptibility to pilot-induced oscillations (PIOs). But that it did is unsurprising since so much of what aeronautical engineers were doing at the time was new, and it was flying, as well, in both the pre-stability augmentation and pre-fly-by-wire flight control eras. Between April 27 and June 1, 1949, flights 2 through 6 were completed with the first X-4. The flights generated data, but problems appeared with Northrop's temperature recorder and radio. After the fourth flight, the engineers initially concluded that the interference was caused by the NACA telemeter system. The telemeter was not used on the fifth and sixth flights, to verify this, but the problems remained. Other difficulties were experienced during the sixth flight. After takeoff, Tucker mistakenly left the recording instruments on through the climb, leaving no recording film for the rest of the planned maneuvers, so they

Another view of the first X-4. The aircraft had a functional design, but it suffered from major stability problems that the technology of the early 1950s could not correct. (NASA)

were aborted. Northrop engineers also reported the left engine had problems during the flight, requiring that it be replaced. This grounded the aircraft for 2 months.

Such delays were often experienced with research aircraft. These were often due, as in this case, to technical problems with equipment and systems. The data instrumentation system was particularly critical. If it was not working, the flight was pointless. Another cause was the flooding of the lakebed, which occurred during most winters. Another was processing a backlog of data. This was the job of female "computers," who had to measure the traces on the film manually, apply corrections and calibrations that transformed the traces into numerical data, and plot these on graphs.

The first and second flights of the second X-4 (AF serial number 46-677) were made in June. During the aircraft's preflight preparation, all NACA instruments were recalibrated. The telemeter in the X-4 burned out before the first flight, however, and was not replaced before the flight was made. Some data were collected, including a rudder release oscillation and a 2-g pull-up. But the lack of telemetry didn't matter since the primary goals for the flight were pilot familiarization and instrumentation checkout. And in any event, both flights were cut short due to fuel leaking from the wing filler caps.[18]

The second X-4 underwent modifications to correct the fuel siphoning. That aircraft's third flight was made on June 23 to test the fix. But as on the two previous flights, fuel continued to be lost and the mission had to be cut short. Despite the aborted flight, data were collected on a snaking oscillation and two pull-ups of 2 g's.

To identify the cause of the continuing fuel siphoning, instrumentation was added to measure vent-line pressures under varying flight conditions. Measurements were taken during the fourth X-4 flight, on June 30. In addition to diagnostic measurements, records were taken at speeds of 300 and 160 mph at different speed brake angles and at altitudes of 10,000 and 8,500 feet.[19]

While the first X-4 still remained grounded, Tucker made flights 5 and 6 in the second X-4 on July 8 and 12, respectively. The fifth flight provided data on accelerated maneuvers at 30,000 feet and at 180, 260, and 300 mph; the sixth was primarily a photographic mission, but data were also obtained on different dive brake angles at 140 mph. Following this flight, the second X-4 was grounded, pending engine changes. The first X-4 resumed flights on July 26, 1949, the second aircraft on the following day. These constituted the seventh flight for each aircraft. Again, a significant shortcoming was identified: a series of directional stability runs was undertaken with the second X-4, but data indicated that hands-off stability runs could not be made, as the time required to trim the aircraft was excessive. As well, Northrop engineers revealed they were "concerned about some component of the X-4 airplane which has proven unsatisfactory in another installation." But they "were unwilling to state at this time what the exact trouble is." A meeting between Northrop and NACA personnel was held, and the Northrop contingent indicated that the landing gear door locks were not satisfactory. The risk was that the doors could open in flight at high speeds. Work began on developing a fix for the problem.[20]

To allow Tucker's contractor flights to continue, the X-4s were restricted from exceeding 300 mph IAS and 1.5 g's of normal acceleration. Each aircraft made its eighth and ninth flights in August. The landing gear door issue was not the only problem the project faced. The second X-4 made a lateral-stability flight on August 3 and a roll-rate measurement flight on August 5. When the film from onboard instruments was developed following the flight, it was discovered that the film drums had been improperly loaded and no data had been collected. Additionally, the aircraft had experienced excess vibrations on both flights, requiring that both engines be removed and replaced.[21]

This was successfully carried out, but Northrop managers requested funding to investigate the vibrations. Pending a decision on their request, the second aircraft was temporarily grounded. The first X-4 remained on flight status, but no flights were made through mid-September. This was due to the removal of the NACA telemetry transmitter so as to allow the installation of

The research airplanes were not typically designed with ease of servicing in mind. The X-4 was an exception. Its aft fuselage could be removed from the forward section, allowing access to the jet engines. (NASA)

engine-temperature-measurement instruments requested by Northrop. Another reason no flights were made was that Northrop engineers were still working on a fix for the landing gear doors. Not until this was completed would the aircraft make another flight.[22]

The second X-4 finally resumed flights on September 30. During flight 10, Tucker made two stalls in the clean configuration and with the gear down. Additionally, an accelerated stall was performed. Based on the flight data, it was clear that modifications would have to be made to the landing gear doors on both aircraft. The task was expected to take 3 weeks.

During the halt in flights, Northrop submitted a revised contractor test plan. This sharply pared the original plan to a level sufficient only for proving the guaranteed performance requirements. This would involve six more flights totaling about 15 hours. In reviewing Northrop's proposed revision, Melvin Sadoff, an NACA aeronautical research scientist at Muroc who wrote the X-4 report, noted several requirements that would be necessary in order to provide the data that the NACA needed for its research efforts: "With regard to the NACA's final acceptance of the abbreviated Northrop program on the X-4, it is considered essential that directional stability data be obtained up to the level flight high speed of the airplane. The tests should be made at sufficiently large sideslip angles to provide satisfactory proof of the structural integrity of the vertical tail at high speeds."[23]

Sadoff also summarized the data from the second X-4's 10th flight:

> The results indicate that the 1 g "stalls" in both the clean and the gear down configurations were mild and were accompanied by a slight dropping of the right wing. The maximum lift coefficients obtained were about 0.71 in both cases. There was no warning prior to these stalls. Rapid recovery was effected with down elevons. From the relative mildness of the airplane motion subsequent to these stalls and because no appreciable buffeting was obtained, it is believed that the stalls were not quite complete. Conceivably, higher values of CL_{max} could be obtained by holding the right wing up with the rudder control. An accelerated stall to about 1.6 g was made at about an indicated speed of 165 mph, (25 mph higher than the 1 g stalls), and the data showed that the stall was essentially complete. The right wing dropped fairly abruptly and large up-elevons at the stall were ineffective in increasing the CL_{max} above about 0.83. Moderate buffeting set in at the stall in the case and persisted throughout the recovery. Recovery was again rapid and complete with the down elevon movement.[24]

Sadoff also raised a more significant issue: whether the X-4 would be suitable from an operational and maintenance standpoint. He listed a series of concerns:

(a) Engine vibration
(b) Engine availability and maintenance (including accessories)
(c) Fuel system peculiarities and sources of trouble
(d) Hydraulic system setup, including protection from vibration and engine failure
(e) Availability of control in case of hydraulic system failure, etc.

Sadoff concluded, "From information available at present, item (a) will not be remedied and will probably be a source of pilot discomfort, although Westinghouse assures us the vibration does not affect the structural soundness of the engine. Items (b) through (e) are currently being looked into by Messrs. Collins, Griffith and myself."[25]

The second X-4 did not make its 11th flight until November 29, 1949. The results were a disappointment; after takeoff, Tucker retracted the landing gear, but it did not lock properly. He aborted the flight, and the only data recorded were of the approach and landing. The Northrop contractor test flights were drawing to a close, with only four flights planned with the second X-4. Sadoff stated that NACA and Air Force representatives needed to meet before the completion of the Northrop flights and make a decision on the number of additional flights the company would need to complete before the X-4s could be accepted by the Air Force and the NACA.[26]

Northrop X-4 Flights Continue

After the delays in the early contractor flights, activity with the second X-4 picked up in mid-December 1949. Flights 12 and 13 were both made on December 7, flight 14 on December 9, and flight 15 on December 14. The most significant event occurred on flight 15. As Sadoff summarized in the biweekly report:

> During Flight 15 at about 0.80 Mach number and about 5g, an inadvertent pitch-up occurred and the airplane acceleration built up to about 6.5g before the pilot was able to regain control of the airplane. During the recovery, the airplane went through a series of violent pitching, rolling, and yawing oscillations, which apparently were associated with the pilot's manipulation of the controls rather than an inherent dynamic instability of the airplane.
>
> Flight 16 scheduled for Friday, December 16 was cancelled so that the nose wheel door may be reworked preparatory to higher speed flights. The interval before the next flight will also be used to analyze the data obtained during Flight 15 so that we won't be proceeding to higher Mach numbers entirely ignorant of the airplane's behavior at lower speeds.[27]

The rapid flight schedule continued into the new year. With the nosewheel door up-lock modified, the second X-4 returned to flight on January 13, 1950. The day's first mission, flight 16, was aborted soon after takeoff after the outside canopy lock opened about an inch. The aircraft landed, the lock was repaired, and flight 17 was made, which collected static-stability data at 35,000 feet at a Mach number of about 0.8. Similar tests had been successfully made at 20,000 feet without incident. At the higher altitude, Tucker reported difficulty achieving the higher acceleration in the test plan due to insufficient longitudinal control. Once the test runs had been completed, Tucker began a rapid descent with the dive brakes open and immediately encountered violent rolling and yawing oscillations he could not control. Tucker closed the dive brakes, and the X-4 rapidly sped up. The aircraft pulled away from the F-86 chase plane and reached a speed of about Mach 0.91. Unfortunately, no data were recorded during the dive.

Engineers decided that the flight would have to be repeated, as the normal acceleration data and the telemeter record were not useful. Further complications were engine malfunctions that occurred on both flights 16 and 17 and caused the aircraft to be grounded for 10 days pending an inspection. Examination revealed that the right engine had sustained damage due to excessive temperatures during flight 17.

While the second X-4 was grounded pending delivery of a new engine, the first X-4 made its 10th and final flight on January 24, 1950. The flight's primary research goal was to check the aircraft's climb performance at 25,000 feet. A secondary goal was the collection of limited longitudinal-stability data in steady, straight flight at 25,000 and 10,000 feet. Finally, data on an oscillation that had occurred with the dive brakes open was also on the flight-test card during the descent. Tucker reported after landing that the friction in all three controls was excessive and made the X-4 very unpleasant to fly. The ground crew began an investigation of the control friction on both aircraft.[28]

Northrop flights with the second X-4 resumed in mid-February 1950 with the completion of flights 18, 19, and 20. The two initial flights investigated the aircraft's longitudinal-stability characteristics in accelerated flight at speeds of up to about Mach 0.84 at 30,000 feet. During the last run on flight 19, Tucker reached Mach 0.88 in steady, straight flight. He reported "a very noticeable buffeting, porpoising, and a yawing and rolling oscillation which were uncontrollable."[29] Tucker compared the buffeting to that of a washboard road, an oft-repeated judgment that quickly became convenient shorthand to describe the X-4's transonic qualities. Sadoff noted in his report: "Although true buffeting existed at this speed, what the pilot probably felt was the porpoising motion which had a period of about 0.6 seconds. The yawing oscillation reached maximum double amplitude of about 6 degrees."[30]

Flight 20 was made on February 17, 1950, but no data were collected because the landing gear failed to lock up. At the time, Northrop and NACA personnel expected the contractor flights to continue, but events intervened.

Changing of the Guard

Northrop contractor flights in the X-4 ended abruptly when the Air Force issued an order on February 20, 1950, halting the flights. The following day, Colonel E.W. Richardson (author of the halt order) and Major L.K. Cox came to the High-Speed Flight Research Station to discuss with NACA engineers their desires regarding the acceptance and future of the two aircraft.

The NACA engineers shared their concerns about remaining work. Pull-up tests had been made by Tucker to the NACA's satisfaction during the contractor flights. The strength of the vertical tail, however, had not yet been demonstrated. This involved making steady sideslips up to maximum level-flight speed at 20,000 feet and was accomplished using either full rudder deflection or 300 pounds of rudder pedal force.

NACA engineers felt that these sideslips would still not give a true indication of the vertical tail's structural integrity until the diameter of the rudder cables was increased. One-sixteenth-inch-diameter cables had been used in the X-4s and were prone to excessive stretching, making it very difficult to obtain reasonable values of sideslip at high speeds. While Northrop engineers argued that the small cables were sufficiently strong, Colonel Richardson agreed with NACA engineers who felt that larger-diameter cables were necessary. As was often the case, money entered the picture. Colonel Richardson told the NACA that the Air Force lacked the funding it would require to change the rudder cables. The NACA agreed to install the larger cables but insisted the sideslip tests had to be completed.[31]

The X-4 rudder cables were not the only safety issue. Ralph Sparks, a Northrop engineer working on the aircraft, later recalled his concern about the two dive brakes, each of which was operated by a separate hydraulic system. If one of the systems failed and the pilot activated the speed brakes, one would remain closed while the other opened, inducing dangerous asymmetrical loads and forces that could not only throw the X-4 out of control, but perhaps break it up as well. Sparks feared the tail might be torn off the aircraft. He discussed his concerns with Walt Williams; Williams told Colonel Richardson and Major Cox that it would be a simple matter to fix the problem and the repair could be done at the same time the rudder cables were replaced.[32]

The repeated problems with the X-4 engines were also a concern. Williams noted that the NACA was not happy about the "burping" of the J30 engines or their excessive vibrations. However, discussions with Westinghouse and the Air Force's Power Plant Laboratory clarified that these conditions were not inherently dangerous. And so the NACA engineers decided that the engines could be operated without modification. They did insist that all engines used on the X-4 have annealed turbine shafts, as both Westinghouse and the Navy had issued technical orders requiring shafts to be annealed to reduce failures. By that time, about one-half of the X-4's engine stock had the annealed shafts.

Major Cox asked the NACA engineers if they had a preference as to which of the two X-4 aircraft they would receive. They replied that "it would be highly desirable" to get the second X-4. The primary reason for their choice was that the second aircraft had already been fitted with the NACA instrumentation, so no time would be lost reequipping it. Perhaps a more significant reason was that the first X-4 was in poor mechanical condition compared to the second, and the NACA personnel knew it.[33]

The second X-4, photographed from a chase plane. As with Northrop's other flying wings, the X-4 had a sleek appearance. It also shared the stability problems that these aircraft displayed. Not until development of the computer fly-by-wire control system would semi-tailless aircraft be practical. (USAF)

By the spring of 1950, the status of the X-4 aircraft was settled. The Air Force originally requested that the NACA maintain both aircraft on flight status, one to be flown by Air Force pilots and the other by the NACA, but the NACA rejected this proposal. The first X-4 would be grounded and used for spare parts, and the second would be kept on flight status. In addition, NACA personnel would replace the existing 1/16-inch rudder cables with 1/8-inch cables and modify the dive brakes' hydraulic system on the second X-4. Once that work was complete, Air Force test pilots would make a short series of evaluation flights and make the high-speed sideslip tests of the vertical fin's structural integrity. NACA pilots would then begin research missions.[34]

Work on the aircraft modifications began in mid-June 1950. In addition to the cable replacement and modifications to the hydraulic system, the engines were replaced. The only major problem was a delay in the engine installation that was due to a fuel leak in the left wing. This was fixed in August, and the installation was nearly complete. Separate from the X-4 modification was preparation for the vertical fin structural tests. Before making any flights, ground load tests would be made using the first X-4. Flight tests of the vertical fin structure would be made once these tests were completed.[35]

The Air Force X-4 evaluation began on August 18 with flight 1 by Captain Charles "Chuck" Yeager. (As with the X-3, these were listed as NACA flights since NACA instrumentation was used.) The second and third flights, by Major

Frank Everest, were made on August 22. The third flight was aborted when the main landing gear did not lock up, a problem the team thought it had resolved. (The solution was to increase the cycling time of the main landing gear). Flight 4 was made without incident. On flight 5, both Everest and Yeager, the chase pilot, noticed oscillations of the wingtips and the outboard portions of the elevons. This was especially noticeable on the left side. After Everest landed, an examination showed the left elevon had about 1½° of play, the right elevon ½°. The X-4's elevons were not mass balanced, and this caused them to flutter. NACA ground personnel began work to eliminate the play in the elevons, for aerodynamic flutter could pose an insidious threat, particularly if encountered at higher speeds and with such magnitude that the ailerons were torn from the plane.

The Air Force evaluation now moved to tests of the X-4's stall behavior. As a safety measure, an 8-foot-diameter spin chute was added to the aircraft so that if the X-4 got into a spin from which the pilot could not recover, he could deploy the spin chute. As the chute opened, it pulled the tail up, forcing the nose down into a dive. Airflow over the wings would be restored and speed increased, allowing the pilot to recover.[36]

The Air Force flights were made in rapid succession. Flights 6 through 11 came between September 13 and 22, 1950, all of them made by Yeager. Flight 6 involved 1-g stalls, an accelerated stall to about 2 g's, stall approaches with the dive brakes at 20° and 30°, and some longitudinal and lateral dynamic stability. Due to instrumentation failure, the flight had to be repeated. After that flight, the spin chute was removed.

The Air Force pilots did have problems: flight 7 had to be aborted when the canopy and landing gear did not lock closed, and flight 8 was a repeat of flight 6. On flight 9, a maximum-speed run was made to Mach 0.89, static-stability data were collected, and an accelerated maneuver was made to the instability boundary at Mach 0.7. Flight 10 suffered an instrumentation failure and had to be repeated as flight 11. This involved accelerated maneuvers to the instability boundary at Mach numbers of 0.6, 0.65, and 0.76; directional, longitudinal, and lateral dynamic-stability data at Mach 0.5 and 0.7; and aileron rolls to the right and left at Mach 0.7. Flight 11 marked the effective end of the Air Force X-4 flights, although eight more flights were made, short ones on which no data were taken. NACA pilot John Griffith made flight 15. The Air Force evaluation was completed with flight 19 and totaled about 13 hours of flight time.[37]

Data from the Northrop and Air Force flights of both X-4 aircraft were summarized in a December 1950 research memorandum:

> The airplane was almost neutrally stable in straight flight at low Mach numbers with the center of gravity located at about 21.4 percent of the mean aerodynamic chord for the clean configuration.

Lowering the landing gear had no significant effect on the longitudinal stability. There was some indication that the stability tended to increase for both configurations as the normal-force coefficient was increased.

The airplane was longitudinally stable in accelerated flight over a Mach number range of 0.44 to about 0.84 up to a normal-force coefficient of about 0.4. At higher values of normal-force coefficient and at Mach numbers of about 0.8 a longitudinal instability was experienced.

The airplane does not meet the Air Force specifications for the damping of the longitudinal oscillations. The pilot, however, did not object to the low damping for small amplitude oscillations. However, an objectionable undamped oscillation about all three axes was experienced at the highest test Mach number of about 0.88[,] which may well limit the X-4 to this speed.

The theory predicted the period of short-period longitudinal oscillation fairly well, while, in general, the theoretical damping indicated a higher degree of stability than was actually experienced. This disagreement was traced to a large error in the estimation of the rotational damping factor.

The directional stability of the airplane was high and essentially constant over the speed range considered, while the effective dihedral increased considerably with an increase in normal-force coefficient. The lateral- and directional-stability characteristics estimated from wind-tunnel data compared favorably with the flight results.

The damping of the lateral oscillation does not meet the Air Force requirements for satisfactory handling qualities.

The dynamic lateral-stability characteristics were estimated fairly well by the theory at low Mach numbers at a pressure altitude of 10,000 feet. At 30,000 feet, however, and at [a] Mach number above about 0.6, the theory indicated a higher degree of stability than was actually experienced.

For the conditions covered in these tests, the stalling characteristics of the airplane at low Mach numbers were, in general, satisfactory. The stall was characterized by a roll-off to the right and by moderate buffeting[,] which served as a stall warning.

The buffet boundary for the X-4 airplane, which was almost identical to that for the D-558-2 airplane, showed a sharp drop-off in the normal-force coefficient for the onset of buffeting as the Mach number exceeded about 0.8.[38]

In addition to the Northrop/Air Force/NACA flights, the ground static-load tests of the first X-4's vertical tail, fin, and rudder were also completed on September 21, 1950. The fin was tested to its design limit of 6,600 pounds. The rudder was loaded to 1,500 pounds at the hinge line near the center hinge. This was approximately 65 percent of a hypothetical combination of maximum loads on the three rudder hinges and about equal to the maximum load on any one hinge in a critical load condition. The results showed that the vertical tail and rudder could withstand the aerodynamic forces they would experience on future NACA research flights.[39]

The NACA's X-4 Research Flights

With the Air Force flights completed, the second X-4 was grounded for instrumentation changes. In addition, several engine problems had appeared that required both engines to be replaced, including governor and starter troubles. This work grounded the aircraft until early November.[40]

Flights resumed on November 7, 1950, with NACA flight 20 flown by Griffith. The pilot made a maximum-speed run to about Mach 0.88 to determine whether elevon motion was contributing to the aircraft's porpoising. Additional test maneuvers included gradual turns to the stall or instability boundary at Mach 0.60 to 0.80, to further define that boundary, and rudder kicks at Mach 0.70 to 0.80, to confirm deterioration of lateral damping. All the tests were made at 30,000 feet. Though instrument malfunctions occurred on the flight, they did not impair the collection of data.

NACA flight 21 was not made until November 17, 1950, again with Griffith as pilot. This time, tests included turns to the instability boundary at speeds of up to Mach 0.88. In addition, aileron rolls were made at Mach 0.40, 0.50, and 0.60. Problems were found in the postflight inspection: minor instrumentation errors had occurred, fuel leaks appeared in the wings, and the left engine suffered from governor problems. These issues were fixed by early December.[41]

Flight 22, on December 6, 1950, was a pilot check for Major R.L. Johnson, and no data were collected. NACA research pilot A. Scott Crossfield made flight 23, which was for aircraft familiarization, the same day. Crossfield later described his first experience with the X-4:

> As the X-4 wobbled down the long, bumpy runway, I gingerly felt out the controls. Then churning jets took hold, and the small X-4 abruptly lunged into the air. Backing off the stall point, I nosed her over gently and leveled out. Then I eased back on the stick and the tiny tailless craft zoomed skyward like a winged

rocket. As predicted, at Mach .88 the X-4 broke into its gentle but potentially dangerous porpoising motion. I opened the speed brakes, and the X-4 slowed instantly, throwing me forward against my shoulder restraining straps.

After about fifteen minutes in the air, I felt at home in the X-4. The plane responded so well, in fact, that it was hard for me to keep in mind that I was flying a marginally stable, experimental race horse.[42]

The flight was cut short when the left engine suffered a flameout. The X-4's biweekly report stated that Crossfield was making a prolonged 4-g maneuver at an altitude of 23,000 feet when the problem occurred. In his biography, Crossfield wrote that he had pulled into a loop and, when going over the top, both engines flamed out. He was able to restart the right engine but not the left one. He made an emergency landing on the lakebed rather than the South Base runway.[43]

Despite these difficulties, Crossfield began a series of flights to explore the X-4's basic handling qualities. The series began with NACA flight 24 on December 15, 1950. Sideslip and aileron roll data were supposed to be collected, but the flight was cut short due to instrument problems. The year's activities came to a close with flight 25, made on December 28, for lateral directional-stability, accelerated longitudinal-stability, and lateral control data at Mach numbers between 0.50 and 0.84. This was the first of 20 flights made to collect data on flight qualities, a series that lasted until May 29, 1951. All but three were made by Crossfield, the others by NACA pilot Walter P. Jones.[44]

The initial results were written up by Walt Williams and Scott Crossfield in 1952 as part of an overview of handling qualities of the X-1, D-558-1, D-558-2, X-4, XF-92A, and F-86A. By this time, Crossfield understood how difficult the X-4 was to fly. He and Williams described the X-4's most serious shortcoming:

> With the X-4 airplane, an undamped oscillation about all three axes at a Mach number of 0.88 has been experienced.... The pitching appears predominant to the pilot. The small undamped yawing oscillation at this speed induces a pitching oscillation at twice the frequency of the yawing oscillation. The pitching is apparently amplified because the natural frequency in pitch is twice that of yaw.... These data were obtained from rudder kicks and stick impulses, and incidentally, in all maneuvers where there is yawing there is pitching at twice the frequency.... [A]t 0.9

Mach number the yawing oscillation diverges, rolling becomes large, and the whole motion is intolerable. The violence is attested by the control motions which result from accelerations on the pilot. Lateral accelerations reached ±1 g. The irregularity of pitching is probably caused by the control motion."[45]

This handling characteristic was judged to be a "Category I" problem, as it was dangerous and imposed serious limitations on the operation of the aircraft.[46] The research memorandum continued, "Also in the first category, the X-4 oscillations about the three axes are determined as having their origin in very low to zero damping in yaw and by the fact that the ratios of natural frequencies and coupled oscillations are similar. Largely because of these oscillations it was considered unreasonable to extend the speed beyond the maximum Mach number reached, nearly 0.93."[47]

A more detailed report of the X-4's handling was written by Melvin Sadoff and Scott Crossfield in 1954. The conclusions stated:

At low speeds marginal stability restricted the aft center-of-gravity travel to 19 percent mean aerodynamic chord and low longitudinal control power restricted the forward limit to 16.5 percent mean aerodynamic chord yielding less than 3 percent permissible center-of-gravity travel. The low longitudinal control power within this center-of-gravity range limited the approach to 1g stalls which was characterized by mild instability roll-off and normal response to recovery control.

Throughout the speed range, typical swept-wing instability and buffet characteristics occurred at lower normal-force coefficients than with tail-on airplanes of similar sweep.

At high speeds the X-4 characteristics deteriorated as follows:

- At Mach numbers above 0.76 a residual yawing and rolling motion persisted at all times.
- At Mach numbers above 0.75 loss of total elevon effectiveness with speed and acceleration severely restricted maneuverability and maximum attainable lift.
- At Mach numbers above 0.85 elevon effectiveness began to decline rapidly in rolling maneuvers.
- At a Mach number of 0.88 the yawing and rolling coupled with the longitudinal motions resulting in persistent oscillation about three axes.

- At a Mach number of 0.90 a high-frequency short-period longitudinal oscillation appeared at normal acceleration greater than 1g.
- At Mach numbers above 0.90 elevon effectiveness had virtually disappeared, angles required for trim in level flight were high and maneuverability was only slight.
- Also, at Mach numbers above 0.90 the lateral-directional oscillation diverged to unsafe values. The tests were limited by the lack of control power to trim and maneuver and the divergent oscillation.[48]

Additional Research Activities

The NACA basic handling qualities program was completed with flight 45, made on May 29, 1951. This included a climb to about 42,300 feet, a speed run at about 38,000 feet, and windup turns at 30,000 feet over a speed range from Mach 0.40 to 0.88. After the flight, the aircraft was grounded for the repair of an oil leak and installation of new turbine blades. The work involved the assembly of a new right engine. During its thrust-stand check, the new engine suffered a failure of the accessory drive.[49]

In the wake of the problems with the right engine, plans for the aircraft were changed. Project managers decided a modification of the wing shape would be made. Like those on most aircraft, the X-4 wing had a rounded leading edge and a thin, knife-edge trailing edge. The modification increased the dive brake's trailing-edge thickness to half that of the hinge-line thickness. Engineers thought a blunt trailing edge on the speed brakes would improve aircraft stability. Accordingly, they blocked the dive brakes open at an angle of ±5°. The brakes could be opened to angles greater than ±5° but could no longer be closed completely.[50] The modifications to the X-4's dive brakes were completed in late July 1951. Strain gauges were also added to the upper and lower segments of the left dive brakes to record hinge-moment data. The research flights were delayed when a test run of the replacement right engine indicated that the throttle mechanism required adjustment. This pushed the start of research flights back to late August.[51]

Walter P. Jones made the first tests of the dive brake modifications on NACA flight 46 on August 20, 1951. The tests involved an unaccelerated stall at 35,000 feet and aileron rolls and turns at Mach 0.71, 0.83, and 0.86. Jones then dove and made a turn and aileron roll at Mach 0.91 at 28,000 feet.

Jones reported a general improvement in the aircraft's handling. In particular, the porpoising and lateral oscillations that had limited the X-4 at speeds of Mach 0.88 to 0.90 were not apparent, with the thickened trailing edges, to a Mach number of 0.91.[52]

Once more, engine problems appeared, delaying flight 47 until October 2, 1951. Crossfield made this flight, which continued the investigation of the effects of the thickened dive brakes on stability and control. The improvements were significant; the X-4's longitudinal oscillations with the thin trailing edges were undamped above Mach 0.88. In contrast, with the thickened speed brakes at a speed of Mach 0.90, the longitudinal oscillations damped out after about two cycles.

Crossfield executed windup turns at Mach numbers from 0.79 to 0.90 for static-stability data and reported after the flight that slight porpoising and instability occurred at about Mach 0.86. When he added a rudder impulse at Mach 0.90, it caused an undamped lateral oscillation of about ±5½° of sideslip and ±10° of angle of bank, with slight porpoising. A similar maneuver had been made with the thinner trailing edges at about the same altitude and Mach number, but subsequent comparison showed that the longitudinal oscillations were less pronounced with the thicker trailing edges.[53]

With initial tests of the thickened dive brake complete, focus shifted to obtaining lift-to-drag ratios for various dive brake settings during landings. Crossfield piloted NACA flights 48 through 51 between October 5 and October 12, 1951. The dive brake deflections ranged from 0° to ±40° and provided landing data on lift-to-drag ratios between 8 to 1 and 3.5 to 1. Jones made flight 52 on October 17, making constant speed runs to determine lift-to-drag ratios at dive brake deflections of 0° to ±60° in the landing configuration.

Joe Walker now joined the X-4 research effort, making NACA flights 53 and 54 on October 18 and 19. These were both pilot-familiarization and research flights involving speed runs, rudder kicks, low-speed stalls at 10,000 feet, dive brake deflections, and the collection of landing pattern data. Research with the X-4 ended for 1951 with NACA flight 55, made by Jones on October 24. This flight provided additional stability and control flight data on the thickened dive brakes.

After the flight, an inspection found that fuel leaks had reappeared. Engineers initially estimated that these could be quickly fixed and flights could be resumed on November 9. The leaks were more serious than first thought, however, and the aircraft was grounded indefinitely.[54]

After considerable effort, NACA flight 56 was finally attempted on January 29, 1952, but was aborted before takeoff due to excessive fuel overflow. The fuel regulator was replaced and set at a lower limiting pressure. This was not the only maintenance problem X-4 personnel faced in the winter of 1951–52. The sideslip transmitter had to be repaired, and the left engine was replaced due to "torching" between the tailpipe and the shroud. This was traced to leaking oil around the front bearing seal.[55]

NACA research pilot Joe Walker discusses his upcoming X-4 flight with a ground crewman. Walker made only one flight in the aircraft, on October 18, 1951. The bulk of the NACA flights were made by Crossfield and Walter P. Jones. (NASA)

Not until March 6, 1952, did Jones finally complete NACA flight 56. This involved measurements of lift-over-drag characteristics at different drag brake deflections, as well as unaccelerated stalls and constant speed runs at various throttle settings. The engine problems reoccurred, this time on the right engine. Flame instabilities, which required investigation, also occurred during the flight. Unlike previous engine difficulties, these were soon fixed, and NACA flight 57 was made on March 13. It was primarily an engine check flight, but data were recorded on directional trim changes at Mach 0.79 and during the landing.

Flight 58, on March 17, was intended to be a continuation of the lift-over-drag studies, but an open circuit in the dive brake actuating solenoid prevented the dive brakes' use. Flight 59, during which lift-and-drag data were collected with the dive brakes at ±50° deflections, was completed March 21. NACA flight 60 was made on March 26 and entailed rudder-fixed aileron rolls, as well as testing of stick and rudder impulses at true Mach numbers between 0.80 and 0.90. Flight 61 was made on March 27, with stick impulses recorded at true Mach numbers of 0.50, 0.60, and 0.70. Landing data were also collected on the flight. In all, Jones made seven consecutive X-4 research flights in March 1952. This brought the dive brake tests to a close.[56]

The X-4's hectic March flight schedule was concluded with a pilot checkout flight on March 27. Stanley P. Butchart made NACA flight 62. The dive brake research was now completed, the X-4 was grounded, and the dive brake data were under analysis.[57]

Landing data initially seemed a less consequential area of study but emerged as a significant issue. Supersonic flight required an entirely new set of design features. These included thin wings, low-aspect-ratio wings, and swept wings, all with high wing loading. As a result, the aircraft had lower lift-to-drag ratios and higher stall speeds than earlier designs. The resulting vertical velocities made it difficult for a pilot to land safely and accurately.

The low lift-to-drag ratio and high stalling speed of high-performance aircraft meant the excess speed ratio required at the start of the flare increased considerably as lift-drag ratio decreased. The flare also had to begin at a relatively high altitude. Additionally, past flight tests had shown that a vertical velocity in excess of 25 feet per second at the start of the flare put too high a demand on pilot skill and was regarded to be impractical. The X-4's large dive brakes enabled a landing maneuver at lift-drag ratios from 8 to 1 down to 3.5 to 1. A research memorandum discussed the results:

> These landings were started at an altitude of approximately 3,000 feet with the engines maintaining zero thrust and with a constant dive-brake angle during the landing maneuver. The patterns become smaller as the lift-drag ratio decreases[,] which requires an increase in acceleration during the approach turn from 1.1g at a lift-drag ratio of 8 to about 1.5g at a lift-drag ratio of 3.5. The higher acceleration results also from the fact that part of the landing flare is made during the final approach turn at the lower lift-drag ratios. This has prevented landings from being made at dive-brake settings greater than 35° because the largest portion of the flare is made during the turn at these settings and there is insufficient elevon control to enable the maneuver to be accomplished at larger dive-brake settings. One factor noted by the pilots was the short length of time, 50 seconds, at an approach lift-drag ratio of 3.5 as compared with about 140 seconds at a lift-drag ratio of 8 during which the pilot could correct and modify his landing approach.
>
> The poor longitudinal control at large dive-brake settings was the pilots' greatest complaint during these flights. They felt that, if sufficient longitudinal control were available, landings could

be performed at still lower lift-drag ratios. Landings at the lowest lift-drag ratios were not felt to require exceptional piloting skill or a great deal of practice. However, it should be remembered that for these landings the lift-drag ratio increased with decreasing speed and although landings were started at a lift-drag ratio of 3.5 the lowest lift-drag ratio at contact was about 6.2 even neglecting ground effect. At high lift-drag ratios ground effect was very noticeable to the pilots, whereas at the lower lift-drag ratios ground effect was not nearly so pronounced.[58]

The memorandum concluded, "Landings of the X-4 airplane to determine the effect of lift-drag ratio showed that the largest portion of the landing flare was made at altitudes above 50 feet at low lift-drag ratio and that, although the vertical velocities during the approach varied from 30 to 90 feet per second, the vertical velocities at contact were less than 5.5 feet per second."[59]

The X-4's Twilight

In the spring of 1952, the X-4 was again grounded for a prolonged period. Several modifications had to be completed before flights resumed. One of these was the fabrication of jigs to support the aircraft during planned moment-of-inertia measurements. A more significant activity was the modification of the elevons' trailing edges. As with the dive brakes, their thickness was increased to 50 percent of hinge-line thickness. Again, this was done to determine whether blunt trailing edges would improve aircraft handling and was completed by the end of April. However, a May 1 ground engine run was unsuccessful. The left engine overheated, requiring replacement.[60]

A successful engine run was made on May 16, and NACA flight 63 was made May 19 with Jones as pilot. Of the planned test maneuvers, the stick impulses and one-half-deflection aileron rolls, performed at 30,000 feet and at Mach numbers of 0.55 and 0.60, were successfully completed. At this point, the right engine began to overheat. Jones aborted the rest of the tests and landed safely. This flight also marked the end of Jones's research flying with the NACA. He left the High-Speed Flight Research Station in July 1952 to work as a Northrop test pilot. Tragically, he died the following October in the crash of a Northrop YF-89D Scorpion.

The malfunctioning engine was replaced, but a ground run on May 26 was unsuccessful due to a stuck fuel valve. The problem was fixed, and a second ground test was made on May 29. Excessive vibrations caused this test to fail as well. Their cause was unknown, and the X-4 remained grounded until a replacement engine could be installed and successfully tested. This proved more difficult than expected. All of the spare J30 engines proved faulty when ground tested, due either to vibration or to excessive bearing heating. To produce a functional engine, maintenance personnel had to assemble parts from spare jets.[61] The effort proved frustrating, as a progress report noted: "In each instance the reassembled engine has experienced excessive vibration. Assembly of another engine is underway."[62] Finally, on July 25, an engine was tested that seemed to be fault-free.

After being grounded for more than 2 months, NACA flight 64 was made on August 6 with Crossfield as pilot. The first test of the thickened elevons was made without incident. Crossfield's opinion was that elevon control had been much improved at higher Mach numbers by the modification. Postflight examination showed the windup turn data were unusable, however, due to instrumentation failure. The maneuvers would have to be repeated on a later flight.

More bad news followed: NACA flight 65 was delayed following a preflight engine run. An investigation showed that an object had passed through the right engine, presumably during landing on flight 64. The aircraft was grounded until the engine was rebalanced and a successful ground run completed. While the aircraft was being serviced, the thickening material was removed from the dive brakes, restoring their original configuration. Subsequent research flights would be made with the thickened elevon configuration and the original dive brake configuration.[63]

After the series of problems, the X-4 made NACA flights 65 through 68 during September 1952. Data from the initial flight were lost due to instrumentation malfunction. The three other flights were successful, with windup turns and aileron rolls at Mach 0.65 to 0.94 and stick and rudder impulses from Mach 0.70 and 0.90. Postflight analysis indicated that the increased elevon thickness improved aileron effectiveness over the entire Mach number range.[64]

Research missions with the X-4s had been flown without serious mishaps, despite each aircraft's having exhibited poor stability at high transonic speeds and unreliable engines. It was therefore ironic that the most serious damage either aircraft suffered happened on the ground, at the hands of a person assigned to protect it. Over the weekend of October 4–5, an Air Force guard on duty at the NACA hanger at South Base accidentally drove an airplane tug into the second X-4's right wing. The impact damaged the wing's underside. The extent of the damage was not immediately evident; an inspection was made to determine whether the wing could be repaired and the X-4 returned to flight, or if the damage was so severe that the aircraft would have to be retired.[65]

Inspection determined that the damage to the aircraft was limited to the wing's skin. Repair was complete by mid-December 1952. The X-4 remained off flight status for several weeks while the moments of inertia about the three axes at various fuel levels and attitudes were determined. This work continued through the end of February 1953, and the aircraft then resumed research flights.[66]

The first of these was made on March 27 with Crossfield as pilot. NACA flight 69 included a speed run to Mach 0.91 and successful windup turns at Mach 0.78 and 0.88. At that point, the fuel gauge malfunctioned and Crossfield had to cut the flight short.[67]

NACA flights 70 and 71 followed at the end of April. The first flight involved tower passes at a low level to check airspeed calibration. The second flight undertook speed runs and windup turns between Mach 0.77 and Mach 0.90, both to check the airspeed calibration and to collect additional data for the longitudinal control study with the thickened elevons. Flight 70 marked the end of this investigation. After it was concluded, the elevons were restored to their original configuration. Work was completed by late May, when Crossfield made NACA flight 72. This flight provided dynamic-stability data without the thickened elevons, using rudder pulses at Mach 0.50 and 0.88 speeds.[68]

X-4 research activity continued with NACA flights 73 and 74 on July 1 and 3. Both flights were made by Butchart to acquire additional data on the aircraft's dynamic stability without the thickened elevons. This was accomplished using elevon and aileron pulses at Mach numbers from 0.50 to 0.88.[69]

Although the X-4 project was entering its final phase, activity increased substantially. During August 1953, seven flights were made beginning with flight 75 on August 4, a checkout flight for Ames Aeronautical Laboratory research pilot George Cooper. Flight 76 on August 11 was a checkout flight for John B. McKay, a new High-Speed Flight Research Station research pilot. McKay also made NACA flights 77 and 78, on August 13 and 19, collecting dynamic-stability data from aileron pulses. However, data from several runs were lost due to instrumentation failures. Once again, this required another research flight to be added to the schedule.

The fast pace continued to the end of the X-4 project. Two days after his previous mission, McKay again piloted the X-4 on NACA flight 79. Crossfield went aloft on August 24 for flight 80. The X-4 was checked out over the next 2 days and flown by McKay on August 26 for the 81st NACA mission. These flights were for dynamic-stability data. The 4 years of X-4 flights by Northrop, the Air Force, and the NACA then came to a close.

The final research mission, NACA flight 82, was made on September 29, 1953. McKay's flight plan involved aileron pulses across the Mach number range and low-speed turns to 2 g's at different dive brake settings. This brought the X-4 project to an end. At the time the mission was flown, there were plans to use the aircraft to check out a number of Air Force and NACA pilots, but plans were dropped, and the second X-4 joined the first in storage. Eventually, the first X-4 was put on display at the U.S. Air Force Academy in Colorado Springs, CO. It subsequently became part of the Air Force Flight Test Museum collection at Edwards Air Force Base, where it awaits restoration. The second X-4 was sent in 1955 to Maxwell Air Force Base, Montgomery, AL. It remained there until March 17, 1972, when it was transferred to the U.S. Air Force Museum at Wright-Patterson Air Force Base, OH, where it is on display, having been magnificently restored.[70]

An Assessment

The X-4 Bantam was a highly productive research aircraft, though one that, at the time, was of impracticable configuration for commercial or military use. More research flights were made with the X-4 than with the X-3, and the X-4 provided data in a wide range of disciplines. Yet the X-3 influenced the design and development of the F-104, one of the most widely used fighters of the mid–20th century. In contrast, the X-4's semi-tailless swept-wing design did not see significant use until much later, following the advent of electronic fly-by-wire flight control technology. The only U.S. aircraft to feature a similar configuration in the 1950s was the Navy's severely underpowered and, indeed, highly dangerous F7U Cutlass, which blended prolonged development with a brief operational service life, entering service in 1954 and retiring almost exactly 5 years later. Of the 320 F7Us built, some 80—fully 25 percent—were lost in accidents.[71]

Crossfield summed up the X-4 project during a 1998 interview:

> Oh, the X-4 was a whole buildup of stability and handling, stability and control, and handling qualities of a tailless airplane. With the X-4, we pretty much found out why we may not have solved the problem…. The X-4 was a very productive program. We did a lot of things with the X-4 that weren't only involved in it's [*sic*] being a tailless airplane. It was a good test bed for other purposes, as we did thickened trailing edges on the X-4. We did variable Lift over Drag (L over D) landings from probably an L over D of two to an L over D of nine with the airplane, which gave us good insight into pilots preferences and that sort of thing, which were useful in coming up with new airplanes like the X-15 and some of the other low L over D airplanes [like] the lifting bodies. But the X-4 was a very good research airplane, for purposes of looking into a tailless configuration, and for other reasons.[72]

Though the configurations of the D-558-2, X-3, X-5, and XF-92A became the basis for numerous U.S. aircraft, only the F7U Cutlass featured the X-4's semi-tailless swept-wing configuration. An early prototype XF7U-1 is shown here on the Langley ramp in 1948. The aircraft entered U.S. service after a prolonged development, but it suffered a high loss rate and was soon retired from service. (NASA)

But for all the flights made with it and all the data returned, the X-4 was conceptually a flawed aircraft. Its instability was described by research pilots as being akin to driving on a washboard road. The X-4 displayed increasingly severe combined yaw, pitch, and roll motions, as well as inadequate damping as Mach number increased. In an attempt to correct the instability, NACA engineers decided to modify the dive brakes and later the elevons, giving them a blunt trailing edge. X-4 research flights indicated that this produced a 25-percent increase in roll rate and improved longitudinal control effectiveness. Above Mach 0.9, however, instability reoccurred. The severity of the porpoising increased rapidly; at Mach 0.94, vertical accelerations reached ±1½ g's. The basic cause of the instability could not be solved by Band-Aid fixes such as thickening the trailing edges of dive brakes and elevons.[73]

Until the advent of the fly-by-wire Northrop B-2A Spirit stealth bomber, the various direct or hydromechanically controlled semi-tailless and flying-wing designs, such as the Horten Ho 229; the Northrop N-9M, XP-79B, and YB-49; and the British de Havilland DH 108 and Armstrong Whitworth AW

52, all suffered from serious stability and control deficiencies that limited their practical use and even endowed them with vicious, life-endangering quirks (indeed, between them, the six types listed here killed a dozen highly skilled airmen). For all their perceived advantages from an aerodynamic viewpoint, all were thus impractical from the start. The semi-tailless X-4 had been built to determine whether eliminating the horizontal stabilizer would prevent interactions between the shock waves formed by the wings and horizontal stabilizers. In fact, the lack of horizontal stabilizers made the instability worse compared with that of a conventional swept-wing/horizontal stabilizer design. The DH 108 demonstrated the risks of what deficiencies could do if encountered at high speed and low level. The X-4 demonstrated the problem but, flown at higher altitudes and lower dynamic pressures, it avoided the disastrous experience of its British cousin. Nevertheless, it clearly had such deficiencies that it did not warrant further development. Northrop played around with the swept semi-tailless configuration, even employing it on a long-range, jet-propelled, nuclear-tipped cruise missile (the disappointing Northrop SM-62 Snark), but, overall, swept-wing semi-tailless aircraft remained impractical for nearly three decades, until the advent of computer-controlled flight.

Ironically, the original X-4 rudder control system gave a hint of what would be needed to correct the aircraft's control problems. Rather than using a cable and bell-crank system, the rudder was electrically operated by a four-speed actuator. This was a proto-fly-by-wire system, which served as a yaw-damping stability-augmentation system. The X-4 system, as noted earlier, was limited to a maximum speed of 25° per second. This system was too slow to the point of being dangerous, and it was replaced with a conventional mechanical system. As long as an aircraft had to be inherently stable, the swept-wing semi-tailless configuration remained impractical. The technology for providing a solution did not exist in the early 1950s.[74]

It was not until the 1970s that practical digital fly-by-wire systems were developed. These systems supplied an artificial inherent stability by providing control inputs faster than human pilots could. The faster inputs eliminated washboard and other unstable motions, allowing the pilot to maneuver the aircraft rather than struggle to control it. The first aircraft to use a digital fly-by-wire control system was a modified F-8 flown at the Dryden Flight Research Center (now called the Armstrong Flight Research Center). In an important innovation, the airplane's mechanical control system was removed. Should the digital system fail, an analog backup computer would take over. NASA engineers realized that fly-by-wire would never be accepted as proven as long as a mechanical backup was still being used.

Once the aircraft was totally dependent on a fly-by-wire system, inherent stability was no longer a design limitation. Among the first applications of this

A photo illustrating the rapid changes in aviation technology at Edwards in the mid-1950s. In the background is a pair of B-36 bombers, originally designed for the bombing of Nazi Germany from U.S. bases. The XB-52 prototype, with the original tandem cockpit design, is in the foreground. Its descendants are still in service a half century later. Beside the XB-52 is the tiny, futuristic X-4. Visible are its control surfaces, which were designed to overcome the absence of horizontal stabilizers. (USAF)

was the Lockheed XST Have Blue stealth test aircraft, first flown in December 1977. This was a swept-wing, semi-tailless aircraft with two inwardly canted tail fins mounted at mid-span of each wing. The design was unstable in the pitch axis and relied on a modified F-16 fly-by-wire system for stability.[75] Even so, for various reasons, its successor, the Lockheed F-117A stealth fighter, had a different vertical fin configuration, effectively giving it a V-tail (like the Beech Bonanza general aviation airplane).

Over the decades to follow, fly-by-wire control systems were fitted to aircraft ranging from business jets, airliners, fighters, and research aircraft to bombers and heavy transports. But for the X-4, such a solution was not yet available. A computer in the early 1950s took up a large room, was slow and unreliable, and required a large maintenance staff to keep it operating. Today, the basic X-4 configuration can be discerned in the lines of a variety of remotely piloted, computer-controlled aircraft. Impractical in the 1950s, the little X-4 was ahead of its time.

A famous photo showing the family of X-planes that were being flown at the High-Speed Flight Research Station in the early and mid-1950s. In the center is the X-3, with the X-1A, D-558-1 Skystreak, XF-92A, X-5, D-558-2 Skyrocket, and X-4 arrayed around it. (NASA)

Endnotes

1. Opening quote from A. Scott Crossfield interview transcript, DFRC Archives.
2. Richard P. Hallion, "Before B-2: The History of the Flying Wing," 2 parts, *Air Power History* 41, nos. 3 and 4 (fall–winter 1994): 4–13, 40–51.
3. Richard P. Hallion, "Rocket Dreams," *World War II* 23, no. 4 (October–November 2008): 57–58. For reminiscences by members of the Komet team, see Wolfgang Späte, *Top Secret Bird: The Luftwaffe's Me 163 Comet* [*sic*] (Missoula, MT: Pictorial Histories Publishing Company, 1989); and Mano Ziegler, *Rocket Fighter* (Garden City, NY: Doubleday and Co., Inc., 1961).
4. The DH 106, which evolved into the Comet I jetliner, was initially conceived as a swept-wing semi-tailless design. However, it ultimately emerged as a conventional wing-fuselage-tail configuration, with four jet engines buried in its wing roots.
5. Quote from Derry's pilot notes, reprinted in Charles Burnet, *Three Centuries to Concorde* (London: Mechanical Engineering Publications Limited, 1979), p. 112.
6. See also Captain Eric Brown, RN FAA, "An Ill-Fated 'Swallow'… but a Harbinger of Summer," *Air Enthusiast* 10 (July 1979): 1–7; and Brian Rivas, *A Very British Sound Barrier: DH 108—A Story of Courage, Triumph, and Tragedy* (Newark, U.K.: Red Kite/Wing Leader Publishers, 2012).
7. For the detailed history of the X-4's design, development, and flight testing, see Richard P. Hallion, "X-4: The Bantam Explorer," *Air Enthusiast Quarterly* 3 (June 1977): 18–25.
8. Total fuel load was 240 gallons, but 10 gallons were "trapped" within the vehicle's plumbing and pump system and unusable.
9. Technical details from Hubert M. Drake, "Stability and Control Data Obtained from First Flight of X-4 Airplane," NACA RM L9A31 (February 7, 1949), Table 1, "Physical Characteristics of X-4 Airplane," p. 6.
10. Jay Miller, *The X-Planes X-1 to X-45* (Hinckley, England: Midland Publishing, 2001), pp. 79–81; see also Hallion, "X-4: The Bantam Explorer," pp. 20–21.
11. Drake, "Stability and Control Data Obtained from First Flight of X-4 Airplane," p. 3.
12. Discussion with NASA research pilot Mark Pestana, Dryden Flight Research Center, July 19, 2010.

13. Drake, "Stability and Control Data Obtained from First Flight of X-4 Airplane," p. 4.
14. Memorandum for Chief of Research, "Progress Report on Acceptance Tests of X-4 Airplanes from January 1 to January 14, 1949." Readers are advised that this and all other flight-test documents and reports mentioned in this chapter are from the DFRC historical archives unless otherwise noted.
15. Hallion, "X-4: The Bantam Explorer," p. 20.
16. Walter C. Williams, "Results Obtained from Second Flight of X-4 Airplane (A.F. No. 46-676)," NACA RM L9F21 (July 18, 1949), p. 3.
17. Ibid., pp. 3–4.
18. Memorandum for Chief of Research, "X-4, January 14, 1949 to June 10, 1949"; Memorandum for Chief of Research, "X-4, June 20, 1949."
19. Memorandum for Chief of Research, "X-4, June 17 through July 1, 1949."
20. Memorandum for Chief of Research, "X-4, July 16 through July 29, 1949"; Memorandum for Chief of Research, "X-4 Airplanes, July 30 through August 12, 1949."
21. Memorandum for Chief of Research, "X-4 Airplanes, July 31 through August 12, 1949."
22. Memorandum for Chief of Research, "X-4, August 27 to September 14, 1949."
23. Memorandum for Chief of Research, "X-4 Airplanes, October 8 to October 21, 1949."
24. Ibid.
25. Ibid.
26. Memorandum for Chief of Research, "X-4, November 19 to December 2, 1949."
27. Memorandum for Chief of Research, "X-4, December 3 to December 16, 1949."
28. Memorandum for Chief of Research, "X-4, December 31, 1949 to January 1, 1950"; Memorandum for Chief of Research, "X-4, January 14 to January 27, 1950."
29. Memorandum for Chief of Research, "X-4, January 27 to February 24, 1950."
30. Ibid.
31. Memorandum for Research Airplanes Project Leader, "Acceptance of the X-4 Airplane."
32. Ibid.; Peebles, *The Spoken Word*, p. 28.

33. Memorandum for Research Airplanes Project Leader, "Acceptance of the X-4 Airplane."
34. Memorandum for Chief of Research, "X-4, February 24, 1950 to March 24, 1950"; Memorandum for Chief of Research, "X-4, May 5 to May 19, 1950"; Memorandum for Chief of Research, "Test Program for X-4 Aircraft Evaluation, May 3, 1950."
35. Memorandum for Chief of Research, "X-4, July 15 to July 28, 1950."
36. Memorandum for Chief of Research, "X-4, August 26 to September 8, 1950."
37. Memorandum for Chief of Research, "X-4, September 22 to October 6, 1950."
38. Melvin Sadoff and Thomas R. Sisk, "Summary Report of Results Obtained During Demonstration Tests of the Northrop X-4 Airplanes," NACA RM A50I01 (December 13, 1950), pp. 11–12.
39. Memorandum for Chief of Research, "X-4, September 8 to September 22, 1950."
40. Memorandum for Chief of Research, "X-4, October 6 to October 20, 1950."
41. Memorandum for Chief of Research, "X-4, November 3 to November 17, 1950"; Memorandum for Chief of Research, "X-4, November 17 to December 1, 1950."
42. Quote from Crossfield and Blair, *Always Another Dawn*, pp. 41–44.
43. Memorandum for Chief of Research, "X-4, November 17 to December 1, 1950."
44. Memorandum for Chief of Research, "X-4, December 15, 1950 to December 29, 1950."
45. W.C. Williams and A.S. Crossfield, "Handling Qualities of High-Speed Airplanes," NACA RM L52A08 (January 28, 1952), p. 5.
46. Indeed, tailless aircraft in general, and the X-4 in particular, inherently had very low damping-in-pitch compared to conventional "tailed" aircraft. The conventional F-86 had a damping-in-pitch factor of +10. A 60° delta like the XF-92A or F-102 had a damping-in-pitch of +3. The X-4 had a damping-in-pitch factor less than +1, and as one study concluded, it "dropped to almost zero at Mach numbers slightly below 1.0." See Joseph Adams Shortal, *A New Dimension—Wallops Island Flight Test Range: The First Fifteen Years*, NASA RP 1028 (Washington, DC: NASA, 1978), p. 278.
47. Williams and Crossfield, "Handling Qualities of High-Speed Airplanes," p. 7.

48. Melvin Sadoff and A. Scott Crossfield, "A Flight Evaluation of the Stability and Control of the X-4 Swept-Wing Semitailless Airplane," NACA RM H54G16 (August 30, 1954), pp. 13–14.

49. Memorandum for Chief of Research, "X-4, May 18 to June 1, 1951"; Memorandum for Chief of Research, "X-4, June 16 to June 29, 1951."

50. Memorandum for Chief of Research, "X-4, June 30 to July 13, 1951." The concept of a blunt trailing wing edge was also tested at supersonic speeds using rocket-launched models launched from the Pilotless Aircraft Research Division over the Atlantic. The test-wing configuration had an NACA 0010-64 airfoil (identical to that of the X-4) with flat-side ailerons with a trailing-edge thickness equal to one-half that of the hinge line. NACA researchers H. Kurt Strass and Edison M. Fields analyzed the data from the rocket flights and found that the increased trailing-edge thickness eliminated control reversal and prevented a large and abrupt decrease in aileron effectiveness in the transonic speed range. The downside was that the aileron modifications increased wing drag at subsonic speeds. Above Mach 1, however, the drag increase was small. See H. Kurt Strass and Edison M. Fields, "Flight Investigation of the Effect of Thickening the Aileron Trailing Edge on Control Effectiveness for Sweptback Tapered Wings Having Sharp- and Round-Nose Sections," NACA RM L9L19 (May 2, 1950), pp. 1–2, 5.

51. Memorandum for Chief of Research, "X-4, July 14 to July 27, 1951"; Memorandum for Chief of Research, "X-4, July 28 to August 10, 1951."

52. Memorandum for Chief of Research, "X-4, August 11 to August 25, 1951."

53. Memorandum for Chief of Research, "X-4, September 22 to October 5, 1951." Initially, flight 47 was made for further investigation of the effect of the thickened dive brakes. Subsequently, this was changed to obtaining data on the X-4's landing characteristics. Finally, the plan was again changed back to collecting data on the thickened dive brakes. The tests of the landing configurations followed the completion of the dive brake tests.

54. Memorandum for Chief of Research, "X-4, October 6 to October 19, 1951"; Memorandum for Chief of Research, "X-4, October 20 to November 2, 1951"; Memorandum for Chief of Research, "X-4, November 3 to November 16, 1951."

55. Memorandum for Chief of Research, "X-4, January 26 to February 8, 1952"; Memorandum for Chief of Research, "X-4, February 9 to February 22, 1952."

56. Memorandum for Chief of Research, "X-4, March 8 to March 21, 1952"; Memorandum for Chief of Research, "X-4, March 22 to April 4, 1952."

57. Memorandum for Chief of Research, "X-4, March 22 to April 4, 1952."

58. Wendell H. Stillwell, "Results of Measurements Made During the Approach and Landing of Seven High-Speed Research Airplanes," NACA RM H54K24 (February 4, 1955), pp. 1–2, 9–10.

59. Ibid.

60. Memorandum for Chief of Research, "X-4, April 5 to April 18, 1952"; Memorandum for Chief of Research, "X-4, April 19 to May 2, 1952."

61. Memorandum for Chief of Research, "X-4, May 17 to May 30, 1952"; Memorandum for Chief of Research, "X-4, May 31 to June 13, 1952."

62. Memorandum for Chief of Research, "X-4, June 28 to July 11, 1952"; Memorandum for Chief of Research, "X-4, July 12 to July 25, 1952."

63. Memorandum for Chief of Research, "X-4, August 9 to August 22, 1952"; Memorandum for Chief of Research, "X-4, September 5 to October 1, 1952."

64. Memorandum for Chief of Research, "X-4, September 5 to October 1, 1952."

65. Memorandum for Chief of Research, "X-4, October 1 to November 1, 1952."

66. Memorandum for Chief of Research, "X-4, November 1 to December 1, 1952"; Memorandum for Chief of Research, "X-4, January 1, 1953 to January 31, 1953"; Memorandum for Chief of Research, "X-4, February 1 to February 28, 1953."

67. Memorandum for Chief of Research, "X-4, March 1 to March 31, 1953."

68. Memorandum for Chief of Research, "X-4, April 1 to April 30, 1953"; Memorandum for Chief of Research, "X-4, May 1 to May 31, 1953."

69. Memorandum for Chief of Research, "X-4, July 1 to July 31, 1953." The monthly report included an item regarding analysis of the X-4 flight data. It read, "Frequency response analysis of the last two data flights is awaiting access to automatic computing equipment here at

Edwards Air Force Base." Before this, data reduction had been done by women who were referred to as "computers." It was at this point that the term's meaning was changed from a human to a machine.

70. Memorandum for Chief of Research, "X-4, August 1 to August 31, 1953"; Memorandum for Chief of Research, "X-4, September 1 to September 30, 1953." The August 1 to August 31, 1953, report indicates that NACA flights 79, 80, and 81 were pilot-familiarization flights. However, Crossfield had made numerous X-4 flights, and McKay made the majority of the final flights. It appears that the familiarization flights entry was an error and that these were research flights.

71. "Vought F7U Cutlass," *http://aviationtrivia.info/Vought-F7U-Cutlass.php*, and "F7U Cutlass," *http://www.absoluteastronomy.com/topics/F7U_Cutlass*, accessed October 5, 2010.

72. Peebles, *The Spoken Word*, p. 79.

73. Hallion and Gorn, *On the Frontier: Experimental Flight at NASA Dryden*, p. 50.

74. Sadoff and Crossfield, "A Flight Evaluation of the Stability and Control of the X-4 Swept-Wing Semitailless Airplane," p. 4; Malcolm J. Abzug and E. Eugene Larrabee, *Airplane Stability and Control: A History of the Technology that Made Aviation Possible* (Cambridge, U.K.: Cambridge University Press, 1997), pp. 175, 311.

75. David C. Aronstein and Albert C. Piccirillo, *Have Blue and the F-117: Evolution of the "Stealth Fighter"* (Reston, VA: American Institute of Aeronautics and Astronautics, 1997).

The initial wind tunnel tests of variable sweep wings were made using an X-1 fitted with movable wings. The design proved impractical, but the results were sufficient to encourage the approval of the X-5. (NASA)

CHAPTER 6

Transformative Pioneer: The Bell X-5

It was like having a whole stable of swept-wing airplanes in one.
—A. Scott Crossfield[1]

The development of swept wings was a major step in making routine supersonic flight a reality.[2] But while swept wings reduced the drag that occurs at transonic and supersonic speeds, they also introduced new problems, principally at low speeds and at high angles of attack, particularly during takeoff and landing. The wing design had to balance the conflicting demands of the two ends of the performance envelope. Engineers tried to capture the beneficial characteristics of both low- and high-speed wing shapes. This, though, could potentially make the aircraft difficult to fly, increasing the pilot's workload and the risks that aviators faced.

Additionally, jet air combat required multiple mission profiles during a single flight. A long-range strike mission might involve a long-range cruise, requiring maximum fuel efficiency, followed by a brief supersonic dash to bomb a target and escape, and, finally, a long cruise back to base. The Navy also faced additional problems. The high landing speeds of swept-wing aircraft would make already-dangerous carrier landings on narrow straight-deck carriers even more difficult. Tactically, swept wings posed a problem for fighters on combat air patrol over a naval task force. A capability for low-speed loitering was needed to maximize coverage. If incoming bombers were detected, fighters would have to accelerate to high speeds to intercept the bombers before the bombers got close enough to attack the carriers.

The shape of aircraft carriers complicated matters further; the vessels were still being designed with straight decks, as they had been from their origins. Before the advent of powerful steam catapults, launching these fighters was difficult. Deck activities were also more difficult since the new, larger aircraft occupied more of the available deck space, which was limited. Of course, the new jet fighters approached and landed at faster speeds than had their propeller-driven antecedents, and this complicated matters on straight decks even more, to say nothing of circumstances created for pilots making a landing approach in the rain, at night, to an airport rolling and pitching in the middle of the ocean.

A potential solution was changing the sweep angle of the wings during flight. For takeoff, landing, and cruise flight, the wings' sweep angle could be nearly straight. As an aircraft's speed increased, the wings could be swept back to reduce drag. The aircraft's aerodynamics could be adjusted to meet the demands of speed and altitude at any time during a flight. Initial research on this innovation had begun previously, as the X-1 was being prepared for flight.

After the Second World War, the NACA moved rapidly to study the application of variable-sweep wings to aircraft. Early NACA studies examined both symmetrical wing sweeping (as with the X-5 and subsequent aircraft such as the F-111) and asymmetrical "oblique" wing sweeping (as later incorporated on the Ames-Dryden AD-1 research aircraft).[3] In early 1946, Charles J. Donlan and William C. Sleeman tested an X-1 model fitted with variable-sweep wings in Langley's 7-by-10-foot High-Speed Wind Tunnel. The wings could be adjusted to sweep angles of 0°, 15°, 30°, and 45°. The design assumed that the wings moved on a fixed pivot point on the fuselage centerline. Results were mixed. Tests showed that variable-sweep wings reduced the inherent low-speed handling problems experienced with high-speed aircraft. Engineers also saw limited success in controlling longitudinal stability by changing the sweep angles. A problem was identified regarding the pivot design, however: A fixed wing-pivot point was not workable. This was because both the airplane's center of gravity and center of pressure shifted as the wings changed position. The net result was too much stability, resulting in excessive trim drag and limited maneuverability.[4]

The wing-pivot system would have to be capable of changing the wing-sweep angle and translating it forward and aft to compensate for the resulting changes in center of gravity and center of pressure caused by the wing-sweep movement. The amount of translation was also dependent on the mass distribution of the airplane and the location of the wing pivot point. The weight of the wings, the locations of the wing and fuselage fuel tanks, and the procedures for emptying the fuel tanks in flight also had to be factored into any assessments of the aircraft's stability. This was a major issue in the view of researchers. In their conclusions, they wrote, "It seems unlikely that satisfactory stability for all flight conditions can be achieved with a variable-sweep wing without recourse to relative translation between the wing and the center of gravity of the airplane."[5]

Nose view of the X-5 with the wings at the 20° sweep angle. Unlike those of later variable-sweep aircraft, the X-5's mechanism moved the wings forward as the sweep angle increased. On the F-111, B-1, and F-14, the pivot point was in a stub wing outboard of the fuselage. This eliminated the need for dual motions. (NASA)

The Evolution of the X-5

Just as the X-4 was influenced by the Me 163, Bell's X-5 design was influenced by an unsuccessful aircraft design that originated in Nazi Germany. This was the P.1101, designed by Waldemar Voigt and built by Messerschmitt's advanced projects development group outside Oberammergau, Bavaria, near the end of the war. Unlike the Me 163, however, the P.1101 never flew. Rather, having been rejected by the Luftwaffe as unsuitable for further development, it had been retained by Messerschmitt as a possible test bed for swept wings. The single prototype, nearing completion, was captured in April 1945 when the Oberammergau development center was overrun by U.S. Army forces. Shortly afterwards, a U.S. technical intelligence team arrived, including Robert Woods of Bell Aircraft. Woods arranged to have the unfinished aircraft shipped to the United States for analysis and eventually turned over to Bell Aircraft in August 1948.

As originally conceived, the wing-sweep angle of the P.1101 could be adjusted on the ground to three fixed settings of 35°, 40°, and 45°, and Bell engineers originally suggested to the Army Air Forces that the P.1101 be used in similar fashion, recommending that it be repaired and fitted with a U.S. turbojet engine and then test-flown. A potential next step would have been to modify the P.1101 wings to allow the sweep range to increase from 20° to 50°, again at three fixed positions. But Bell's P.1101 advocates also suggested redesigning the P.1101 so that its sweep angle could be changed in flight. This capability would be useful in an operational fighter, as the wings could be fully extended for takeoff and landing, then swept back to achieve high-speed flight.

Another Bell proposal was to use the P.1101 as an engine test bed. The jet engine was attached beneath the aircraft, at its center of gravity. This made engine changes relatively easy. Among the engines proposed for tests on the P.1101 were the J34, J35, J46, and J47. Another possibility was a 36-inch-diameter ramjet. Finally, a 4,000-pound liquid-fuel rocket also could be tested, by placing a fairing over the nose inlet and fitting the aircraft with new fuel tanks.

In the end, use of the P.1101 itself as a research aircraft proved impractical. The aircraft was too small, major technical problems existed with the proposals, and the aircraft had been damaged when it was dropped during delivery to Bell Aircraft. Rather, Woods and Bell engineers concluded that designing a new aircraft based upon its basic configuration would be preferable. The proposed model would be similar in design configuration to the P.1101 but larger and more advanced. Bell also hoped that the resulting research plane could be modified into a lightweight production jet fighter. (Eventually, the X-5 would be proposed as a NATO export fighter but rejected on grounds remarkably similar to those given by the Luftwaffe in its rejection of the earlier P.1101.) Given the collapse in aircraft orders following the end of World War II, however, such approval was unlikely.[6]

Bell's Robert Wood and his design engineers began work on the new aircraft. A major problem was the development of a practical wing-sweep mechanism. The sweep angle could be varied from 20.25° to 58.7°. Limit switches prevented the wings from exceeding these angles, which would cause interference between the wing root and fuselage. As the wings swept back and forward, the X-5's center of gravity and center of pressure shifted. These characteristics had to be kept in close proximity to prevent stability problems.

The solution was complex. As the wings' sweep angle increased (reducing the wingspan and aspect ratio), the X-5's center of gravity moved aft. To counter this, the complete wing-root assembly moved forward along a track inside the fuselage. When the sweep angle was reduced (increasing the wingspan and aspect ratio), the wing assembly moved backward as the wingtips moved forward. The net result was to keep both the center of gravity and center of

Nose view of the X-5 with the wings swept back to 60°. The aircraft was a low-speed demonstrator for variable-swept wings, as it lacked the supersonic-speed capacity necessary to take full advantage of the maximum sweep angle. (NASA)

pressure within limits, no matter the sweep angle. As the wing's sweep angle changed, so did the wing characteristics. At a 20° wing sweep, the X-5 had a wing area of 184.3 square feet and an aspect ratio of 6.09. With the wings swept back to the maximum 58.7° angle, these values were reduced to a 166.9-square-foot area and 2.16 aspect ratio.[7]

Each wing also required a special fairing "glove" where the leading edge of the wing met the fuselage. This was designed to be movable to ensure that the wing had a smooth airfoil whatever the sweep angle. The wings' leading edges also had slats, which could be extended to increase lift and reduce stall speed. One unusual feature was the speed brakes. Normally, these are located on the aft fuselage, as on the D-558-1. The X-5 had its speed brakes on the nose, just behind the inlet. This proved to be a very poor location, however, and thus the brakes proved generally ineffective.

As on the P.1101, the X-5's engine, an Allison J35-A-17A axial flow jet engine, was slung under the fuselage. The engine produced 4,900 pounds of thrust. Unlike the exotic flush inlets on the D-558-2 or the wing inlets of the

X-4, the X-5 had a simple, straight nose inlet that ran directly to the front of the engine. "This design," a Bell Aircraft press release noted, "holds air-duct losses to a minimum, scooping greater quantities of air at high altitudes where the decreased oxygen content of the atmosphere lowers jet engine performance."[8] Like the X-3 and X-4, the X-5 had an emergency ejection seat. The long main landing gear struts retracted into the fuselage above the engine, and the nose gear retracted into the nose, under the air inlet tunnel.

Unlike the other early X-planes, the X-5 was not particularly sleek, having a configuration more akin to then-contemporary transonic jet fighters than exotic supersonic research airplanes. Bell described it as having a "flying guppy" configuration, with an underslung engine, fat forward fuselage, and boom tail. The X-5 was 33.6 feet long and stood 12.2 feet tall from the ground to the tip of the fin. Its wing employed an NACA $64_{(10)}A011$ airfoil at the wing pivot point, changing to an NACA $64_{(08)}A008.28$ section at the wingtip. Maximum wingspan was 32.75 feet; with the wings fully swept back, the wingspan was just 19.4 feet. The aircraft weighed 10,006 pounds fully loaded and 7,894 pounds without fuel.[9]

Bell Aircraft made a formal proposal to the Air Force for building a pair of X-5 research aircraft on February 1, 1949. (The first aircraft was to be operated by the NACA, the second by the Air Force.) The response was rapid; just 3 days later, Air Force Headquarters directed that a contract be written and signed. The "X-5" was to be used to demonstrate the best sweep angle for lightweight interceptors and the tactical advantages of variable-sweep wings. But the USAF had no interest at that time in funding an operational aircraft, and, indeed, variable sweep would not appear on an Air Force combat aircraft for another 15 years.[10]

The contract signing initiated a series of reviews of Bell's design. Engineers from the Air Force Power Plant Laboratory issued their report on May 9, 1949. They objected to the placement of the fuel tank directly over the jet engine and requested a redesign. This would have meant designing an entirely new aircraft, delaying the project significantly. And so the Power Plant Laboratory engineers withdrew their objections, instead agreeing on August 5 to approve the existing configuration. (However, they asked that shielding of the fuel tank be improved, which it was.) They stressed that their approval applied only in the case of the X-5's use as a research aircraft and not as a production fighter.

These were not the only doubts about the X-5 design. Engineers at the Wright Field Aircraft Laboratory in Ohio issued a critical report on August 29, 1949, in which they urged numerous design changes to make the aircraft both more airworthy and compliant with Air Force design specifications. More serious was the engineers' questioning of the project's value. The 20°

minimum angle was judged to be too low to be of any real use. More substantive, it seemed, was that the X-5 data would duplicate data from aircraft either already available or under construction. The engineers concluded, "In other words, the X-5 does not fill any particular gap in either high-speed or sweep-back research."[11] What was missed in this was that the greatest value of the X-5 would be in simply demonstrating the *act* of in-flight variable wing sweep itself.[12] The NACA, in contrast, strongly supported the X-5's development. NACA researchers had decided by mid-1948 that the aircraft would complement their earlier wind tunnel work. Following Bell's initial proposal that a variable-sweep research aircraft be designed and built, a team from Langley went to Wright Field to argue for Air Force approval. This did much to win needed military support for the project at a time when the service faced many competing demands for scarce funding.

Contractor and Air Force Proving Flights

Ground tests with the first X-5 (AF Serial 50-1838) began on February 15, 1951, at Bell's Niagara Falls facility. The next several months entailed aircraft system testing, load and structural testing, and taxi runs. The Air Force also completed engineering inspections. On June 9, 1951, the disassembled aircraft was crated and loaded onto a Fairchild C-119 cargo plane for the long flight to Edwards. The test flights and research plan for the pair of X-5s were similar to those of earlier X-planes. Initial demonstration flights would be made by Jean L. "Skip" Ziegler, Bell's chief test pilot. Once the first X-5 had been proven airworthy, Air Force familiarization flights would follow. With these complete, the first X-5 would then be turned over to the NACA, which would begin research flights. The second X-5 (AF Serial 50-1839) would be flown by Air Force pilots in a separate test effort.

Ziegler took the first X-5 aloft on June 20, 1951. After takeoff, he climbed to 15,000 feet, using reduced power to keep his speed below the wheels-down limit. Once at altitude, he tried out the X-5's control response and found it to be stiff. He reached a top speed of Mach 0.56 and a maximum altitude of 15,974 feet. So far, the flight had been a success, and Ziegler began to descend.

At that point, he discovered the fuel cells were showing negative pressure. This meant their internal pressure was lower than that of outside air. If the reading was valid, as the X-5 descended the increasing outside air pressure could cause the fuel cells to rupture. Fuel would then spill onto the engine, triggering a fire. Ziegler made maneuvers to determine whether the reading was correct, and after several minutes he determined that the fuel-cell pressure reading was false. He landed several minutes later without incident.

The fuel-cell pressure gauge error and several other problems had to be addressed, and the aircraft was grounded for 5 days. The June 25 flight went off but yielded no data. The next two flights, on June 27 and 28, reached Mach 0.638 and 0.696. Zeigler undertook the first wing-sweep test on July 27. This involved only a partial movement, rather than the full range of 20.25° to 58.7°. The Bell contractor tests continued into late August 1951, with nine flights made.

Brigadier General Albert Boyd, the Air Force Flight Test Center commander, received permission from the Wright Air Development Center to make an evaluation flight in the X-5 on August 23. General Boyd took off, climbed to 40,000 feet, and moved the wings back to their full 58.7° sweep angle. He then descended to 30,000 feet, reached a speed of Mach 0.92, and made several more test maneuvers. Boyd's total flight time was 28 minutes. The NACA progress report on the X-5 stated that the primary goal of Boyd's flight was to demonstrate a landing with a 40° sweepback. Data were obtained on three landing configurations:

- Landing at alternate gross weight, slats out, and with wings at a 20° sweep
- Landing with slats out and wings at a 20° sweep
- Landing with flaps at 35°, slats out, and at a sweepback of 40°

The first two landings were made without incident, but during a landing approach at 40°, Boyd accidently raised the flaps by striking the flap switch. The X-5 experienced a stall roll-off, striking the ground on its nose and right main wheels before Boyd could recover. The impact caused minor damage to the tire tread. No structural damage was listed.[13]

The Bell test effort with the first X-5 ended on October 8, 1951, when Ziegler made his final flight in the NACA aircraft. The first X-5 was grounded pending the installation of NACA instrumentation. The initial payload measured the following quantities:

- Vertical, longitudinal, and transverse acceleration
- Sensitive longitudinal acceleration
- Rolling angular velocity
- Pitching angular velocity and acceleration
- Yawing angular velocity and acceleration
- Airspeed and altitude
- Angle of sideslip and angle of attack
- Control positions
- Wing-sweep angle
- Elevator and aileron stick forces[14]

Along with instrument installation, the X-5 was inspected. The fuel cells were replaced, and functional checks of them were made. These preparations were expected to be completed by the week of December 17, 1951. Once the work was complete, Air Force demonstration flights could begin. These were to be made by Lieutenant Colonel Frank K. "Pete" Everest.[15]

Everest's first two flights were made on December 20. The first was for pilot familiarization, and no data were collected. A second flight the same day reached Mach 0.844 and 22,380 feet. Everest made two more flights on December 21 and 27. His final pair of flights came on January 7 and 8, 1952. The tests involved clean stalls with wing sweeps of 20°, 40°, and 60° and multiple accelerated turns at the three sweep settings of clean, slats out and flaps down, and flaps down. Thomas W. Finch, NACA X-5 project manager, summarized the initial results of the flights in two research memorandums. In the first, he said:

> At low speed for 20° sweepback an increase in longitudinal stability occurred as maximum lift was approached. At 40° and 60° sweep a reduction in stability occurred at the higher lift coefficients. During the tests at 30,000 feet to investigate the effects of lift coefficients at Mach number of approximately 0.8—for the 20° sweep, there occurred a reduction in longitudinal stability at lift coefficient of approximately 0.4. No change in stability was noticed at 40° sweep up to lift coefficient of 0.5 (the limit of tests to date). For 60° sweep an abrupt pitch-up occurred at a lift coefficient of 0.6. Stick forces were of the order of 20 and 35 lbs/g at the high Mach numbers.
>
> Structural integrity demonstration required 5.86 g at Mach of 0.8 at 12,000 feet which corresponds to a lift coefficient of approximately 0.5. Pull-ups made at 20° and 60° sweep at this speed and altitude were limited to load factors less than 4gs due to the high stick forces.[16]

And in the second, he said:

> There was a slight increase in stability at 20° sweep from M = 0.75 to M = 0.79, and the stability at 60° sweep remained essentially the same for a Mach number range of 0.7 to 0.8. At 40° sweep there is an appreciable increase in stability at M = 0.81 above that for M = 0.71 and M = 0.76. During the tests to investigate the effects of lift coefficients up to M ≈ 0.8, instability was found for the following conditions: (1) for 40° sweep there was a decrease in stability at M ≈ 0.75 and at M ≈ 0.81 a mild pitch up occurred at a C_{An} [airplane normal-force coefficient] of 0.5. (2) for 60° sweep an abrupt pitch up occurred at a C_{An} of 0.6 and M ≈ 0.8.
>
> The only indication of instability occurred at 20° sweep and 20,800 feet with a decrease in stability above a C_{An} [of] 0.4.

A load factor of 5.86g could not be demonstrated at M = 0.8 and 12,000 feet because of high stick forces. At lower Mach numbers of 0.7 and 0.75 the stick forces were essentially the same, and the lift coefficients for instability were being approached or exceeded. In view of these results it was decided to accept the airplane since it became apparent that the longitudinal stability evaluation required a more complete analysis, and the flight testing was entering into the research program planned for the airplane.[17]

NACA X-5 Research Flights Begin

With the X-5 officially transferred to the High-Speed Flight Research Station, Joe Walker was selected as the initial NACA X-5 pilot. He made his checkout flight on January 9, 1952. Walker's first research flight came on January 14, 1952, and dealt with static and dynamic longitudinal and lateral stability and control. Ultimately, the bulk of the flights in the X-5 focused on this type of research. Walker was kept busy flying the X-5, completing 17 flights between January 9 and April 1. Though most of the flights were for stability and control, three were for airspeed calibration and another was for a gust loads investigation at 20° and 60° sweep angles. Finally, on February 12, Air Force pilot J.C. Meyer had a check flight in the NACA's X-5. (This was the only flight not made by Walker during this period.)

Not everything went smoothly. The March 13 flight was aborted after takeoff, and Walker's first flight on March 17 was aborted as well due to "poor voltage, no data."[18] The problem was corrected, and a second flight that day was made for lateral and longitudinal stability and control data at a 60° sweep angle.

The test data from the Bell acceptance flights had been analyzed, and a research memorandum emerged. The report offered a more detailed look at the data than had initial observations in Finch's progress reports. The memorandum on the X-5's horizontal-tail load measurements noted:

> During sweep changes at an altitude of 20,000 feet, the trends of the balancing tail loads variation with sweep angle at Mach numbers of 0.50, 0.56, and 0.85 were similar with the larger down tail load occurring at approximately 36° sweep angle at each Mach number tested. The largest balancing tail load in a down direction over the entire sweep range from 20° to 59° occurred at a Mach number of 0.85.

During level-flight-trim points at 20° sweepback at an altitude of about 20,000 feet and an airplane weight of about 8,800 pounds, the tail load increased in a down direction as the Mach number was increased from 0.54 to 0.84.

During pull-ups at a Mach number of about 0.83 and at sweep angles of 20°, 45°, and 59°, the wing-fuselage combination was stable at 20° and 45° sweepback and unstable at 59° sweepback at normal-force coefficients less than 0.3. At normal-force coefficients near 0.3 the stability of the wing-fuselage combination changed for these sweep angles, becoming unstable at a sweep angle of 20°, experiencing a reduction in stability at 45°, and became stable at 59° as the normal-force coefficient increased. For the normal-force-coefficients range covered in these tests the aerodynamic center of the wing-fuselage combination moved rearward as the sweep angle was increased from 20° to 59°. A larger change in the wing-fuselage aerodynamic center was experienced with the sweep for the high normal-force-coefficient range than was experienced for the low normal-force-coefficient range.[19]

In April 1952, A. Scott Crossfield and Walter P. Jones began making X-5 flights. Crossfield's check flights came on April 2, Jones's on April 29. Crossfield had already talked with Walker about the X-5's handling. Crossfield recalled later, "The X-5 handled in the air like a three-wheeled automobile. It was loose and danced crazily. Even so, we thought it would make a fine research tool."[20] The X-5's most serious shortcoming was its spin characteristics. Both Walker and Crossfield would experience these in full fury.

Crossfield's flight plan called for making several accelerated stalls. After reaching 25,000 feet, he pulled back on the throttle and the stick. He wrote later:

As the X-5 slowed, she began to buffet. Suddenly her nose veered sharply to the left. In a split second, the X-5 turned 180 degrees. Then she dropped precipitously into a spin.

A kaleidoscope of brown desert, blue sky, and white clouds passed dizzily in review in my windshield as the X-5 wound up steadily towards the desert floor. I pressed the stick hard to forward left and bent on full right rudder—the prescribed spin recovery maneuver—but the X-5 stubbornly refused to conform. After a drop of over 10,000 feet, the X-5 pulled out.[21]

Walker had experienced the X-5's spin behavior the month before; he had entered a spin at 40,000 feet and had not recovered until reaching 20,000 feet. He described the experience in his pilot report: "As the airplane pitches, it yaws to the right and causes the airplane to roll to the right. At this stage aileron reversal occurs; the stick jerks to the right and kicks back and forth from neutral to full right deflection if not restrained. It seems that the airplane goes longitudinally, directionally, and laterally unstable in that order."[22]

During the spring and summer of 1952, pilots flew the X-5 research plane for longitudinal control effectiveness, static lateral stability and control characteristics, and dynamic longitudinal and lateral stability and control data. Between May 3 and May 16, four research flights were made, three by Crossfield and one by Jones. Maneuvers included speed runs, aileron rolls, sideslips, elevator and rudder pulses, and stall approaches. The bulk of the maneuvers were flown with the wings at a 60° sweep angle. Speeds ranged from Mach 0.47 up to 0.94, altitudes from 36,000 to 42,000 feet. The initial results were as follows:

> Preliminary evaluation of the records and pilot's notes indicated that all speed runs were easily controllable with elevator. The nose down trim change reported in the speed run…occurred about 0.93 which is in agreement with previously reported data.
>
> The aileron effectiveness is low and approximately constant up to M = 0.9. The rudder effectiveness determined from sideslip data is noticeably improved below M = 0.70 as compared to an approximate constant effectiveness between M = 0.70 and M = 0.90. Almost total aileron control available is required for sideslip angles of about 5° at Mach numbers below 0.70.
>
> The values of the period and time-to-damp of the longitudinal and lateral oscillations obtained from pulses below M = 0.90 were in agreement with previously reported data. Data have not yet been reduced from maneuvers performed above M = 0.9.[23]

Crossfield and Jones continued to make longitudinal and lateral stability data flights into late June 1952. Walker made his next flight on June 25, 1952. These flights continued static and dynamic longitudinal and lateral stability data collection. Walker made flights on July 2 and 10. The July 2 flight and most of the July 10 flight collected additional static longitudinal and lateral stability data at 59° wing-sweep angles. These involved speed runs, pushovers and pull-ups, aileron rolls, and gradually increasing sideslips.

Walker's July 10 flight also generated data on lift and drag at a 20° sweep angle. He made speed runs as well as pushovers and pull-ups with the wings at a 20° sweep. The pushover was made to a g-meter reading of 0 g, followed by a pull-up into the longitudinal instability boundary. These runs were made to obtain accelerated maneuver data starting from zero lift. During this flight,

Walker also made fast-rate stabilizer pull-ups into the instability region while flying in a speed range of Mach 0.70 to 0.96. He performed these maneuvers to get baseline data, which would be compared to data collected following the installation of modified wing-root fillets.

By July 25, Walker had made another three research flights, with all the tests conducted at a 59° sweep angle. As on his earlier flights, he performed gradually increasing sideslips, pushovers and pull-ups, and a speed run. One of the flights was made with the modified wing-root fillets. A wind tunnel test with a model that resembled the X-5 indicated that changing the wing-root shape would prevent the reduction of longitudinal stability that characterized the X-5.

For these tests, stabilizer pull-ups were made from Mach 0.70 to 0.965, in a 2° dive from 40,000 to 38,000 feet. Mindful of how fast the aircraft could lose altitude in a spin, pushovers and pull-ups were made at Mach 0.70 to 0.84 and 40,000 feet, pull-ups at Mach 0.965 and 38,000 feet. The results were summarized as follows:

> Static longitudinal instability was encountered on all pull-ups both in the original configuration and with modified wing root fillets. The pilot reported increased stability at lower normal-force coefficients with the modified wing root fillets at the higher Mach numbers tested while the instability seemed to occur at slightly higher load factors.
>
> Data from the speed run performed in a 20° degree dive has not been reduced but the pilot's Machmeter reading of 0.93 indicates a Mach number greater than 0.98 has been reached. The speed run was easily controlled with elevator with the pilot reporting maximum stick forces of about 10 pounds push at the trim change and about 15 to 20 pounds pull at the maximum Mach number.[24]

Walker expanded the longitudinal and lateral stability and control flights in late July and early August 1952. To extend the speed range of the X-5, shallow dives were made to exceed Mach 1. He began the dives at angles of 20° and 30°, starting at 45,000 feet, and pulled out at 38,000 feet at a wing-sweep angle of 59°. The test maneuvers were much the same as those on earlier flights: aileron rolls, gradually increasing sideslips, pushovers and pull-ups, and stabilizer pull-ups. (The latter were done at both 59° and 20° wing-sweep angles.) During the July 25 flight, Walker reached a maximum speed of Mach 0.986. He achieved Mach 1.006 on both the August 1 and 7 flights. The preliminary results of the three flights were summarized in the X-5 progress report:

Preliminary inspection of the records and pilots comments indicate that near M = 1.0 the maneuvers were performed without any difficulties. About 35 pounds aileron force was required for a full deflection roll and about two-thirds the available aileron control was required in sideslips to $\beta \approx 1.5°$.

The dives were easily controlled with elevator with a maximum push force of about 60 pounds being encountered in the dive at…–3°. Elevator forces up to about 180 pounds was required in the pullout from the dives near M = 1.0.

Longitudinal instability was encountered in all pull-ups. The trend of the instability boundary above M = 0.96 will not be known until the data has been reduced from the pullouts.[25]

Additional research flights were made in September at the 59° sweep angle before being halted. The X-5 did not fly again until October 21, with Walker at the controls. Pilots of the era would likely have described Walker's experience that day as "eventful." The progress report noted:

At 59° sweepback a 30° dive was made to M = 1.04 with a stabilizer setting of –2.5°. Trim force for 1g was about 45 pounds push at maximum speed. An elevator pull-up to about 2g was completed above M = 1.0 without encountering any reduction in stability. A stabilizer pull-up was started above M = 1.0 with a reduction of stability being encountered at better than 2g as the Mach number decreased. The remainder of the flight was to be composed of pushovers to 0g followed by pull-ups through the reduction of stability boundary starting from the trimmed stabilizer deflection. However, a violent spin occurred following the reduction of stability during a pull-up at a Mach number near 0.7. As the airplane yawed to the right following the reduction in longitudinal stability it abruptly snap-rolled and went into a spin at an altitude of about 44,000 feet. There was a high rate of roll (greater than 3 radians/sec) about the longitudinal axis. The elevator hinge moments caused the elevator to float up; the forces were too high for the pilot to apply full down elevator. The recovery was not affected until the stabilizer control had been in the full leading-edge up position (+4.4°) for several seconds with ailerons and rudder opposing the spinning direction. Recovery was completed at an altitude of about 37,000 feet.[26]

Following the spin, mechanics inspected the aircraft and the flight data were analyzed for any indication that the aircraft had been overstressed. The progress report noted:

> Strain gage data indicated that compression loads imposed on the sweep mechanism jackscrews approached limit load. It may be necessary to examine and test the various components of the sweep mechanism. The engine was removed for inspection and cracks were found in the nozzle diaphragm as well as evidence of rubbing between the turbine wheel and the diaphragm. The engine will be replaced as soon as the oil tank can be modified to accommodate a –B engine.
>
> A "g" limitation that has existed for the X-5 wing is being lifted by replacement of a number of rivets on each wing panel aft of the pivot point by high sheer bolts. The present limitation of 5.65g will be then lifted to 7.33g.[27]

Given the complexity of the inspection and the resulting repair work, it is not surprising that the X-5 was grounded until December 5, 1952. The aircraft made a total of seven flights in December, another five in January 1953. These flights, unlike those made earlier in the year, had a wider range of goals. Only three of the December flights dealt with longitudinal- and lateral-stability and control data; two were checkout flights for Stanley P. Butchart; another was a photographic flight; and one was aborted after takeoff due to an inoperative stabilizer motor. The January 1953 flights involved two made for vertical-tail load measurements during maneuvers, another for stalls and maneuvers at a 20° wing sweep, and the check flight of Major Arthur A. "Kit" Murray. The last was made to compare the behavior of the first X-5 with that of the second, which was being flown by the Air Force.[28]

The other two flights in January and the first flight in February all had an unusual pair of goals: "investigation of flight at speeds below minimum drag of the test airplane and testing the controllability of a highly swept-wing aircraft in the wingtip wake of a straight-wing aircraft."[29] The tests originated with a verbal request made by Wright-Patterson engineers to Walter Williams during a visit to Edwards. The data they sought would be used in the design of a tanker capable of refueling an interceptor aircraft in flight. Originally, the delta-wing XF-92A was suggested as the test aircraft. Analysis indicated that preliminary results could be obtained at a much earlier date using the X-5 flying with a 59° sweepback behind an F-80 and a B-29 bomber.

Multiple exposures showing the full range of travel of the X-5 wings. The sweep angle could be adjusted in flight depending on test requirements. One unusual effort undertaken with the aircraft involved the X-5 flying behind a B-29 in a test of how a swept-wing aircraft would handle while taking on fuel from a straight wing/propeller-powered tanker. (NASA)

Walker made the research flights. The first, on January 27, 1953, was flown with the X-5 trailing an F-80 Shooting Star, the first production U.S. jet fighter. The X-5's wing sweep was 59° at an altitude of 25,000 feet. The first part of the formation tests involved stabilized test points recorded at intervals from 290 to 190 mph. A second set was done in a continuingly decreasing speed run between 290 and 190 mph. Finally, a continuously increasing speed run was made from 190 to 290 mph. In the X-5, Walker took a position 10 to 15 feet behind the F-80's wingtip, which he used as a reference point. His pilot report on the January 27 flight noted:

> Accurate position could be maintained at any of the test speeds and during the accelerating and decelerating runs once the position was established. Getting into position was difficult at these test speeds. Throttle control of speed was effective only for minor

position changes once position was established. At other times, except at high speed, power change was so slow that speed changes were difficult and slow. A fast acting effective speed brake combined with a control switch on the throttle is the only practical means of speed control for join up. If the speed brakes were capable of variable positioning, throttle regulation would be made easier in case of two dissimilar aircraft attempting to maintain an accurate position relative to each other.

The variations in power required to maintain position at different speeds was most apparent during the deceleration and acceleration speed runs. At minimum speed of 190 mph there was still ample reserve power. The power required had not started increasing rapidly down to 190 mph. It was relatively less difficult to maintain position at 190 mph than at 250 mph because of larger airplane drag changes with slight changes of angle of attack.[30]

The other two flights, on January 29 and February 6, 1953, were with a B-29 at 40,000 feet. The X-5's wing sweep was again 59°, with the stabilizer incidence at –2°. Level formation runs were made with the B-29 at speeds of 230, 220, 210, 200, and 190 mph. Walker commented later that he experienced "less difficulty" maintaining position with the B-29 than with the F-80, as the bomber "didn't bounce around as much," adding, "It was not difficult to maintain fore and aft and vertical position. There was plenty of elevator and rudder control. However, lateral control with the ailerons gradually deteriorated as speed was reduced."[31] A problem appeared at 190 mph, when Walker extended the X-5's wing slats. He later wrote, "This configuration is not recommended. As soon as slat extension started, extreme sensitivity in roll developed. The airplane gained nose up trim. The ailerons and elevator became noticeably stiffer. It appeared that the static longitudinal stability stick-fixed and stick-free decreased markedly. The result was an all out effort to maintain the wings level and increased difficulty maintaining vertical position…. It should be possible to reduce speed below 190 mph in the clean configuration without encountering as much control difficulty as with the slates extended at 190 mph."[32]

Walker flew the third and final formation test on February 6, 1953, again trailing a B-29. The flight went smoothly, with Walker's postflight report noting:

Because the airplane [X-5] buffeted at 176 mph and the stability decreased at that speed, 180 mph was set as the minimum speed for tests, clean configuration, of ability to fly formation below minimum drag. A record was obtained while getting into position on the lead airplane which was flying at 190 mph. No particular difficulties were encountered which would not be present at any speed during the join up.

The only noticeable handicap to maintaining position at 180 mph was the small amount of control remaining and large deflection required. This was minimized for the X-5 because of the component of thrust acting as an additional longitudinal control.

It actually appeared easier to maintain position at 180 mph than at 240 mph because of greater drag at trim and larger drag changes with small angles of attack changes. It was found, for example, that a slight tendency to overshoot could be quickly stopped merely by raising the nose of the airplane slightly.

Based upon observations during these flights, for the purposes of aerial refueling it would be feasible to fly below the speed for minimum drag of a highly swept wing airplane and may be more easily done than at the speed for minimum drag, providing reserve power is available for maneuvering.[33]

Initial X-5 Research Results

As NACA research flights with the X-5 began, the flight data were being simultaneously analyzed. This was a complex process that began with data reduction and was followed by the writing of a rough draft, a review by High-Speed Flight Research Station staff, and further reviews and comments from other NACA laboratories. Not until early 1953 were the initial research memorandums published.

The first of these dealt with flight measurements of the X-5's stability characteristics in sideslips with the wings at a 59° sweep angle. The flight conditions were at Mach 0.62 to 0.97 between 35,000 and 40,000 feet. The results indicated the following:

> Throughout the Mach number range the apparent directional stability is positive. It is constant from a Mach number of 0.62 to 0.90 and increases to a value about 60 percent higher as the Mach number increases to 0.97.
>
> The apparent effective dihedral is positive and high, doubling in value between Mach numbers of 0.75 and 0.97. The dihedral is so high at the highest Mach number that the ailerons can only trim out about 2.5° of sideslip and can be easily overpowered by the rudder.

The cross-wind force coefficient per degree of sideslip is stable and constant to a Mach number of 0.94, above which it increases rapidly to a Mach number of 0.97.

There is little or no change in pitching moment due to sideslip.[34]

Another research memorandum looked at the lift and drag measurements at different sweep angles, including a comparison of the lift and drag at 59° and 20° sweep angle configurations. The data indicated the following:

At an altitude of about 42,000 feet the drag force for the 20° sweep configuration in unaccelerated flight was considerably less than that for the 59° sweep configuration for flight speeds below a Mach number of 0.81; above a Mach number of 0.82 the reverse is true.

At an altitude of 42,000 feet and a Mach number of 0.74 the total drag force for the 59° configuration was more than twice that for the 20° configuration at any given lift coefficient below maximum lift.[35]

Other important research was devoted to determining the X-5's buffeting characteristics, as these produced bending stresses and moments, shear loads, and torque on the aircraft. Buffeting also affected controllability. Flight measurements of the X-5's buffeting were made at a 58.7° sweep angle, at a speed range of between Mach 0.65 and 1.03, and at altitudes between 37,000 and 43,000 feet. Maximum airplane normal-force coefficients were reached for Mach numbers up to 0.96. The research memorandum's concluding remarks on the X-5's buffeting read:

At all airplane normal-force coefficients the horizontal tail was found to experience buffeting.... At angles of attack below maximum airplane normal-force coefficient the peak buffet-induced tail-bending stresses were 20 percent of the maximum observed tail steady-state bending stress; the peak buffet-induced tail shear loads were approximately 5 percent of the tail design limit load.

Wing buffeting began at moderate angles of attack but above the wing buffet boundary there was no appreciable increase in wing buffet intensity with increase in Mach number or angle of attack. At angles of attack below maximum airplane normal-force coefficient, the peak buffet-induced wing bending stresses were 5 percent of the maximum observed wing steady-state bending stress.

Coefficients of incremental normal acceleration greater than ±0.05, considered to be high-intensity buffeting on other research airplanes, were not experienced by the X-5 airplane below normal-force coefficient. The pilot considered the buffeting to be "unobjectionable" throughout the entire test region.[36]

Though most of the research was focused on the X-5's basic aerodynamics, stability and control, along with the effects of the swept wings, changing the shape of the wing roots to improve stability was also examined. This effort illustrated the value of actual flight testing as a means of verifying wind tunnel results. Replacing the original 52.5° sweepback leading edges with rounded leading-edge fillets showed improved stability in the wind tunnel, but flight tests produced different results. The research memorandum noted:

A comparison was made between two configurations of the Bell X-5 research airplane at 59° sweepback, one with the original wing-root fillets and the other with the wing-root fillets shown by low-speed wind-tunnel to eliminate the loss of stability at high-lift coefficients. The data obtained from the flight investigations, however, show that the longitudinal stability characteristics, as well as the buffet and drag characteristics, were essentially unaffected by the modification.[37]

Dark Day: The Loss of Ray Popson and the Second X-5

While NACA research pilots were flying missions in the first X-5, Air Force test pilots were conducting their own flight tests with the second aircraft. As the first X-5 underwent contractor flights in 1951, the second X-5 (AF serial number 50-1839), meant for use in the Air Force test effort, was under construction. It was completed in early October and arrived at Edwards aboard a C-119 cargo plane on October 9, 1951. It was test-flown by Ziegler on December 10 and delivered to the Air Force 8 days later. The Air Force test effort was an extension of Bell Phase I testing and involved stall testing with wing slats closed. Subsequently, the X-5 would make takeoffs with slats closed. The goal was to determine whether they could be closed permanently. Other tests involved the nose-mounted speed brakes. The X-5 had experienced severe buffeting during the Bell flights at speeds at which the aircraft were to be used. The Air Force wanted more data on the cause.[38]

On October 13, 1953, Major Raymond A. "Ray" Popson took off from Edwards for a familiarization flight in the second X-5. Such flights were common Air Force practice for test pilots at Edwards. Popson was an experienced and skilled test pilot. Major Arthur A. "Kit" Murray was the chase pilot, flying an F-86. The takeoff and climb to 40,000 feet were uneventful. Popson then began a series of stalls with the wing sweep at 20°, 40°, and 60°, as well as level flight accelerations. These maneuvers were followed by a dive that incorporated a 20° sweep angle and pull-up. During the pull-up, Popson swept the wings back to 60°. He then entered a dive, reaching a speed of Mach 0.96 and leveling off at 35,000 feet.

The first indication of trouble appeared at that point. Popson radioed Murray that the X-5 had lost oxygen pressure. Murray answered that Popson should immediately descend, which he did. During the descent, made with the speed brakes extended, Popson indicated he had 25 to 50 pounds of oxygen pressure. This was sufficient for continuing the flight.

The NACA X-5 parked on the ramp at South Base. The X-5 aircraft had a bulky design that led to poor flight characteristics. Spins were a particular problem and resulted in the loss of the second X-5 as well as the death of Air Force pilot Ray Popson. (NASA)

The two aircraft leveled out at 10,000 feet. Popson radioed Murray that the X-5 had 120 gallons of gas remaining and he wanted to "feel the aircraft out some more" before landing. The pair climbed to 12,000 feet above sea level (about 10,000 feet above ground level), and Popson began a series of stalls at 20° and 40° sweep angles. He then began a third series of stalls at 60°, but the X-5 slowly rolled over onto its back and entered a spin to the right. Murray radioed Popson to eject during the third turn, but received no reply. The X-5 struck the ground after four to six turns, in a 60° diving turn. Popson made no ejection attempt and died on impact.[39]

Although the accident investigation board concluded that the cause of the crash was loss of control leading to an unintentional spin at an altitude too low for successful recovery, board members felt that several factors had contributed to the loss of control. One of these factors was that analysis of crash debris indicated that the wings had been at a 45° to 47° sweep angle when the X-5 hit the ground. As the sweep angle was known to be 60° at spin entry, the board believed Popson had attempted to move the wings to a 20° sweep angle. The reaction to sweeping the wings forward during a spin was unknown, but in straight and level flight, a trim change had been noted during wing-sweep changes.

The X-5's cockpit pressurization system was not operational at the time of the flight. This meant Popson would have been using 100-percent oxygen from takeoff until reporting the loss of oxygen pressure. However, the supply of oxygen would have lasted about 35 minutes. Popson reported the loss of oxygen pressure after 26 minutes of flight time. Roughly 2 minutes later, he radioed that he had 25 to 50 pounds of oxygen pressure. The X-5's crew chief told the accident board he was certain a full supply of oxygen was on board the aircraft before it took off. If the numbers Popson reported were an accurate reading, this would indicate excessive leakage or a partial malfunction within the oxygen system.[40]

The medical official on the accident panel expressed the opinion that the conditions described could induce some degree of hypoxia, but to an extent that was unknown. Although Popson's actions and radio communications during the 20° and 40° sweep-angle stalls had seemed normal, hypoxia could have been a contributing factor in the accident, he asserted. Popson's intentions for the 60° stalls at 12,000 feet were unknown; they had not been part of the original familiarization flight plan. Full exploration of the X-5's stall characteristics at so low an altitude "would have been unwise," the accident report noted.[41] But Popson had extensive experience and should have been able to recover successfully. The board considered the possibility that Popson had made mistakes in attempting to recover from the spin, such as holding the ailerons against the spin rather than with it, or using excessive elevator trim. The accident report stated, "This is considered less likely, however, than the assumption of partial

In-flight photo of the X-5 over Edwards Air Force Base with the wings in the midrange position. As many of the other X-planes did, the X-5 suffered from poor stability and control. The stall/ spin behavior was very poor, requiring 10,000 feet to make a recovery. This was the cause of the loss of Major Popson during a familiarization flight in the second aircraft. (NASA)

hypoxia[,] which would reduce the pilot's 'keenness' or 'edge' of reaction." (But the report did not officially endorse the hypoxia theory.)[42]

As was routine in such incidents, panel members questioned Major Murray. He was asked if Popson's voice had sounded normal during radio communication, or if there had been any indication he was suffering from hypoxia. Murray responded, "At the time I did not [think there was anything unusual], he was perfectly normal, it seemed…." At a later point, a panel member asked, "Again, he seemed normal, his words were used properly, no slurring of speech?" Murray replied, "When talking through an oxygen mask a voice sounds garbled, at the time I was under the impression that he was in a normal condition, gave no hesitation in answering."

One member also asked Murray: "Have you ever thought there was any indication that the flight characteristics of this aircraft differed from the NACA aircraft?"

Murray, who had about 40 hours of flight time piloting both of the X-5s, replied, "They differ quite a bit in the high speeds in that [the Air Force's] airplane tends to become uncontrollable [at] .93 to .96 and we have noticed a great difference in the stall characteristics. In accelerated stalls and unaccelerated stalls the airplane will recover as soon as the elevator was put forward and after speed was regained lateral control came back."

Joe Walker also testified before the accident panel. One of the members noted that Popson had stalled the X-5 with a 60° wing sweep, in a clean configuration, and entered a spin. He asked Walker if he had experienced any similar conditions. Walker replied:

> In a 1g stall, clean configuration, 60° sweep I have experienced several different conditions. The airplane exhibited increasing loss of lateral control and abrupt yaw to the left. The most vicious stall approach was with slats extended and occurred with no warning. This took the form of a half snap roll to the left. If excess right rudder were used it would probably have been to the right. It seemed like I had perfect control of the airplane before the snap roll. Application of trim by actuation of the stabilizer with the electrical motor results in excess control which pitches the airplane into a spin condition near the stall.[43]

Walker was asked later if he had anything he wanted to add to his testimony. He replied, "I would like to say a 1g stall approach at 60° is accompanied by large loss of altitude. You get an increase of drag with an increase of angle of attack. Below 170 mph use of full throttle still requires about 5,000 feet altitude to gain sufficient speed to pull out of the dive."[44]

The final conclusion was, "The Board is of the opinion that this accident was the result of loss of control of the aircraft resulting in an unintentional spin at insufficient altitude for recovery but it is felt that several other factors or conditions could have contributed to this loss of control. They are as follows: 'Wing Sweep Control and Oxygen System and Pressurization.' The panel recommended that stalls only be performed above 20,000 feet in research aircraft with unknown qualities."[45]

Although not mentioned in the accident investigation, a breakdown in communications between the Air Force and the NACA had occurred. Crossfield recalled later that following Walker's and his own X-5 spin, a note had been added to the X-5 pilot's handbook prohibiting any maneuvers that could result in a spin at an altitude below 20,000 feet. When Crossfield learned that Popson had made aggravated stalls at 12,000 feet, he later recalled, "I was sick. We had failed in a basic NACA mission—getting information to the right place in time.... If there had been better coordination between [the] Air Force and NACA, [Popson] might be alive today."[47]

The medical safety division had its own comments: "One fact apparently overlooked is that even after descending to 12,000 feet...where stalls were practiced for about 10 minutes, the cabin pressure would have been near 13,000 feet to 14,000 feet and hypoxia possibly induced at a higher altitude would not

The first X-5 in January 1952, after it was transferred to the NACA. A total of 122 NACA research flights were made with the X-5, most of them piloted by Joe Walker. In contrast, A. Scott Crossfield made 10 flights between 1952 and 1954. He later commented that the low-slung engine resulted in a misalignment of the drag axis, the principal axis, and the thrust axis. "So," he later said, "it could get into some interesting maneuvers and motions…."[46] (NASA)

be completely recovered from since mild hypoxia is actually induced at these altitudes. Concur generally with findings."[48]

The X-5's Later Years—1953–1955

The NACA continued to fly the surviving X-5 following the Popson crash. The number of flights made in the aircraft each year gradually declined, however. In 1953, a total of 31 flights were made with the X-5 (four by Crossfield, one by Murray, and the rest by Walker). Research goals included collecting data on vertical-tail loads, gust loads, effects of wing transition on aircraft trim, longitudinal stability and control, and wing twisting and bending tail loads.

The X-5 made a total of 27 flights in 1954, with Walker, Crossfield, Stanley P. Butchart, and John B. "Jack" McKay as pilots. Much of the research work continued to focus on longitudinal and lateral stability and control, as well as vertical-tail loads. Additional research included measuring the effects of dynamic pressure on buffet. Most of the flights were made between January and June of that year. The X-5 then was grounded, awaiting delivery and installation of a new nose gear housing from the Electrol Company. The aircraft did not fly again until December 14, when Butchart conducted an instrumentation check flight. The following day, McKay made the first of four pilot checkout flights.

The X-5 project made its final research flights in 1955, totaling 19 flights in all. The first flight, made on January 27, was an instrumentation check by Butchart and reached Mach 0.922. The next eight flights, made by Butchart and McKay between January 28 and March 23, were for longitudinal-stability and control data. Six more flights, starting on March 23 and continuing through April 8, were for lateral-stability and control measurements. Flights then halted until the fall.[49] A limited number of additional flights were still necessary to collect lateral control effectiveness data and to obtain an angle-of-attack calibration. McKay made these on October 19, 20, and 24, 1955. The 134th and final NACA flight was made on October 25 by Neil A. Armstrong. During the pilot check flight, a landing gear door separated. Armstrong landed safely, but the aircraft never flew again.[50] The X-5 was put into storage for the next several years. In March 1958, it was sent to the U.S. Air Force Museum at Wright-Patterson Air Force Base. The aircraft was subsequently restored and now is on display in the museum's Research and Development Gallery.[51]

As the X-5 flights were winding down, the final set of research memorandums on the project was completed, reviewed, and approved. The first of these, which dealt with wing loads at a sweep angle of 58.7°, stated:

> Flight measurements on the Bell X-5 research airplane at a sweep angle of 58.7° have shown the wing loads exhibit nonlinear trends over the angle-of-attack range from zero to maximum wing lift. These nonlinearities were, in general, more pronounced at angles of attack above the "pitch-up" where there is a reduction in the wing-panel lift-curve slope and an inboard and forward movement in the center of load. These characteristics have been found to exist in the results of wind-tunnel tests of swept wings and emphasize the need of model testing for accurate wing design data when nonlinearities exist.
>
> No apparent effects of altitude on the wing loads were evident over the comparable lift ranges of these tests at altitudes from 40,000 to 15,000 feet.[52]

The second memorandum looked at the loads on the X-5's horizontal tail. Its conclusions read:

> An investigation of the horizontal-tail loads on the Bell X-5 research airplane at a sweep angle of 58.7° has indicated that the horizontal-tail loads are nonlinear with lift throughout the lift

ranges tested at all Mach numbers except at a Mach number of approximately 1.00. The balancing tail loads reflected changes which occur in the wing characteristics with increasing angle of attack. The nonlinearities of the horizontal-tail loads were generally more pronounced at the higher angles of attack near the pitch-up where the balancing tail loads indicate that the wing-fuselage combination becomes unstable.

No apparent effects of altitude on the balancing tail loads were evident over the comparable lift ranges of these tests at altitudes from 40,000 feet to 15,000 feet.

Comparisons of balancing tail loads obtained from flight and wind-tunnel tests indicated discrepancies in absolute magnitudes, but the general trends of the data agree. Some differences in absolute magnitude may be accounted for by the tail load carried inboard of the strain-gage station and the load induced on the fuselage by the presence of the tail. These loads were not measured in flight.[53]

Research with the X-5 was primarily focused on longitudinal and lateral stability and control. Most of the research flights were made for these purposes, and the resulting research memorandums were both lengthy and detailed. One such memorandum noted:

An investigation of the dynamic stability of the X-5 research airplane at 58.7° sweepback at altitudes of 40,000 feet and 25,000 feet over a Mach number range of 0.5 to 0.97 shows the following: The longitudinal motions were well damped over the entire Mach number range tested except for residual oscillations resulting principally from engine gyroscopic coupling with the lateral oscillatory mode. This engine gyroscopic coupling results in motion on both the longitudinal and lateral oscillatory modes for either a longitudinal or lateral disturbance. The lateral oscillatory mode exhibits moderately good damping except for nonlinear damping characteristics above a Mach number of 0.80 where the motion is well damped at large amplitudes and poorly damped for double amplitude sideslip angles less than 2°. Small inadvertent aileron control motions often produced apparently undamped small amplitude oscillations in the Mach number range above 0.80.[54]

Another memorandum expanded on this, describing lateral-stability issues such as roll coupling, pitching characteristics aggravated by directional divergence and aileron overbalance, an abrupt wing-dropping tendency, wing heaviness, and rudder flutter. Direction divergence, for example, meant the X-5 had suddenly entered a sideslip of 25°, resulting in a spin. The memorandum also noted, "The problem of aileron overbalance occurred less frequently but was no less disconcerting to the pilot because the stick would jerk from side to side unless restrained."[55]

Perhaps the most damning criticism of the airplane was reserved for the section "Pilots' Impressions," which made clear the demands of flying the X-5 (emphasis added):

> The X-5 airplane at 58.7° sweepback is considered to have the least desirable lateral stability and control characteristics *of any of the airplanes tested*, including straight-wing, swept-wing, semitailless, and delta-wing configurations. One pilot, while checking out in the X-5 airplane, *discontinued a speed run at M = 0.85 and an altitude of 35,000 feet because he strongly doubted his ability to keep the airplane right side up.*[56]
>
> The outstanding deficiency of the X-5 airplane is the lateral-directional oscillation or "Dutch roll" caused by the high positive dihedral effect. This oscillation is annoying but tolerable for research flying over the entire speed range at 40,000 feet, except over the range of M = 0.86 to M = 0.88 where the residual, small amplitude, virtually undamped oscillation is most noticeable. The dihedral effect decreases with a decrease of altitude but never reaches a satisfactory value. The airplane exhibits positive lateral stability during sideslip maneuvers and requires large aileron deflections for small rudder deflections; however, it is impossible to maintain a steady sideslip without rolling oscillations. Normal turning maneuvers tend to be jerky with abrupt increases and decreases of bank angle, apparently caused by small yawing motions and angle-of-attack changes. In straight and level flight, lateral-directional oscillations can be initiated by control motions, power changes, or turbulent air.
>
> The aileron effectiveness is low at all Mach numbers and, except for the adverse dihedral effects in some conditions, the rolling characteristics are normal with rolling velocities proportional to aileron deflection and increase as Mach number increases. The rolling characteristics improve with decrease of altitude, but maximum rolling velocity is limited because of the excessive force necessary to obtain large aileron deflections. Near the 1g stall there is little or no lateral control and nearly zero stick force.[57]

An Assessment

The X-5 left a mixed legacy. Like its progenitor, the Messerschmitt P.1101, the aircraft was flawed, with poor stability and vicious stall/spin behavior that cost the life of one of its pilots. At the same time, while the wing-sweeping mechanism used on the X-5 was impractical, the aircraft had proven the basic fundamental value of in-flight variable wing sweeping (in contrast to the X-4, whose stability problems had proven the semi-tailless configuration impractical in the pre-fly-by-wire era). Additionally, because it could vary its sweep, researchers gained a wide range of data on wing-sweep at various angles; NACA test pilot Scott Crossfield memorably recalled that having the X-5 was like "having a whole stable of swept-wing airplanes in one."[58] Absent the X-5, collecting such a quantity and variety of data would have required multiple aircraft with different wings.

Though the X-5, despite its stability problems, had demonstrated that the concept of variable-sweep wings was workable, manufacturers were slow to embrace the idea of variable-sweep wings, in part because of traditionalist design tendencies, but in large measure because the technology was still immature and not yet ready for practical application. The mechanism needed for the complex wing movements added weight and complexity, and the benefits did not justify this burden.

A lone prototype U.S. fighter was built in the 1950s using variable-sweep wings of a configuration similar to that of the X-5. This was the Grumman XF10F-1 Jaguar, which began flight testing in early 1952. A "shoulder wing" design like the X-5, it, too, used a single pivot point and shifted the wing roots fore and aft, though coupling this with an imaginative delta-wing "flying tail" to help control trim changes. But again like the X-5, it was impractical for routine use. Worse, the XF10F-1 was in any case a thoroughly bad design, plagued by miserable flying qualities and an unreliable engine. These deficiencies, coupled with changes in aircraft carrier design (including the angled deck and mirror landing system and the steam catapult) and better aircraft exemplified by the forthcoming Vought XF8U-1 Crusader, resulted in its termination. The cancellation must have come as a relief to company test pilot Corwin H. "Corky" Meyer, who stated revealingly afterward, "I had never attended a test pilots' school, but for me the XF10F-1 flight test program provided the complete curriculum."[59]

The NACA, and later NASA, played the leading role in transforming the variable-sweep wing concept into a viable configuration.[60] The change came about as the result of a British proposal by famed Vickers corporation designer Barnes Wallis for a supersonic airliner with variable-sweep wings called the "Swallow." Wallis's imaginative study was largely impractical but did incorporate a novel form of pivot location that ultimately hastened the development of practical, operational variable-sweep aircraft. Vickers requested that NASA review the design, and at the behest of John Stack and project engineer Charles Donlan, four different Swallow configurations were eventually tested. Configurations I through III had better stability margins than the X-1 model had shown but were unacceptable. Configuration IV incorporated a different concept for the variable-sweep wing. Unlike on the X-5 and the XF10F-1, the pivot point was outboard of the fuselage, at the extremities of a small, fixed forward wing. The outboard pivot, combined with the geometry of the fixed forward wing, favorably changed the way the aerodynamic load shifted as the wing sweep changed. The means of building a variable-sweep aircraft without the complications of the X-5 or XF10F-1 wing designs was now at hand.[61]

The first U.S. variable-sweep aircraft to enter service was the F-111A, first flown in 1964.[62] It had originally been designed as a strike aircraft for the U.S. Air Force and a fleet air defense interceptor for the Navy. (The Navy version was subsequently canceled.) It was followed by the Navy's F-14 fleet air defense fighter and the Air Force B-1B strategic bomber. The NATO and Saudi air forces operated the Panavia Tornado strike aircraft. The Soviets also operated and exported a number of variable-sweep aircraft, including the MiG-23/27 fighter, the Su-17/22 and Su-24 strike aircraft, and the Tu-22M and Tu-160 strategic bombers. The original Boeing supersonic transport (SST) design also featured variable-sweep wings, though fixed-sweep wings replaced these during the design process. (The American SST project ended in 1971 when Congress withdrew the funding.)

But variable-sweep wings subsequently proved to be of largely transitory value, however, for they added cost and weight to a design and complicated the designer's challenge in the era of stealth. Today, while "legacy" variable-sweep aircraft such as the B-1B and Tu-160 remain in service, few designers look to them as viable options for future aircraft. As Richard P. Hallion noted in 2010:

> On the whole, the variable-geometry wing has not enjoyed the kind of widespread success that its adherent hoped. While it may be expected that, from time to time, variable-sweep aircraft will be designed and flown for particular purposes, overall the fixed conventional planform, outfitted with all manner of flaps and slats and blowing, sucking, and perhaps even warping technology, continues to prevail.[63]

Endnotes

1. Opening quote from Crossfield and Blair, *Always Another Dawn*, p. 155.
2. The best survey of the advent and significance of variable sweep is Robert L. Perry's *Innovation and Military Requirements: A Comparative Study*, RAND Report RM-5182PR (Santa Monica, CA: The RAND Corporation, 1967). See also Richard P. Hallion, "Sweep and Swing: Reshaping the Wing for the Jet and Rocket Age," in Richard P. Hallion, ed., *NASA's Contributions to Aeronautics*, vol. 1: *Aerodynamics, Structures, Propulsion, Controls*, NASA SP-2010-570-Vol 1 (Washington, DC: NASA, 2010), pp. 57–64; and James R. Hanson, *The Bird Is on the Wing: Aerodynamics and the Progress of the American Airplane* (College Station, TX: Texas A&M University Press, 2004), p. 123.
3. NACA-NASA interest in variable-sweep wings is documented in NASA Langley Research Center, "Summary of NACA/NASA Variable-Sweep Research and Development Leading to the F-111 (TFX)," NASA LRC Working Paper LWP-285, 1966; and Edward C. Polhamus and Thomas A. Toll, "Research Related to Variable Sweep Aircraft Development," NASA TM 83121, 1981, pp. 5–6. For the earliest example of oblique-wing wind tunnel testing, see John P. Campbell and Hubert M. Drake, "Investigation of Stability and Control Characteristics of an Airplane Model with Skewed Wing in the Langley Free-Flight Laboratory," NACA TN No. 1208, May 1947.
4. Charles J. Donlan and William C. Sleeman, "Low-Speed Wind-Tunnel Investigation of the Longitudinal Stability Characteristics of a Model Equipped with a Variable-Sweep Wing," RM L9B18, May 23, 1949.
5. Hanson, *The Bird Is on the Wing*, p. 123; Donlan and Sleeman, "Low-Speed Wind-Tunnel Investigation," pp. 1, 3, 8; Jay Miller, *The X-Planes: X-1 to X-45* (Hinckley, U.K.: Midland Publishing, 2001), pp. 87–88.
6. Hanson, *The Bird Is on the Wing*, p. 124; Miller, *The X-Planes: X-1 to X-45*; Bell Aircraft Corporation, "Bell X-5 Ready For Flight Tests," for release June 14, 1951.
7. John T. Rogers and Angel H. Dunn, "Preliminary Results of Horizontal-Tail Load Measurements of the Bell X-5 Research Airplane," NACA RM L52G14 (August 15, 1952), p. 4; Donald R. Bellman, "Lift and Drag Characteristics of the Bell X-5 Research

Airplane at 59° Sweepback for Mach Numbers from 0.60 to 1.03," NACA RM L53A09c (February, 17, 1953), p. 7. It should be noted that reports and documents frequently give X-5 wing-sweep angles of 59° or 60°. This was apparently rounding up, rather than an actual modification to the wings.

8. Bell Aircraft Corporation, "Bell X-5 Ready for Flight Tests," press release.

9. Data from Jack Nugent, "Lift and Drag of the Bell X-5 Research Airplane in the 45° Sweptback Configuration at Transonic Speeds," NACA RM H56E02 (July 11, 1956), Table I, pp. 10–11.

10. The Air Force role in developing the X-5 is minutely and definitively detailed in Warren E. Green's *The Bell X-5 Research Airplane* (Wright-Patterson AFB, OH: Wright Air Development Center, March 1954).

11. Miller, *The X-Planes: X-1 to X-45*, p. 89.

12. See Perry's *Innovation and Military Requirements: A Comparative Study*.

13. Memorandum for Chief of Research, "Progress Report of Engineering and Instrumentation for the X-5 Airplane During the Period August 25 to September 7, 1951."

14. Thomas W. Finch and Donald W. Biggs, "Preliminary Results of Stability and Control Investigation of the Bell X-5 Research Airplane," NACA RM L52K18b (February 11, 1953), p. 4.

15. Memorandum for Chief of Research, "Progress Report of Engineering and Instrumentation for the X-5 Airplane During the Period December 1 to December 14, 1951."

16. Memorandum for Chief of Research, "Progress Report of Engineering and Instrumentation for the X-5 Airplane During the Period December 15, 1951 to December 28, 1951."

17. Memorandum for Chief of Research, "Progress Report of Engineering and Instrumentation for the X-5 Airplane During the Period December 29, 1951 to January 11, 1952."

18. Hallion and Gorn, *On the Frontier*, p. 402 (quoting flight records).

19. Rogers and Dunn, "Preliminary Results of Horizontal-Tail Load Measurements of the Bell X-5 Research Airplane," pp. 8–9.

20. Crossfield and Blair, *Always Another Dawn*, p. 155.

21. Ibid.

22. Hallion and Gorn, *On the Frontier*, pp. 47–48.

23. Memorandum for Chief of Research, "Progress Report for the X-5 Research Airplane for the Period May 3 to May 16, 1952."

24. Memorandum for Chief of Research, "Progress Report for the X-5 Research Airplane for the Period July 12 to July 25, 1952"; James

A. Martin, "Longitudinal Flight Characteristics of the Bell X-5 Research Airplane at 59° Sweepback with Modified Wing Root," NACA RM L53E28 (August, 10, 1953), p. 1.

25. Memorandum for Chief of Research, "Progress Report for the X-5-1 Research Airplane for the Period July 26 to August 8, 1952."

26. Memorandum for Chief of Research, "Progress Report for the X-5-1 Research Airplane for the Period October 1 to November 1, 1952."

27. Ibid. At the time, 7.33 g's was the Air Force loads design standard.

28. Hallion and Gorn, *On the Frontier*, p. 403 (flight records).

29. De Elroy Beeler, Acting Chief, NACA High Speed Flight Research Station, to NACA Liaison Officer, Wright Patterson Air Force Base, "Preliminary Investigation of Handling the X-5 Airplane Below Minimum Drag in Close Proximity with Other Aircraft," March 5, 1953, and Joseph A. Walker, NACA HSFRS, "Investigation of Flight at Speeds Below Minimum Drag, Flight No. 60," January 27, 1953, p. 1, DFRC Archives. These tests were not an investigation specifically into wingtip vortices. Later, pilots and engineers would realize that the wingtip vortices from a jumbo jet could cause a smaller airplane to lose control and crash during a landing approach. This led to increases in separation between aircraft on final approach.

30. Joseph A. Walker, NACA HSFRS, "Investigation of Flight at Speeds Below Minimum Drag, Flight No. 60," January 27, 1953, p. 1, DFRC Archives.

31. Joseph A. Walker, NACA HSFRS, "Investigation of Flight at Speeds Below Minimum Drag, Flight No. 61," January 29, 1953, p. 1, DFRC Archives.

32. Ibid.

33. Joseph A. Walker, NACA HSFRS, "Investigation of Flight at Speeds Below Minimum Drag, Flight No. 63," February 6, 1953, p. 1, DFRC Archives. Aerial refueling became a standard practice in both the Air Force and Navy. In particular, aerial refueling had become critical to Strategic Air Command operations within a few years of the X-5 tests. Aerial refueling extended the range of bombers and allowed airborne alert missions. Subsequently, tactical aircraft and even transport aircraft were outfitted for aerial refueling.

34. Joan M. Childs, "Flight Measurements of the Stability Characteristics of the Bell X-5 Research Airplane in Sideslips at 59° Sweepback," NACA RM L52K13b (February 11, 1953), pp. 4–5.

35. Donald R. Bellman, "Lift and Drag Characteristics of the Bell X-5 Research Airplane at 59° Sweepback for Mach Numbers from 0.60 to 1.03," p. 8.

36. Donald W. Briggs, "Flight Determination of the Buffeting Characteristics of the Bell X-5 Research Airplane at 58.7° Sweepback," NACA RM L54C17 (May 24, 1954), pp. 1, 10–11.

37. Martin, "Longitudinal Flight Characteristics of the Bell X-5 Research Airplane at 59° Sweepback with Modified Wing Root," pp. 6–7.

38. Miller, *The X-Planes: X-1 to X-45*, p. 91; Hallion and Gorn, *On the Frontier*, p. 401 (flight records).

39. USAF, "Report of Major Aircraft Accident—X-5, 50-1839A, Section 0—Description of Accident" (Edwards AFB, CA: AFFTC, October 27, 1953), first page. This section of the accident report has no page numbers. It is typed text on a blank page.

40. Ibid.

41. Ibid., first and second pages.

42. Ibid., second page.

43. Ibid., eighth page.

44. Ibid., ninth page.

45. Ibid., "Accident Board Action Findings, Recommendations," no page number.

46. NASA, Fact Sheet "X-5," *http://www.nasa.gov/centers/dryden/news/FactSheets/FS-081-DFRC_prt.htm*, modified July 3, 2013.

47. Crossfield and Blair, *Always Another Dawn*, pp. 155–156.

48. USAF, "Report of Major Aircraft Accident—X-5, 50-1839A," October 27, 1953, "Remarks Medical Safety Division," no page number.

49. Hallion and Gorn, *On the Frontier*, pp. 402–404 (flight records).

50. Ibid., p. 404. See also Memorandum for Research Aircraft Project Leader, "Progress Report for the X-5-1 Research Airplane for the Period July 1 to July 31, 1955."

51. X-5 Fact Sheet, *http://www.nationalmuseum.af.mil/factsheets/factsheet.asp?id=630* (accessed October 5, 2010).

52. Richard D. Banner, Robert D. Reed, and William L. Marcy, "Wing-Load Measurements of the Bell X-5 Research Airplanes at a Sweep Angle of 58.7°," NACA RM H55A11 (April 5, 1955), p. 8.

53. Robert D. Reed, "Flight Measurements of Horizontal-Tail Loads on the Bell X-5 Research Airplane at a Sweep Angle of 58.7°," NACA RM H55E20a (April 4, 1955), pp. 6–7.

54. Edward N. Videan, "Flight Measurements of the Dynamic Lateral and Longitudinal Stability of the Bell X-5 Research Airplane at 58.7° Sweepback," NACA RM H55H10 (October 6, 1955), p. 1.

55. Thomas W. Finch and Joseph A. Walker, "Flight Determination of the Lateral Handling Qualities of the Bell X-5 Research Airplane at 58.7° Sweepback," NACA RM H56C29 (May 31, 1956), pp. 12–13.

56. Ibid., p. 12.

57. Ibid., p. 13.

58. Crossfield and Blair, *Always Another Dawn*, p. 155.

59. Corwin H. Meyer, *Corky Meyer's Flight Journal: A Test Pilot's Tales of Dodging Disasters—Just in Time* (North Branch, MN: Specialty Press, 2006), p. 216.

60. The NACA, which existed as an agency from 1915 to 1958, gave way to the National Aeronautics and Space Administration (which had a broader mandate encompassing both aeronautics and astronautics) in the reorganization of Federal aerospace taking place after the shock of Sputnik. See Roger D. Launius, "An Unintended Consequence of the IGY: Eisenhower, Sputnik, and the Founding of NASA," AIAA Paper No. 2008-860, 2008; and T. Keith Glennan (edited by J.D. Hunley and in association with Roger D. Launius), *The Birth of NASA: The Diary of T. Keith Glennan*, NASA SP-4105 (Washington, DC: NASA, 1993).

61. Polhamus and Toll, "Research Related to Variable Sweep Aircraft Development," pp. 9–12.

62. Robert W. Kress, "Variable-Sweep Wing Design," AIAA Paper No. 83-1051 (1983) is an excellent survey of this and other efforts.

63. See the previously cited Hallion, "Sweep and Swing: Reshaping the Wing for the Jet and Rocket Age," p. 64.

The XF-92A is shown parked on the lakebed soon after final assembly. The aircraft spent most of its research career in a bare-metal finish. The fuselage was wider at its midpoint than at the nose or tail, which was long the standard design used in high-speed aircraft. (USAF)

CHAPTER 7

Progenitor of the Delta:
The Convair XF-92A

The pilot never really flew that airplane, he corralled it.
—A. Scott Crossfield[1]

The Consolidated-Vultee (Convair) XF-92A was not built as a research airplane but as a flying mockup for a proposed supersonic interceptor, hence its prototype fighter designation. It was not, however, intended as a combat aircraft, and thus it occupies a similar place in research aircraft development as the Bell XP-59A, the first American turbojet, which itself had a fighter designation while actually functioning as a technology demonstrator. Its design evolution shows the ambitious plans of the immediate post–World War II period, the unknowns of supersonic flight, and the impractical concepts proposed to overcome them. From this environment came the birth of the semi-tailless delta-wing aircraft. This configuration would eventually be used by nations around the world in fighters, strike aircraft, reconnaissance airplanes, and bombers, as well as in a pair of supersonic airliners—but it was proven first by the Convair XF-92A.

The Birth of the XF-92A

The war against Imperial Japan had barely ended in the first week of September 1945 when the Army Air Forces announced a design competition for three different fighters: the first was for an all-weather fighter capable of attacking enemy aircraft at night or in bad weather; the second was for a long-range escort fighter to protect bombers; and the third was for a short-range point-defense supersonic interceptor, intended as a last-ditch defense against enemy bombers. This third project became the XP-92. Consolidated-Vultee Aircraft Corporation (CVAC, subsequently Convair) was among potential contractors the Army approached on the three projects. In response, the firm assembled a small design team at their Downey, CA, plant. The team consisted of Jack Irvine, Frank W. Davis, Adolph Burstein (chief of design), Thomas Hemphill, and Ralph H. Shick, chief of aerodynamics.[2]

Out of this team came the Convair Model 7002, later known as the XF-92A. The first challenge the four men faced was the point-defense interceptor's propulsion system. Existing jet engines lacked the thrust necessary for reaching supersonic speeds, and rocket engines lacked sufficient burn time to take off, climb to altitude, engage an enemy bomber, and land. As a result, engineers came up with a hybrid propulsion system that used a ramjet combined with an auxiliary jet engine, similar to that employed a decade later on the French Mach 2+ Nord 1500-02 Griffon II experimental fighter. Several ducted rocket motors were mounted within the XP-92's ramjet both to provide thrust and to act as igniters and flame holders. The auxiliary jet engine was fitted in the aft fuselage for the return to base and landing.

The initial XP-92 airframe design featured a cylindrical fuselage, large swept wings, and a V-tail. The wing sweep was 35° on the leading edge. The Consolidated-Vultee design was submitted to the Army Air Forces, where it was selected for development in May 1946. The first step in refining the design involved wind tunnel testing. These tests showed a number of problems. The wing suffered from tip stall at angles of attack as low as 5°, as well as poor lateral control characteristics. The design team set to work modifying the XP-92 configuration.

Replacing the V-tail with a conventional design resolved some of the stability problems, but the wings required more work. The Convair design team looked at wing slots, fences, and gloves as possibilities. The solution proved far simpler. The wing's trailing edge was changed to a straight line, making the wing a 45° triangle rather than a conventional swept wing. This was the first time the shape had been used on a jet aircraft. The design was further refined to a pure 60° delta wing in a series of July 1946 wind tunnel tests.[3]

The adaptation of a delta wing for the XP-92 thus was a byproduct of swept-wing refinement, not a choice from the outset based on theoretical work or emulation, despite NACA research aerodynamicist Robert T. Jones's having enunciated the thin, sharply swept delta more than a year previously.[4] More importantly, in contrast to popular myth, the XP-92 (and the XF-92A and, for that matter, all subsequent Convair delta aircraft) owed nothing to the work of German aerodynamicist Alexander Lippisch, who had designed the Me 163 and who had conceived a very thick-wing 60° delta glider, the Lippisch DM-1, intended as a low-speed test bed for a proposed ramjet-powered delta-wing fighter, the P.13. The Convair team rejected his concept of a delta wing, which envisioned a very thick wing with a very thick vertical fin (in contrast, the delta wing that they chose had—for its time—a very thin 6.5-percent thickness-chord ratio). Lippisch's DM-1 had more than twice the thickness-chord ratio

Another early photo of the XF-92A. The canopy was considered problematic by pilots because the framework hampered visibility. The sensitivity of the flight-control system, which required a light touch by pilots, also presented difficulties. (USAF)

of the XP-92, and its vertical fin was so large that the pilot sat within it, the clear cockpit windscreen being formed by its leading edge. More significantly, when the DM-1 glider was tested in Langley's Full-Scale Tunnel in 1946, the results were "very disappointing; the lift coefficient was low, the drag was high, the directional stability was unsatisfactory, and the craft was considered unsafe for flight tests."[5] The Convair thin-wing approach was altogether more satisfactory, and for it, Convair's XP-92 design team deserves great—and sole—credit.

Model 7002—From Flying Mockup to Research Airplane

The final design of the XP-92 was striking, with the 60° delta wing, a triangular vertical fin, and a tubular fuselage that extended well behind the fin.[6] The cockpit was in a bullet-shaped nose mounted within the circular ramjet-intake duct. In the event of an emergency, the forward fuselage could be jettisoned as an escape capsule in a manner reminiscent of the D-558-1 and -2. After separation, a parachute would slow the capsule, and the pilot would then bail

A research aircraft in wolf's clothing. During the Air Force test program, the XF-92A was painted in bogus Soviet markings as a "MiG 23" for the movie *Jet Pilot*. The aircraft apparently did not appear in the final film. (USAF)

out using his own parachute. Ironically, the airplane, which resembled a craft straight out of the world of Buck Rogers, was armed with conventional weapons—four 20-millimeter cannons.

The new design retained the rocket-augmented ramjet engine. Because a ramjet must be in flight before it can produce thrust, a set of eight 1,500-pound-thrust rockets, burning liquid oxygen and alcohol/water, would be used for the takeoff. The XP-92 did not make use of conventional landing gear for takeoff but rather was mounted on an eight-wheel cart containing the liquid-oxygen and alcohol/water tanks necessary for the takeoff run. Once the plane lifted off, a pair of large wing drop tanks supplied the fuel to boost the XP-92 to a top speed of Mach 1.65.

At that point, 16 50-pound ducted rockets fueled by liquid oxygen and gasoline and mounted inside the ramjet ignited. The rockets started the ramjet and stabilized the flame within the ramjet combustion chamber. The ramjet increased the airplane's speed to Mach 1.75 at 50,000 feet, speed and altitude that could be maintained for 5.4 minutes. The XP-92 was designed as a last-ditch/point-defense interceptor to destroy high-speed bombers and cruise missiles before they could reach their target. Once the mission was complete, the XP-92 would fly back using the auxiliary jet to land on a runway with its tricycle landing gear.

A full-scale metal mockup of the XP-92 was built, but Army Air Forces personnel had already begun to have doubts about its design. The rocket-augmented ramjet engine was seen as too complex for use in a near-term project, and the sled launch system seriously limited its utility. Other doubts were raised about Convair's proposed hydraulic-powered, nonreversible control system, and weight increases had reduced performance. Even if these issues could be dealt with, the Air Force was in the midst of postwar budget cuts, and the number of personnel and aircraft were at a low point. No funding was available for so advanced and risky a concept as the XP-92. The interceptor program ended in June 1948.

But construction of the subscale demonstrator went ahead, for it had value even if completely separated from the futuristic interceptor program that had spawned it. The research aircraft that eventually became the XF-92A originated in meetings between Air Force and Convair personnel in September 1946. Building a subscale transonic test vehicle would provide data on the behavior of the delta wing at low and high speeds. Delta wings offered a number of advantages, including large wing area, a thin airfoil cross section, and a low aspect ratio. In addition, the wings were light in weight relative to their surface area while being very strong, an added benefit in any aircraft design.

On November 7, 1946, the Army Air Forces contract with Convair was amended. Two XP-92 prototypes were to be built. In addition, a single Model 7002 would be constructed to test the wing and tail configuration. The Model 7002 that emerged had little in common with the exotic XP-92. The cylindrical fuselage had a small diameter at the nose and tail, but the center section was much larger in diameter to accommodate its centrifugal-flow jet engine. The Model 7002's wing was the same size, airfoil, and configuration as that planned for the XP-92, though its tail fin was larger than the planned interceptor's. To keep development costs down, existing components and systems were used in building the aircraft. The Model 7002 was powered by an Allison J33 jet engine from a Lockheed P-80 and had the canopy and ejection seat from Convair's YP-81, the nose gear of a Bell P-63, the brakes of a Lockheed P-80, the pilot stick and rudder pedals from a Vultee BT-13, and the main landing gear of a North American FJ-1.

But in other ways, the Model 7002 was as exotic as its ramjet-powered predecessor. The Model 7002 had the 100-percent hydraulically powered, non-reversible flight controls that were planned for the XP-92. Because the Model 7002 was a semi-tailless configuration—lacking a conventional horizontal stabilizer—the plane employed elevons combining pitch and roll control, similar to the X-4 then under development. Convair closed its Downey facility in the summer of 1947, as a result of tightening military budgets following the end of World War II, and transferred the unfinished Model 7002 airframe to the company's San Diego facility between June and July. The final assembly of the Model 7002 was completed in San Diego on October 31, 1947. In November, Convair sent the aircraft by Navy cargo ship to San Francisco for wind tunnel testing in the full-size tunnel at the Ames Aeronautical Laboratory. This testing was completed in early January 1948, and the aircraft returned to San Diego for final testing and installation of its J33-A-21 turbojet engine. The completed Model 7002, now designated the XF-92A, was then shipped from the San Diego harbor aboard the Navy landing craft LST-827 and arrived at the harbor in Los Angeles on March 26, 1948. The aircraft was then loaded on a truck and shipped over the San Gabriel Mountains to Muroc Air Force Base, where it arrived on March 31, 1948.[7]

Phase I Flight Tests

Convair's chief test pilot, Ellis D. "Sam" Shannon, started tests of the XF-92A on May 25, 1948, by making high-speed taxi runs across the Rogers lakebed. The first "hop" came on June 9, 1948, during the fifth taxi test. The aircraft reached 10 or 15 feet above the lakebed, and he flew straight for about 2 miles before touching down again. Shannon found the controls were very sensitive to the smallest inputs. Touching the stick and rudder pedals was enough to create control problems. With the first taxi tests and short hop behind them, the team took the XF-92A back to the hangar, where the plane was fitted with a more powerful J33-A-23 jet engine that had water injection to increase thrust. The aircraft resumed taxi tests in September. These were successfully completed, and with the aircraft systems checked out, Shannon could make the first flight.

A delta-wing aircraft model attached to a rocket booster for a high-speed test. Such tests were used for preliminary research on new wing configurations. (NASA)

Shannon made his first actual flight in the XF-92A on September 18, 1948, and it lasted 18 minutes. He found that the hydraulic control system was overly sensitive and had a lag in its control movements. Tiny movements of the stick and rudder pedals caused the XF-92A to wallow in all three axes, he told engineers following the flight. During a second flight, on September 29, he found the same conditions. After another flight, on October 13, the XF-92A was grounded through November 1948 while the ground crew harmonized its flight controls.

Testing resumed once sufficient modifications had been made, and by the end of 1948, Shannon had made a total of 10 flights. A second Convair test pilot, Bill Martin, joined the Phase I test effort, making his first taxi test on December 21, 1948. Martin's first flight was on February 9, 1949. The contractor flights initially focused on general handling qualities and performance.

An unusual characteristic of the XF-92A that the pilots quickly identified was its remarkable low-speed stability. Shannon discovered to his surprise that even with the indicated airspeed below 90 mph and the angle of attack as high as 30°, the aircraft would not stall. This was due to the delta wing's lack of an abrupt break in its lift curve at the stall. Instead, the XF-92A exhibited a stabilized high sink rate due to the increase in drag. This loss of altitude continued despite the use of full throttle.

Another unusual characteristic was that the aircraft would not spin. Tests of a model in the Langley spin tunnel had indicated that if the Model 7002's center of gravity was between 24 and 29 percent of the mean aerodynamic chord, a spin was impossible. By August 1949, the Phase I tests moved to transonic flights. To reach these speeds, the pilots had to put the underpowered XF-92A into steep dives. In the end, neither pilot exceeded Mach 0.925, as the nonafterburning J33 could not power the XF-92A through the speed of sound. Phase I tests ended on August 26, 1949, after a total of 47 flights by Shannon and Martin.

With the contractor flights completed, the Air Force now began Phase II flights. The two pilots assigned to the tests were Captain Charles E. Yeager and Major Frank Everest. Phase II flights began on October 13, 1949, and concluded on December 28. The two pilots completed a total of 25 flights and were highly enthusiastic about the little delta. The Phase II flights also included very steep dives attempting to reach speeds slightly above Mach 1. Even assisted by a dive, however, the J33-A-23 engine lacked sufficient thrust to reach Mach 1. Despite this, Everest was impressed with the aircraft. He later noted, "We found that the delta planform handled very well during the transition from subsonic to supersonic speed, in comparison with the straight-wing F-94 and the swept-wing F-86, which encountered severe buffet and loss of control effectiveness in this speed range."[8]

While Phase II flights were underway, the Air Force issued a contract to Convair to replace the J33-A-23 engine with an afterburner-equipped J33-A-29 engine and lengthen the aft fuselage. This would increase the available thrust with afterburner to 7,500 pounds, compared to the 4,250 pounds with water injection available with the J33-A-23. Convair engineers estimated that the XF-92A's level speed would be increased to Mach 0.98, higher than the maximum dive speed with the J33-A-23 engine. Moreover, the maximum dive speed would be Mach 1.2. To improve visibility for the photo-tracking cameras, the XF-92A's bare metal exterior was also painted white. Original plans called for Yeager to make a ferry flight of the XF-92A from Edwards to Convair's San Diego facility. Yeager took off on May 12, 1950, but suffered an engine failure requiring an immediate emergency landing on the lakebed. The aircraft was not damaged but had to be taken south by truck. The aircraft spent the next 14 months in San Diego undergoing the engine change. The XF-92A did not return to Edwards until July 1951, and Yeager made the first flight with the new engine on July 20.

Yeager and Everest now embarked on a second series of flights to evaluate the XF-92A's performance with the new engine, which proved to be a disappointment. They found that the afterburner would flame out above 38,000 feet, and the J33-A-29's increased thrust failed to raise the aircraft's Mach

The XF-92A in flight over a cloud deck late in the Air Force test flight program. The airplane had been painted white, as had other X-planes, to allow the aircraft to be photo-tracked against the dark blue desert sky. The dark orange or dark red finishes originally used on the X-1 and the D-558-1 Skystreak were difficult to spot against the dark sky. (USAF)

number. In fact, the XF-92A's performance was not better than it had been with the J33-A-23 engine. To compound matters, while the J33-A-23 engine had few maintenance issues, the J33-A-29 was beset by reliability problems. Completing the initial 18 flights of the power plant demonstration program required six engine changes.

Problem areas included the fuel control system, the improper sequencing of the afterburner, and the backward flow of the turbine cooling air. The last issue resulted in molten metal in the aft compressor inlet, which triggered fire warning lights in the afterburner and faulty turbine wheel seal clearances.[9]

Despite the unreliable engine, Yeager and Everest made 10 research flights in the XF-92 by the end of the year. Peak altitude achieved with the aircraft was 41,443 feet on August 8, 1952, and the top speed was Mach 1.01 on February 2, 1953. The only serious failure occurred on September 14, 1951, when the engine suffered a turbine failure shortly after takeoff, forcing an emergency landing. The aircraft was repaired and test flights resumed. Another 11 flights were made in 1952 before the Air Force flights ended.[10]

Initial Results

As they had with earlier contractor and Air Force test flights of research aircraft, NACA personnel wrote research memorandums on the XF-92A's handling and flight qualities. The NACA had access to the data collected and conducted the data reduction and analysis. From this, the XF-92A's characteristics were determined. The first of these, on preliminary measurements of static longitudinal stability and trim, covered the power plant demonstration flights following the replacement of the original J33-A-23 engine with a J33-A-29 fitted with an afterburner, as well as Air Force performance testing. The flights covered Mach numbers up to 0.75 to 0.97, at altitudes from 11,000 to 40,000 feet. The research memorandum noted:

> The airplane had a stable variation of control angle with speed up to some Mach number between 0.75 and 0.87. A nose-down trim change extended from a Mach number of 0.87 to a Mach number of about 0.93, at which point a nose-up trim change was encountered.
>
> The apparent longitudinal stability was constant up to a Mach number of about 0.75. As the Mach number increased above 0.75 the apparent stability increased rapidly to approximately five times the low-speed value at a Mach number of 0.96. The static longitudinal stability increased threefold as the Mach number

increased from approximately 0.75 to 0.94; this result indicates that most of the increase in apparent stability was caused by an increase in static longitudinal stability.[11]

Air Force Phase II flights tested the XF-92A's performance, and, as a result, no maneuvers were made during Phase II flights specifically to obtain dynamic-stability data. However, several random disturbances occurred that could be analyzed to identify dynamic longitudinal-stability characteristics. The situation was complicated by the fact that under certain flight conditions, pilots observed "undesirable lateral and longitudinal oscillations" during this stage of the flights.[12] NACA researchers thought these could indicate "the possibility of cross coupling between the lateral and longitudinal modes of motion."[13]

To obtain the stability data, two different techniques were used. The first was simple: the period of the oscillations and time it took to damp out the aircraft's motions were measured. The other technique, involving the use of a Reeves Electronic Analog Computer (REAC), represented a glimpse of the future. The actual control deflections were used as the REAC input. A solution, in the form of a time history, was produced for a transfer-function equation with a particular set of transfer-function coefficients. The coefficients were varied on each run until the output most nearly matched the actual flight record.

Though the REAC represented an advance in data processing, it was significantly limited by the primitive computer technology of the early 1950s. The effects of trim changes due to Mach number and altitude changes were not included in the calculations. Agreement was considered good between the period and static-stability measurements acquired using the two methods, though there were differences in the time and cycles needed to damp and in the damping factor. These differences were thought to be due to such factors as the method of analysis, small control motions during the maneuver, or nonlinear damping.

An example of the analysis and the information that could be determined from it was a time history of an XF-92A dive from 38,000 feet to 34,000 feet at Mach 0.94. The control deflections were small during the dive. The REAC was used to analyze the dive from 2 to 16 seconds, using only the longitudinal control inputs. The REAC calculations showed good agreement with actual flight data. From this, the NACA researchers concluded that no serious coupling was occurring between lateral and longitudinal modes, as the aircraft underwent both lateral and longitudinal motion. (An earlier concern had been raised over the possibility that the XF-92A's lateral and longitudinal motions were coupled, indicating major stability problems.)[14]

After Phase II flights were completed, several Air Force test pilots made familiarization flights in the XF-92A. These included Colonel Albert Boyd,

Major Jack Ridley, Captain J.E. Wolfe, Captain Arthur "Kit" Murray, and Lieutenant Colonel Richard L. Johnson. After one landing, Colonel Boyd, the Edwards base commander at the time, was asked by Shannon, "Colonel, didn't you find the airplane a little sensitive laterally?" Boyd replied, "No, not sensitive, but if I find the guy that didn't show me where the lateral trim switch is, I'll shoot him. I had to hold five pounds pressure on the stick for the whole flight, and my arm is about to fall off."[15]

Following XF-92A tests with the J33-A-29 engine, the Air Force test team noted that, "Since the XF-92A was designed purely as a research airplane and never intended for operational use, the aircraft systems, maintenance, and accessibility were not stressed in the design."[16] The Air Force report also stated that "the 'delta-wing' configuration exhibits characteristics that could be used advantageously in future Air Force tactical aircraft." Given the advantages shown by the delta wing, the report recommended improvements for a new delta-wing aircraft:

- Install a higher rated power plant in conjunction with the design of a more efficient inlet duct
- Improve the centering and breakout forces of the power control system
- Improve the over-sensitivity of the longitudinal and lateral control system
- Improve the directional stability characteristics and decrease the excessive dihedral effect (the rolling moment of an aircraft due to sideslip)
- Decrease the high side forces produced by the vertical tail being located too near the airplane's center of gravity
- Improve the poor low-speed flying characteristics during approach and landing
- Modify the directional control system to eliminate the trim changes caused by a change in temperature
- Improve directional control on the ground and cross-wind handling characteristics by increasing the landing gear tread and the wheel size
- Improve general ground handling characteristics and reduce landing ground roll by installation of an adequate brake system
- Improve forward visibility at high angles of attack
- Improve the restricted visibility resulting from the "greenhouse" canopy
- Relocate the landing gear position relative to the center of gravity to eliminate tail heaviness on the ground
- Redesign the aft fuselage to permit engine accessibility for maintenance

- Redesign the landing gear control system for easier operation by the pilot
- Install an improved hydraulic system[17]

Crossfield Flies the First Delta

The final three flights of the Air Force power plant demonstration program were completed in early 1953. Crossfield and the NACA engineers then began a separate series of research flights. The NACA personnel were eager to try out the new wing configuration. They were also aware of the aircraft's shortcomings, in particular, those of the J33-series engines. One of the first things ground personnel did was replace the J33-A-29 jet with an afterburner-equipped J33-A-16 engine capable of producing a maximum thrust of 8,600 pounds. The modification gave the XF-92A a lengthened tail cone enclosing the afterburner.

Crossfield was named NACA project pilot, and his introduction to the aircraft was not encouraging. Crossfield had a "first flight jinx"; he always seemed to have difficulties on his first flight of a new airplane, and the XF-92A "hop" was no exception. Pete Everest was originally scheduled to make the final Air Force flight before the XF-92A was turned over to the NACA. The XF-92A was towed out onto the lakebed and pointed into the wind. But the wind shifted and quickly grew too strong, so the final Air Force flight was canceled. Crossfield and Everest were meeting with Williams at the time, and Williams suggested that Crossfield taxi the airplane back to the NACA hangar at the main base and lift it off the lakebed to get a feel for its handling. Crossfield agreed.

He climbed into the XF-92A, started the engine, closed the canopy, and began a fast taxi toward the main base. The XF-92A was heavy with fuel and wobbled into the air. By this time, the lakebed shoreline was fast approaching. Crossfield pulled back on the stick to raise the nose and slow the airplane. The decrease in speed was only slight, and he thought the XF-92A was going to hit a sand dune and be destroyed. Crossfield then spotted a dirt road heading into the desert and pressed the left brake to turn the aircraft toward it. The brake seized up, then failed, but not before turning the aircraft toward the road. When the XF-92A reached the road, the tires burst, but the airplane continued straight ahead. After about a hundred yards, it came to a stop. Crossfield triggered the fire extinguishers and jumped out. Crossfield and the XF-92A were unharmed. The dirt road was promptly, if unofficially, dubbed "Crossfield Pike."[18]

The NACA XF-92A research effort involved 25 flights focused on two areas. The first 15 flights would collect the stability and control characteristics of the basic aircraft design. The subsequent 10 flights would then look at the

The XF-92A in the desert after Crossfield's first high-speed taxi test. The dirt road was soon named "Crossfield Pike." The aircraft sustained only minor damage. (NASA)

effectiveness of wing fences positioned at 60 percent of the wing semispan. Data on drag; static longitudinal, lateral, and directional stability and control; buffeting; wing loads; and airfoil section characteristics would be obtained both with and without the fences.[19]

Crossfield made his first XF-92A flight on April 9, 1953, for pilot checkout and static longitudinal-stability data. He then flew the airplane three times in April, including one flight that reached the highest altitude by an NACA pilot in the airplane—41,364 feet. Following one flight in May, the research program hit its stride. A total of eight flights were made between June 3 and June 24 and included the fastest NACA XF-92A flight, which reached Mach 0.962. All these flights were made for longitudinal-stability and control data. The procedure was to make sideslips, aileron rolls, and rudder pulses at altitudes from 18,000 to 30,000 feet at indicated airspeeds of 160 to 420 mph.

In the case of the rudder pulses, Crossfield stabilized the aircraft at the planned test speed and altitude and then made an abrupt pulse of the rudder while the other control surfaces were held in a fixed position until the aircraft returned to stabilized flight. Test maneuvers were done in both a clean configuration and with landing gear down. The month's final flight, on June 26, was for low-speed stability and control data.[20]

After that, the aircraft was grounded to undergo the installation of the wing fences. Wing fences had been installed on the D-558-2 as one of several potential cures for pitch-up. The fence itself was simple, running from the wing's front edge back to the 60-percent chord. The leading and trailing edges of the fence were fairing curves.[21]

The first two flights made with the fences installed took place on July 3. The fences were then modified and reinstalled on the XF-92A, which was again flown on July 22. The changes proved unsuccessful; one of the fences buckled under the flight stresses. Following the incident, the aircraft remained grounded for nearly a month. Crossfield took the airplane aloft on August 17, but the engine suffered a malfunction and forced the research flight to be cut short.

In contrast to the long delays the Air Force endured during test flights, the engine problem was repaired in 3 days and the XF-92A was back in the air on August 20. Crossfield made two flights that day, both for longitudinal-stability and control data with the modified fences.

Not until September 30 did the aircraft again go aloft. The two flights on this date marked the start of flights to collect data on the airplane's low-speed lateral and directional control with the original wing fences. Two more flights followed with the same research goals, on October 2 and October 5. The fences were removed as the research program drew to a close. The earlier test maneuvers were repeated to identify what effects the fences had on the aircraft's low-speed lateral and directional control.

A pair of flights was made on October 14, 1953. At the end of the second mission, Crossfield touched down on the lakebed. As the XF-92A rolled out, the nose landing gear collapsed. The aircraft ground-looped and came to a stop on its nose and one wingtip. Once Crossfield was sure the aircraft would not tip over, he climbed out of the airplane. Inspection revealed considerable damage to the nosewheel, forward fuselage, and right wingtip. Taken together, the extent of the damage, the amount of time and money that would have been needed to restore the XF-92A to flight status, and the fact that the research program was nearly complete meant that the aircraft would be grounded permanently.[22]

Even as the XF-92A project ended, the data generated during the NACA research flights were being analyzed. There was quite a bit of information, and because data reduction in that era took time, results were somewhat slow in coming. But come they did. And since the XF-92A was the first delta-wing aircraft from which any data had been collected in flight, what the Air Force and NACA engineers and pilots produced was of considerable value. A 1955 research memorandum on the aircraft's lateral-stability and control characteristics noted:

The static lateral stability characteristics as measured in sideslips appear satisfactory although there is a rapid increase in apparent dihedral effect at the lower speeds. There is adequate rudder power over the entire speed range tested.

The lateral control as measured in aileron rolls appears adequate over the entire speed range tested although there is a considerable reduction in aileron effectiveness at the lower speeds.

The dynamic lateral stability of the airplane was generally in the unsatisfactory region when compared to U.S. Air Force requirements for satisfactory values of reciprocal of cycles to damp to half amplitude and ratio of roll angle to sideslip velocity.

Although the airplane appears to have satisfactory static lateral stability and control characteristics, the pilots object to the overall lateral handling characteristics primarily because of the high roll-to-sideslip ratios which probably resulted from the relatively low static directional stability and relatively high effective dihedral. These adverse characteristics were aggravated at low speeds by high adverse yaw and rough air and at high speeds by high airplane response to small control deflections. The apparent high side force and poor hydraulic control system added to the objectionable characteristics.[23]

The research memorandum also included comments on the control system issue: "Part of the difficulties encountered on the XF-92A may be attributed to the poor hydraulic control system. Evaluation of ground calibration has shown the control system to have high friction and breakout forces and appreciable lag of surface-to-stick motion. These characteristics are particularly objectionable at low speeds where large control deflections are required to maneuver and also at high speeds where the airplane is sensitive to small control displacements."[24]

Though the bulk of the NACA flights had been made for longitudinal- and lateral-stability and control data, the tests of the wing fences proved successful. The research memorandum stated: "Installing wing fences on the airplane improved the handling characteristics at the lower speeds, in the pilots' opinion, probably because of the increase in static directional stability attributed to the fences."[25]

The XF-92A was eventually patched up as a static display for air shows and was later sent to the University of the South, at Sewanee, TN, where it remained until 1969. It was returned to the U.S. Air Force Museum at Wright-Patterson AFB, OH, and thoroughly restored; it is now on display, along with the X-3, X-4, and X-5, in the museum's Research and Development Gallery.[26]

In-flight photo of the XF-92A during one of its NACA flights. The only significant difference in finish was the X's on the nose and tail, which were put on for photo reference. The right wing had tufts attached to the upper surface to make visible changes in the airflow that occurred under different flight conditions. (USAF)

An Assessment

The XF-92A occupies an honored place among the world's pioneering aircraft, but it was not an airplane that was popular with its pilots. An NACA research memorandum noted: "All the pilots who have flown the XF-92A (during the joint NACA-Air Force program and the NACA research program) have reported that the airplane exhibited poor lateral handling characteristics, particularly at low speed."[27] Crossfield later said of the airplane, "It was under-powered, under-geared, under-braked, and overweight." After the gear collapsed on Crossfield's last flight, he noted, "It was finished and no one shed any tears."[28]

At the same time, the potential that the XF-92A represented was clear. The Air Force technical report noted, albeit in understated tones, "The 'delta-wing' configuration exhibits characteristics that could be used advantageously in future tactical aircraft."[29] Yeager was impressed with the high roll rate of the aircraft, which would be useful in a dogfight. He commented, "When I'm doing a maximum rate of roll, it feels like the seat of my pants are pushing down into the seat while at the same time the centrifugal force is pulling my head up toward the canopy."[30] Though Crossfield did not lament the airplane's demise, his Air Force counterparts found elements of it to their liking. And the Air Force itself saw the planform's potential.

On another note, the shortcomings of the XF-92A's control system underscored that the building of a successful supersonic aircraft was not merely an issue of aerodynamics. A proper control system had to provide handling qualities that would allow the pilot to fly his aircraft to its limits rather than struggle against it. Some of the most skilled pilots in America flew the XF-92A, and even they found it a difficult airplane to control in spite of its desirable qualities. It is clear in retrospect that control systems evolved in the same way other aircraft elements did in this new era of aviation and that fits and starts were part of the process.

Of course, the story of delta-wing aircraft development did not end with XF-92A. On October 24, 1953, just 10 days after the XF-92A's final flight, Convair's YF-102 prototype took off from Edwards. The new design was based on what Convair engineers had learned from the XF-92A. The new delta-wing aircraft featured a pointed nose to house the radar system along with side air inlets. The NACA was eager to test the new aircraft and had begun negotiations with the Air Force to receive an early prototype. But like the XF-92A, the YF-102 had its problems. The first prototype

The solution to performance problems that plagued the F-102 was a major redesign of the aircraft. On the top is the original YF-102. Like the XF-92A, it had a fuselage that was widest at the midsection. This produced excessive drag. The solution, developed by Richard T. Whitcomb, was the "area rule." The fuselage was reduced in width, forming a shape referred to as a "Coke-bottle" or "wasp-waist." The production F-102 saw considerable improvement in performance as a result of the modification. (NASA)

Ground photo of the XF-92A during NACA research flights. The poor visibility from the canopy is evident. So is the forward position of the main landing gear, which made the aircraft tail-heavy, and a pole, visible under the aft fuselage, that was necessary to prevent the aircraft from resting on its tail. (USAF)

The YF-102 prototype interceptor was developed using data acquired with the XF-92A. The new interceptor was beset by performance problems and crashed only 9 days after its first flight. (NASA)

crashed on November 2, only 2 weeks after its first flight, and the brief test program was just long enough to demonstrate the design's poor performance.

Test flights with the second YF-102A began on January 11, 1954, and although Convair had expected it, they found that the plane could not exceed Mach 0.98 and had a maximum ceiling of only 48,000 feet, well below the required performance set by the Air Force. The design underwent extensive changes, which included cambered wing leading edges and new wingtips. The wings were also moved farther aft on the fuselage, which itself was lengthened by 11 feet. The vertical fin was also moved aft, and, most important, the center fuselage was redesigned (thanks to NACA research aerodynamicist Richard Whitcomb) with a "Coke-bottle" shape to reduce drag. This last feature represented one of the great breakthroughs made during the early supersonic era.[31]

Two NACA ground personnel with a prototype F-102. The family resemblance between the XF-92A and the F-102 is apparent. Both had a bulky fuselage that resulted in excessive drag and poor performance. (NASA)

Endnotes

1. Opening quotation from Crossfield and Blair, *Always Another Dawn*, p. 167.
2. For the XF-92A's evolution and flight research program, see Richard P. Hallion, "Convair's Delta Alpha," *Air Enthusiast Quarterly* 2 (June 1976): 177; Robert E. Bradley, "The Birth of the Delta Wing," *American Aviation Historical Society* (winter 2003): 243.
3. Hallion, "Convair's Delta Alpha," pp. 177–178; Bradley, "The Birth of the Delta Wing," pp. 245–247.
4. See Hallion, "Lippisch, Gluhareff, and Jones," passim.
5. Letter, Major Howard C. Goodall, USAF, to Paul E. Garber, "DM-1 Glider Disposal," November 28, 1949, in the Gluhareff Dart accession file, Registrar's Office, National Air and Space Museum, Smithsonian Institution, Washington, DC.
6. For details, see Hallion, "Convair's Delta Alpha," passim.
7. Bradley, "The Birth of the Delta Wing," pp. 254–258. The point-defense role would eventually be filled by surface-to-air missiles (SAMs), which provided quicker response and could be built, deployed, and operated far more cheaply than aircraft.
8. Hallion, "Convair's Delta Alpha," p. 181.
9. "High-Speed Flight Research Station: Research Airplane Project Panel 1952 Annual Report," pp. 8–9.
10. Hallion, "Convair's Delta Alpha," pp. 181–182; Bradley, "The Birth of the Delta Wing," p. 259. The following chronology of reports offers some idea of the engine problems faced by the XF-92-A:
    10/3/1951: Installed in airframe.
    10/4–8/1951 Ground runs—would not start on "normal," had to use emergency fuel supply.
    10/10/1951 AF flight 10—afterburner would not light normally.
    10/11/1951 Engine removed—turbine rotor #5-6-7 replaced.
    11/28/1951–1/9/1952 Reinstalled—experienced fuel control problems, changed controls several times/two small fuel fires (no damage).
    1/10/1952 Removed from aircraft—nozzle vanes cracked/diaphragm replaced.
    6/4/1952 AF flight 11—two cracks found in aspirator.
    6/5/1952 AF flight 12—molten metal found in aft impeller area.
    6/9–11/1952 Ground runs—cracks in afterburner.
    6/11/1952 Engine removed from aircraft—cooling air diffuser overheated.

7/18/1952 Test cell run.

7/22/1952–8/5/1952 Installed in airframe/ground runs.

8/6–8/1952 AF flights 13–14

8/15/1952 AF flights 15–16

8/18/1952 Removed from aircraft—air baffles cracked—metal found on aft impeller area.

11. Thomas R. Sisk and John M. Mooney, "Preliminary Measurements of Static Longitudinal Stability and Trim for the XF-92A Delta-Wing Research Airplane in Subsonic and Transonic Flight," NACA RM L53B06 (March 27, 1953), p. 5.

12. Euclid C. Holleman, John H. Evans, and William C. Triplett, "Preliminary Flight Measurements of the Dynamic Longitudinal Stability Characteristics of the Convair XF-92A Delta-Wing Airplane," NACA RM L53E14 (June 30, 1953), p. 1.

13. Ibid., pp. 4–5.

14. Ibid., p. 5.

15. Letter, William F. Chana to James Young, April 4, 2001; "Comments on Derek Horne Convair XF-92A Website," Edwards AFB History Office F-92 file. The quoted text is from the letter.

16. Joseph W. Redd, Jr., Major Charles E. Yeager, and Lieutenant Colonel Frank K. Everest, "Performance Flight Tests of the XF-92A Airplane, USAF S/N 46-682, with a J33-A-29 Power Plant," AFFTC Technical Report No. 53-11, Edwards AFB, CA: Air Force Flight Test Center, 1953, pp. 4–5.

17. Ibid.

18. Crossfield and Blair, *Always Another Dawn*, pp. 165–167. When a pilot was killed in a crash at Edwards Air Force Base, a street was named for the pilot as a memorial. Crossfield was the only living pilot at the time with a street named after him.

19. "High-Speed Flight Research Station: Research Airplane Project Panel 1953 Annual Report," pp. 10–11.

20. Hallion and Gorn, *On the Frontier*, p. 405 (flight records); Thomas R. Sisk and Duane O. Muhleman, "Lateral Stability and Control Characteristics of the Convair XF-92A Delta-Wing Airplane as Measured in Flight," NACA RM H55A17 (May 26, 1955), p. 1; Euclid C. Holleman, "Flight Measurements of the Lateral Response Characteristics of the Convair XF-92A Delta-Wing Airplane," NACA RM H55E26 (August 5, 1955), p. 5.

21. Sisk and Muhleman, "Lateral Stability and Control Characteristics of the Convair XF-92A Delta-Wing Airplane as Measured in Flight," p. 19.

22. "High-Speed Flight Research Station: Research Airplane Project Panel 1953 Annual Report," p. 10; Hallion and Gorn, *On the Frontier*, p. 405 (flight records).

23. Sisk and Muhleman, "Lateral Stability and Control Characteristics of the Convair XF-92A Delta-Wing Airplane as Measured in Flight," p. 12. Other research memorandums on the XF-92A include Clinton T. Johnson, "Flight Measurements of the Vertical-Tail Loads on the Convair XF-92A Delta-Wing Airplane," NACA RM H55H25 (October 27, 1955); and Earl R. Keener and Gareth H. Jordon, "Wing Pressure Distributions over the Lift Range of the Convair XF-92A Delta-Wing Airplane at Subsonic and Transonic Speeds," NACA RM H55G07 (November 30), 1955.

24. Ibid.

25. Ibid.

26. Crossfield and Blair, *Always Another Dawn*, p. 167; Convair XF-92A Fact Sheet, National Museum of the United States Air Force.

27. Sisk and Muhleman, "Lateral Stability and Control Characteristics of the Convair XF-92A Delta-Wing Airplane as Measured in Flight," p. 1.

28. Crossfield and Blair, *Always Another Dawn*, pp. 165, 167.

29. Redd, Yeager, and Everest, "Performance Flight Tests of the XF-92A Airplane, USAF S/N 46-682, with a J33-A-29 Power Plant," p. 4.

30. Fred Stoliker, Bob Hoey, and Johnny Armstrong, *Flight Testing at Edwards: Flight Test Engineers' Stories 1946–1975* (Edwards, CA: Flight Test Historical Foundation, n.d.), pp. 29–30.

31. In late 1949 and early 1950, Langley researchers conducted wind tunnel tests of models of aircraft with swept wings and optimized fuselage shapes. The results were disappointing. The models had a higher total drag than transonic theory had predicted for the combined drag of the fuselage and wings. Richard T. Whitcomb, one of the researchers working on the study, realized he needed to understand the details of the flow fields around different wing/fuselage combinations at transonic speeds. The first clue was found in Schlieren photos, which showed shock waves forming at the model's nose; a second where the wing and fuselage pushed the air out of their way; and a third at the wings' trailing edge. This investigation was followed in November 1951 by another test series focused on measuring the transonic drag caused by interference between the wings and fuselage. Whitcomb drew two conclusions from this series. The first was that even small changes in the shape of the fuselage caused disproportionate changes in the amount of drag. The

second was that the drag from the wings and fuselage was the result of both interacting together and not, as had been assumed, the result of simple addition. In thinking about these conclusions, Whitcomb realized that if the middle of the fuselage were pinched in, the air would flow over the area and would not form the strong shock waves shown in the Schlieren photos.

Convair had learned of the "area rule" and hurriedly applied it to their YF-102A prototype. Whitcomb assisted with the effort. On December 20, 1954, a YF-102A modified with an area-rule fuselage went supersonic without difficulty. The modifications proved successful, and the Air Force accepted its first production F-102A on June 24, 1955. The F-102A showed that a delta-wing aircraft could fulfill the promise hinted at in the XF-92A. These planes were soon followed by Convair's F-106 interceptor and B-58 medium bomber, which were also semi-tailless delta-wing aircraft. Other U.S. semi-tailless delta-wing aircraft were Lockheed's Blackbird family—the A-12, YF-12, M-21, SR-71, and D-21, as well as North American Aviation's XB-70 Valkyrie. France undertook the development of a family of semi-tailless delta-wing aircraft, beginning with the Dassault MD 550 Mirage I test aircraft, the Mirage II and Mirage III fighters, and the Mirage IV strategic bomber (the same sequence of a test aircraft, two fighters, and a bomber that Convair had followed). Another French delta aircraft, the Nord 1500-02 Griffon II, was designed to be a ramjet-powered fighter similar to the original XP-92 concept and, flown by Andre Turcat, successfully demonstrated the concept. British researchers extensively developed deltas, beginning with the Avro Type 707 research aircraft, which served as a flying mockup of the Vulcan delta-wing strategic bomber. The Boulton Paul P.111 and P.120 served as transonic delta-wing research aircraft. The Fairey Delta 2 extended this research to supersonic speeds and, in modified form, influenced the "ogee" wing planform of the Anglo-French Concorde SST, one of only two commercial deltas, which introduced airline passengers to Mach 2 flight. The Soviet Tu-144 also featured a delta wing, of the so-called "double delta" planform. Sweden introduced a remarkably advanced multipurpose fighter, the delta-wing Saab 35 Draken, following this with the JA-37 Viggen and the JAS-39 Gripen. With the end of the Cold War, several air forces now fly the Eurofighter, a combination of a classic semi-tailless delta planform with small canards. Finally, on the horizon are several proposed delta-shaped Unmanned Aerial Vehicles (UAVs), which eliminate the vertical tail. Thus, across a span of six decades, the descendants of the XF-92A fly, marking it as one of the most successful of the NACA's configuration demonstrator X-planes.

Regarding these aircraft, see Bill Gunston, *Early Supersonic Fighters of the West* (New York: Charles Scribner's Sons, 1975); Marcelle Size Knaack, *Post–World War II Fighters 1945–1973* (Washington, DC: Office of Air Force History, 1986); and John W.R. Taylor, *Jane's Pocket Book of Research and Experimental Aircraft* (New York: Collier Books, 1976). Regarding Whitcomb and his "Area Rule," see Richard T. Whitcomb, "A Study of the Zero-Lift Drag-Rise Characteristics of Wing-Body Combinations Near the Speed of Sound," NACA RM L52H08 (September, 3, 1952); Richard P. Hallion, "Richard Whitcomb's Triple Play," *Air Force Magazine* 93, no. 2 (February 2010): 68–72; and Jeremy Kinney, "Richard Whitcomb and the Quest for Aerodynamic Efficiency," in Richard P. Hallion, ed., *NASA's Contributions to Aeronautics*, vol. 1: *Aerodynamics, Structures, Propulsion, Controls*, NASA SP-2010-570-Vol 1 (Washington, DC: NASA, 2010), pp. 89–133.

The third D-558-1 in flight with scattered clouds in the distance and the desert below. The Skystreak did not have the impact the XS-1 had on aviation technology, but it did contribute to the understanding of transonic flight. (NASA)

Round One: A Reflection

The United States research-airplane program has been a fruitful one which resulted in a systematic and orderly approach to extending man's flight capabilities in both the atmosphere and space.
—Kenneth S. Kleinknecht[1]

In the final years of the Second World War, knowledgeable authorities recognized that aviation was poised on the cusp of a revolution. The piston-powered propeller airplane was in decline, the jet was in the ascendant, and the rocket and missile were an uncertain emerging technology. Aircraft were already entering the transonic region, and the ballistic missile had already traversed it and was even nudging the hypersonic. The next clear challenge in piloted, winged flight was the achievement of supersonic flight.

But supersonic flight required a reliable knowledge base, and at this pivotal moment in aeronautical history, the NACA and other Federal institutions lacked the ability to produce it using conventional means. The standard tool of aeronautical research—the wind tunnel—was unable to cope with the distorted flows caused by shock impingement at transonic velocities. Theory was contradictory. Flight experience was replete with examples of aircraft that had already crashed and pilots who had already died in the grips of "compressibility." It was in this environment that the military services, the NACA, and the industry formed a robust partnership to seek a new kind of research tool, one that would use the sky itself as a laboratory—the transonic and supersonic research airplane.

The decade following the initial research flights of the X-1 and D-558-1 was a dynamic period in the history of aviation, arguably exceeded only by the first decade after the invention of the airplane by the Wright brothers in 1903. It marked a great divide between what came before and what came after. When the decade began, jet aircraft represented a new and unreliable technology and Mach 1 seemed to many an unattainable goal. By decade's end, supersonic flight was routine, humanity had placed small satellites in orbit, and space now beckoned. In the same fashion that aviation progressed in the first years after the Wrights, researchers, designers, engineers, and pilots were feeling their way into the supersonic era. Not surprisingly, aircraft of both eras had severe shortcomings in control, handling, stability, and performance.

Years after the First World War, an authentic reproduction of a World War I Sopwith Camel was built and test-flown to see how well the plane flew. By then, designers, engineers, and pilots well understood how an airplane should fly and what handling qualities it should have. The description of the Camel's flight characteristics was telling:

> Once in the air…the pilot is faced with almost total control disharmony. The Camel is mildly unstable in pitch and considerably unstable in yaw, and both elevator and rudder are extremely light and sensitive…the ailerons are in direct and quite awe-inspiring contrast. The Camel…has four enormous…barn doors [for ailerons] which require an equally enormous force to be moved quickly. And when you have moved them, the wing section is so degraded…that the roll response is very slow indeed…. At the same time, aileron drag is quite staggering.[2]

While the wording of NACA research memorandums relating to the Round One research aircraft was not as "colorful," one need only compare this description of the Sopwith Camel to the shortcomings of the X-planes of the early transonic and supersonic era to understand that both were flying into the unknown:

> D-558-1: Landing gear and brake problems, vulnerability of the control cables to damage, an unreliable capsule escape system, nose-heavy above Mach 0.80, wing heaviness at high Mach numbers, rolling-yawing oscillation, and elevator vibrations approaching the maximum load limit.
>
> D-558-2: Long and slow takeoff using the original jet engine and JATO rockets, pitch-up during maneuvers leading to loss of control, poor high-speed stability resulting in uncontrolled rolls, an unreliable capsule escape system, and oscillations during landing.
>
> X-3: Unreliable and underpowered jet engines, tire failures, very high takeoff and landing speeds, failure to reach design performance, flawed control system, and dangerous combined oscillations in flight. The most serious issue was inertial coupling. Walker encountered forces during the inertial coupling flight that reached the fuselage's maximum-load limit. Had they been slightly greater, both plane and pilot would have been lost.
>
> X-4: Severe stability and control issues, flight control problems, jet engine problems, and poor handling at speeds near Mach 1.

X-5: Complexity and weight of the wing-sweep mechanism, undesirable lateral-stability and control characteristics, violent stall/spin characteristics, and slow recovery. The aircraft was so unstable under some conditions that one pilot doubted he could keep it flying right side up.

XF-92A: Overly sensitive longitudinal and lateral controls combined with a lag in the response, unreliable and underpowered engines, poor directional stability, poor low-speed control during approach and landing, and poor brakes.[3]

Indeed, somewhat ironically, having shortcomings proved in some respects to offer an advantage. They allowed the NACA, the Air Force, the Navy, and contractors to anticipate and correct deficiencies before operational aircraft were built using their configurations.

It is well worthwhile, then, to review these aircraft from the point of view of what they contributed:

D-558-1: With a largely similar configuration to the more famous XS-1, this aircraft complemented the results achieved with the X-1. The rocket-powered X-1 provided data at speeds above Mach 1, and the jet-powered D-558-1 covered the high transonic speed range. As a result, the X-1 did not have to make low-speed flights; this accelerated the overall collection of data. Additionally, this aircraft was the first to test vortex generators, which improved wing aerodynamics at transonic speed and became standard on jet aircraft.

D-558-2: Research with this pioneering swept-wing aircraft showed how to avoid the stability problems inherent in these wings, in particular that the horizontal stabilizers should be mounted low on the fuselage. When this aircraft was being designed, all operational U.S. and British jet aircraft had straight wings. Swept wings introduced the potential for much higher performance. The D-558-2 was also used in external stores testing, which allowed combat aircraft to fly at high speeds while carrying streamlined weapons and fuel tanks. Information derived from the D-558-2 program made all swept-wing aircraft that came after it safer and certainly more controllable.

X-3: In terms of performance, this was the biggest disappointment among the early X-planes. It never came close to reaching its design speed of Mach 2 due to its underpowered jet engines. But it did show that low-aspect-ratio wings were practical, and such wings were subsequently used on aircraft such as the F-104, F-5/T-38, and X-15. The X-3's most valuable contribution was to reveal inertial coupling to be anything but theoretical. The fully instrumented X-3 greatly enhanced the NACA's understanding of the phenomenon and was passed to industry as well.

X-4: The semi-tailless swept wing was the only configuration tested in the 1950s that proved impractical. It would be another three decades before computer fly-by-wire systems would make the semi-tailless swept-wing configuration a workable reality, in the first generation of stealth aircraft and in many other aircraft and remotely piloted systems that have followed.

X-5: The aircraft pioneered variable-sweep wings, but at a terrible price. While its wing pivot concept was impractical, it did validate the concept of variable sweep, encouraging further development that spawned the fixed outboard pivot point, used on subsequent aircraft such as the F-111, MiG-23, B-1, F-14, and Tu-160.

XF-92A: This accidental research airplane had more than its share of poor flying characteristics, control system flaws, design shortcomings, and engine deficiencies. Unloved by its pilots, it nevertheless demonstrated the value of the delta-wing configuration, which became one of the iconic planforms of the supersonic—and indeed hypersonic—era. The XF-92A directly led to a notable family of delta successors, and from this sprang as well (though not solely because of it) Richard Whitcomb's concept of area ruling.

The X-series family was generally hailed for its contributions to aeronautical science but was not without some critics. For example, Clarence L. "Kelly" Johnson, head of the famed Lockheed "Skunk Works," dismissed the X-planes as drawing resources and technical effort that could best be focused on the development of practical aircraft designs. But in retrospect it is hard to imagine, given the utter unknowns of supersonic flight, that any wind tunnel or rocket-boosted model tests could alone have produced the volume of data needed to determine which designs would work and which would not. The X-planes also provided practical experience operating exotic aircraft with unfamiliar designs and as-yet-unidentified problems. Had there been no X-planes, designers would have had to try out different configurations on prototype production aircraft. This would have been a waste of time and money and would have interfered with the building of U.S. air power. And despite his public dismissal, Kelly Johnson himself quietly took full advantage of NACA research when he designed the Lockheed F-104. That task would have taken considerably longer and cost much more than it did had the NACA not undertaken X-plane research.[4]

This book has traced the development and significance of seven of those research airplanes. Each had its own distinctive "personality," and each contributed to aeronautical advancement in its own way. While each program had its own trials, tribulations, and difficulties, in great measure all worked together to advance the cause of flight.

Beyond these "Round One" airplanes was "Round Two": the hypersonic X-15 that took piloted, winged flight across the divide from the atmosphere into space. If more glamorous, more exciting, and better known than its predecessors, it was nevertheless largely dependent for its success upon the structure, organizational culture, and expertise that the military services, the NACA (and NASA thereafter), and the industry had developed during the earlier Round One effort.

As the Round One aircraft wound down and Round Two began its own gestation, a shocking event occurred that dramatically reshaped not only American but global perspectives on air and space: the Soviet Union's launch of Sputnik, the world's first artificial satellite, on October 4, 1957. The significance of Sputnik's launch became even more apparent in ensuing weeks and was the impetus for a permanent U.S. space program and a new agency to run it.[5] Less than a week after Sputnik I was launched, the American Rocket Society called for the establishment of an "Astronautical Research and Development Agency" that would be responsible for nonmilitary space activities. The Rocket and Satellite Research Panel of the National Academy of Sciences made a similar suggestion on November 21, 1957.

President Dwight D. Eisenhower responded with several actions. These included announcing the establishment of the position of the Special Assistant to the President for Science and Technology, and he named Massachusetts Institute of Technology (MIT) president James R. Killian, Jr., to the post. Soon after, the President's Scientific Advisory Committee (PSAC) was established, with Killian named its chairman. Killian's first assignment in his new position was to review the alternatives for a U.S. space program. His report, titled "Memorandum on Organizational Alternatives for Space Research and Development," was completed on December 30, 1957, and offered two options. The first was for the DOD to establish a central space laboratory that could undertake basic space research as well as military-related work. This laboratory might also have the authority to sponsor research in civilian institutions.[6] His second was using the NACA as an alternative to a military-sponsored central space laboratory, an idea first proposed by James McCormack, a vice president of MIT, and James B. Fisk, of Bell Telephone Laboratories.[7] In Killian's proposal, space activities would be split between the DOD and "some other agency or agencies external to the DOD" that "might engage in basic research."[8] Killian continued, "One obvious way of doing this would be to encourage the NACA to extend its space research and to provide it with the necessary funding to do so."

In February 1958, Eisenhower asked Killian to study options for organizing the U.S. space effort. Killian appointed a PSAC panel headed by Nobel laureate Edward Purcell that included the University of California's Herbert York, NACA chairman James H. "Jimmy" Doolittle, and Polaroid's Edwin Land. The Purcell committee members were favorably disposed to accepting Killian's recommendation regarding the NACA, particularly since other contenders (including the National Science Foundation and the Atomic Energy Commission) had various shortcomings. Accordingly, in early March, the committee recommended a reorganized NACA as the organization best prepared to manage civilian space activity. Draft legislation was soon written, leading to the establishment of the National Aeronautics and Space Administration, the follow-on agency to the NACA, and began operations on October 1, 1958. The "new-old" Agency absorbed the NACA's existing laboratory structure—the Langley, Lewis, Ames, and Edwards facilities—joining them to the Development Operations Division of the Army Ballistic Missile Agency (subsequently the Marshall Space Flight Center) and partnering with the California Institute of Technology's Jet Propulsion Laboratory (JPL).

Each of the Centers brought different skills, traditions, cultures, and experiences to the new Agency. These had been shaped in the course of the transonic-supersonic revolution, which had made the NACA the only organization realistically qualified to take America into space. On October 5, 1958, 4 days after opening its doors, NASA Administrator T. Keith Glennan said, "All right. Let's get on with it!"[9] Thus began the Mercury program, first to put an American astronaut into orbit.

Mercury was where the legacy of the Round One research programs paid off. In contrast to the academic research culture of Ames, Langley, and Lewis, the High-Speed Flight Station was more operationally oriented. This was due to its focus on flying research aircraft, the lack of wind tunnels or similar ground research facilities, and the close ties it maintained with the military services. The experiences of Round One airplanes, and particularly the High-Speed Flight Station pilots, ground crews, and researchers, became the basis for planning Mercury.[10]

From December 1946 onward, the High-Speed Flight Research Station personnel had been flying piloted rockets, with hundreds of successful flights to the facility's credit. No one else on Earth, in the United States, Europe, or the U.S.S.R., had such experience. The Round One pilots—Air Force, Navy,

NACA, Marine, or contractor—were the first to see the sky turn black and see Earth's curvature, its hallmark as a planet. Their flights reached speeds and altitudes not exceeded until the first Soviet and American space missions. They wore the first partial pressure suits and then, later, full pressure suits anticipating the spacesuits of the 1960s in order to survive cockpit depressurization at the altitudes at which they flew. Their ground crews developed and mastered the procedures for checking out the aircraft; maintaining the temperamental rocket engines; and handling liquid oxygen, pure hydrogen peroxide, alcohol/water mixtures, anhydrous ammonia, and the other dangerous chemicals used in the engines. High-Speed Flight Station engineers had done the first test work with the reaction controls necessary to stabilize an orbiting spacecraft operating in a vacuum. Indeed, the very design developed for testing on the X-1B became the basis for the Mercury spacecraft's thrusters. And it was the High-Speed Flight Research Station's control room that the Mercury project copied when casting about for a way to monitor the spacecraft.

In many respects, the NACA's human contribution to the X-series program was its most significant. The transonic and supersonic revolution was, like history itself, the working of men and women over time. Those of the NACA who had advanced flight through the speed of sound were, to a great degree, the men and women who now advanced flight into space.[11] Robert Gilruth, who pioneered the interim "wing flow" method of transonic research and who had favored a thin wing for the XS-1, became Director of the Space Task Group, responsible for America's first piloted space program, Project Mercury, and later Director of the Manned Spacecraft Center, now the NASA Lyndon B. Johnson Space Center. Walter C. Williams, who had gone to Muroc from Langley to head the Muroc Flight Test Unit, remaining there to lead the High-Speed Flight Station into the NASA era, became Operations Director for Project Mercury, and later NASA's Chief Engineer, a singular distinction. Hartley Soulé, the NACA's Research Airplane Projects Leader, supervised establishment of its tracking network. Gerald Truszynski, who had instrumented and tracked the XS-1 at Pinecastle and Muroc, remaining through the Round One era at Edwards as chief of instrumentation at the HSFS, eventually became NASA Associate Administrator for Tracking and Data Acquisition in the Apollo and Shuttle eras.

Fittingly, one of their colleagues, a young research pilot who flew the X-1, the X-5, and later (in the early years of NASA) the X-15, went on to fly into space and become the first human to set foot on another celestial body: Neil A. Armstrong. He was humanity's link from the surface of Earth through the atmosphere and into space and from the subsonic to the transonic, supersonic, hypersonic, and onwards to escape velocity and footprints on other worlds.[12]

Progress always extracts a price, and flight has always extracted a particularly high tribute from those who have sought to advance its frontiers. The early Round One X-series was no different: between 1948 and 1957, accidents and incidents related to the Round One program claimed nine airplanes—seven research airplanes and two launch aircraft—and the lives of five aircrew (two in airplanes discussed in this work). It is to them—pilots Howard Lilly, Raymond Popson, Jean Ziegler, Milburn Apt, and aircrewman Frank Wolko—that this book is dedicated.[13]

Endnotes

1. Kenneth S. Kleinknecht, "The Rocket Research Aircraft," in Eugene M. Emme, ed., *The History of Rocket Technology: Essays on Research, Development, and Utility* (Detroit: Wayne State University Press, 1964), p. 210.

2. Brian Lecomber, "Flying the Sopwith Camel and Fokker Triplane," *Flight International* (April 8, 1978), quoted in Robert P. Harper, Jr., and George E. Cooper, "Handling Qualities and Pilot Evaluation," 1984 Wright Brothers Lectureship in Aeronautics (New York: American Institute of Aeronautics and Astronautics, 1984), p. 7.

3. Hallion and Gorn, *On the Frontier*, pp. 56–59.

4. Miller, *The X-Planes X-1 to X-45*, pp. 285–289. Years later, it should be noted, Johnson himself sought to acquire "X-series" status for his Model CL-1200 Lancer, a proposed derivative of the F-104, which did in fact receive the designation X-27, though it was never actually built and flown.

5. Robert A. Divine, *The Sputnik Challenge: Eisenhower's Response to the Soviet Satellite* (New York: Oxford University Press, 1993), pp. 7–9; Roger D. Launius, "An Unintended Consequence of the IGY: Eisenhower, Sputnik, and the Founding of NASA," AIAA Paper No. 2008-860 (2008).

6. J.R. Killian, Jr., "Memorandum on Organizational Alternatives for Space Research," accessed on July 5, 2011, *http://history.nasa.gov/sputnik/iv1.html*.

7. Brian R. Page, "The Creation of NASA," *Journal of the British Interplanetary Society* 32 (October 1979): 449–450.

8. Killian, "Memorandum on Organizational Alternatives for Space Research."

9. Loyd S. Swenson, Jr., James M. Grimwood, and Charles C. Alexander, *This New Ocean: A History of Project Mercury*, NASA SP-4201 (Washington DC: NASA, 1966), p. 109.

10. William M. Bland, Jr., "Project Mercury," in Emme, ed., *The History of Rocket Technology*, pp. 212–240.

11. As related in Sylvia Doughty Fries, *NASA Engineers and the Age of Apollo*, NASA SP-4104 (Washington, DC: NASA, 1992).

12. As noted in Hallion, *Supersonic Flight*, pp. 203–204.

13. The aircraft were the Bell X-1-3, X-1A, and X-1D; the Bell X-2 #1 and X-2 #2; the Bell X-5 #2; the Douglas D-558-1 #2; and two Boeing EB-50 launch aircraft (one lost with the ground explosion of the X-1-3 and one scrapped after the in-flight explosion and loss

of the X-2 #2). The aircrew were Jean Ziegler, Frank Wolko, and Milburn Apt (both X-2s); Ray Popson (X-5 #2); and Tick Lilly (D-558-1 #2). Additionally, Bell pilot Joseph Cannon was seriously injured in the explosion of the X-1-3, fortunately surviving to fly again.

Technical Specifications for the Round One Aircraft

Aircraft Type:	Bell XS-1[1]	Douglas D-558-1	Douglas D-558-2		Douglas X-3	Northrop X-4	Bell X-5	Convair XF-92A
			Jet only	All rocket				
Engine Number, Manufacturer, Type Static Thrust (lb)	1 RMI XLR-11 6,000	1 GE TG-180 5,000	1 West. J34 3,000	1 RMI XLR-8 6,000	2 West. J34 4,850 ea.	2 West. J30 1,600 ea.	1 Allison J35 4,900	1 Allison J35 5,600
Propellants (gallons and type of propellant)[2]	311 LOX 293 DEA	230 kerosene	260 gasoline	345 LOX 378 DEA	970 kerosene	240 gasoline	340 kerosene	560 kerosene
Weights — T.O./Launch (lb)	12,250	10,105	10,572	15,787	21,900	7,820	9,960	15,560
Weights — Landing (lb)	7,000	7,711	7,914	9,421	17,500	6,452	7,850	11,808
Height (ft)	10.85	12.14	12.67	12.8	12.52	14.8	12.2	17.75
Length (ft)	30.90	35.71	42.0		66.75	23.25	33.6	42.80

Aircraft Type:		Bell XS-1[1]	Douglas D-558-1	Douglas D-558-2 Jet only	Douglas D-558-2 All rocket	Douglas X-3	Northrop X-4	Bell X-5	Convair XF-92A
Wing	Airfoil Section	NACA 65-108	NACA 65-110	NACA 63-010 root to NACA 63-012 tip		Douglas Modified Hexagon[3]	NACA 0010-64	NACA $64_{(110)}A011$ to $64_{(08)}A008.28$	NACA $65_{(06)}$-006.5
	Span (ft)	28.0	25.0	25		22.69	26.1	31.9 max / 20.0 min	31.33
	Wing Area (sq ft)	130	150.7	175.0		166.50	200	184.3 max / 166.9 min	425
	Root Chord (ft)	6.18	6.21 MAC[4]	9.04		10.58	10.25	5.61 min MAC	27.13
	Tip Chord (ft)	3.09		5.1		4.11	4.67	10.05 max MAC	0.0
	Flap Area (sq ft)	11.6	n/a	12.58		17.22	16.7	15.9	n/a
	Aileron Area (sq ft total)	6.30	7.94	9.8		8.08	17.2 [elev.]	7.24	76.19 [elev.]
Horizontal Tail	Airfoil Section	65-006	65-008	63-010		hexagon	none	65A-006	none
	Area (sq ft)	26	35.98	39.9		n/a	n/a	31.5	n/a
	Elevator Area (sq ft total)	5.2	8.6	9.4		43.24	17.2 [elev.]	6.9	76.19 [elev.]
Vertical Tail	Area (sq ft)	25.6	25.68	36.6		23.73	16.0	29.5	75.35
	Rudder Area (sq ft)	5.2	7.92	6.15		5.44	4.1	4.7	11.50
Perf.	Mach No. at Altitude, ft (mph)	1.45 / 35,000 / (960)	0.832 / sea level / (632)	0.825 / 20,000 / (585)	2.01 / 62,000 / (1,290)	1.21 / 30,000 / (822)	0.92 / 30,000 / (625)	1.03 / 30,000 / (700)	1.01 / 30,000 / (686)

1. Specification for XS-1 no. 1 (46-062) at time of first supersonic flight, October 14, 1947. 2. LOX: Liquid Oxygen; DEA: Diluted Ethyl Alcohol. 3. Douglas, not an NACA, airfoil section. 4. MAC: Mean Aerodynamic Chord.

Acknowledgments

Writing a book as lengthy and complicated as a history of the early X-planes could not have been done without the help of many people. They include Tony Springer at NASA Headquarters, who provided funding for this and earlier projects; Christian Gelzer, the project supervisor; and Peter W. Merlin, who tracked down half-century-old weekly progress reports on the X-planes in the Dryden archives. Thanks to Karl A. Bender and Freddy Lockarno, at the Dryden Flight Research Center's Technical Library, for tracking down NACA Research Memorandums describing the data collected and problems experienced with the early X-planes. Thanks as well to Albion Bowers for his explanation of rocket science. Sarah Merlin receives my thanks for the first round of copyediting. Thanks also to Dr. Richard P. Hallion, who added significantly to the text, and to the copy editors at NASA Headquarters.

Finally, I wish to recognize the courage of the test and research pilots, be they NACA, contractor, or military, who flew the X-planes. They were the explorers of an undiscovered territory. Like the Wright brothers, they had to find their way without guideposts. The body of experience that had been built up over the previous decades was of no use in understanding the demands of transonic and supersonic flight. The engineers, wind tunnel researchers, and pilots were on their own. But in their efforts to overcome the unknowns, they were unknowingly setting the stage not simply for supersonic flight, but for a far greater leap. The procedures, safety rules, and experience gained in breaking the sound barrier were later used when the NACA became NASA, the agency whose new role was to explore space.

Curtis Peebles

Selected Bibliography

I. Reports and Memorandums, by Type

General

Beeler, De E., and George Gerard. "Wake Measurements Behind a Wing Section of a Fighter Airplane in Fast Dives." NACA TN No. 1190, 1947.

Briggs, L.J., and H.L. Dryden. "Pressure Distribution over Air Foils at High Speeds." NACA Report No. 255, 1926.

Briggs, L.J., and H.L. Dryden. "Aerodynamic Characteristics of Twenty-Four Airfoils at High Speeds." NACA Report No. 319, 1929.

Briggs, L.J., and H.L. Dryden. "Aerodynamic Characteristics of Circular-Arc Airfoils at High Speeds." NACA Report No. 365, 1931.

Briggs, L.J., G.F. Hull, and H.L. Dryden. "Aerodynamic Characteristics of Airfoils at High Speeds." NACA Report No. 207, 1924.

Buckingham, Edgar. "Jet Propulsion for Airplanes." NACA Report No. 159, 1923.

Caldwell, F.W., and E.N. Fales. "Wind Tunnel Studies in Aerodynamics Phenomena at High Speeds." NACA Report No. 83, 1920.

Chief, Bureau of Aeronautics, United States Navy. "Transfer of Aircraft to the NACA Under Public Law 266 of the 81st Congress." December 27, 1950.

Chief of Naval Operations, United States Navy. "Transfer of Aircraft to the NACA Under Public Law 266 of the 81st Congress." January 5, 1951.

Day, Richard E. *Coupling Dynamics in Aircraft: A Historical Perspective.* NASA SP-532. Edwards AFB, CA: NASA Dryden Flight Research Center, 1997.

Harper, Robert P., Jr., and George E. Cooper. "Handling Qualities and Pilot Evaluation." Wright Brothers Lectureship in Aeronautics. New York: American Institute of Aeronautics and Astronautics, 1984.

Jones, Robert T. "Wing Plan Form for High-Speed Flight." *Collected Works of Robert T. Jones.* NACA Report No. 863, in NASA TM X-3334. Washington, DC: NASA, 1976.

Loftin, Laurence K., Jr. *Quest for Performance: The Evolution of Modern Aircraft.* NASA SP-468. Washington, DC: NASA, 1985.

Marschak, Thomas A. *The Role of Project Histories in the Study of R&D*, Report P-2850. Santa Monica: The RAND Corporation, January 1964.

McAvoy, William H., Oscar W. Schey, and Alfred W. Young. "The Effect on Airplane Performance of the Factors That Must Be Considered in Applying Low-Drag Cowling to Radial Engines." NACA Report No. 414, 1931.

Moss, Sanford A. *Superchargers for Aviation.* New York: National Aeronautics Council, Inc., 1942.

National Advisory Committee for Aeronautics, High-Speed Flight Station, "Research Aircraft Projects Panel 1952 Annual Report."

National Advisory Committee for Aeronautics, High-Speed Flight Station, "Research Aircraft Projects Panel 1953 Annual Report."

Parks, James H. "Experimental Evidence of Sustained Coupled Longitudinal and Lateral Oscillations from a Rocket-Propelled Model of a 35° Swept Wing Airplane Configuration." NACA RM L54D15, 1954.

Phillips, William H. "Effects of Steady Rolling on Longitudinal and Directional Stability." NACA TN No. 1627, 1948.

Polhamus, Edward C., and Thomas A. Toll. "Research Related to Variable Sweep Aircraft Development." NASA TM 83121, 1981.

Saltzman, Edwin J., and Theodore G. Ayers. *Selected Examples of NACA/NASA Supersonic Flight Research.* NASA SP-513. Edwards AFB, CA: NASA Dryden Flight Research Center, 1995.

Shortal, Joseph Adams. *A New Dimension—Wallops Island Flight Test Range: The First Fifteen Years.* NASA RP-1028. Washington, DC: NASA, 1978.

Stack, John, W.F. Lindsey, and R.E. Littell, "The Compressibility Burble and the Effect of Compressibility on Pressures and Forces Acting on an Airfoil." NACA Report No. 646, 1938.

Stillwell, Wendell H. "Results of Measurements Made During the Approach and Landing of Seven High-Speed Research Airplanes." NACA RM H54K24, 1955.

Strass, H. Kurt, and Edison M. Fields. "Flight Investigation of the Effect of Thickening the Aileron Trailing Edges on Control Effectiveness for Sweptback Tapered Wings Having Sharp- and Round-Nose Sections." NACA RM L9L19, 1950.

Thompson, Milton O., with J.D. Hunley. *Flight Research: Problems Encountered and What They Should Teach Us.* NASA SP-2000-4522. Washington, DC: NASA, 2000.

Weick, Fred E. "Drag and Cooling with Various Forms of Cowling for a 'Whirlwind' Engine in a Cabin Fuselage." NACA TN No. 301, 1928.

Whitcomb, Richard T. "A Study of the Zero-Lift Drag-Rise Characteristics of Wing-Body Combinations Near the Speed of Sound." NACA RM L52H08, 1952.

Williams, Walter C., and A. Scott Crossfield. "Handling Qualities of High-Speed Airplanes." NACA RM L52A08, 1952.

Wood, Donald H. "Tests of Nacelle-Propeller Combinations in Various Positions with Reference to Wings. Part I. Thick Wing–NACA Cowled Nacelle–Tractor Propeller." NASA Technical Report No. 415, 1933.

Williams, Walter C. Letter to NACA Headquarters. "Choice of Color for Research Aircraft at Edwards." NACA HSFRS, December 3, 1951.

Bell XS-1 (X-1)
Angle, Ellwyn E., and Euclid C. Holleman. "Determination of Longitudinal Stability of the Bell X-1 Airplane from Transient Responses at Mach

Numbers up to 1.12 at Lift Coefficients of 0.3 and 0.6." NACA RM L50I06a, 1950.

Beeler, De E., and John P. Mayer. "Measurements of the Wing and Tail Loads During the Acceptance Tests of Bell XS-1 Research Airplane." NACA RM L7L12, 1948.

Carman, L. Robert, and John R. Carden. "Lift and Drag Coefficients for the Bell X-1 Airplane (8-Percent-Thick Wing) in Power-Off Transonic Flight." NACA RM L51E08, 1951.

Drake, Hubert M., and John R. Carden. "Elevator-Stabilizer Effectiveness and Trim of the X-1 Airplane to a Mach Number of 1.06." NACA RM L50G20, 1950.

Drake, Hubert M., Harold R. Goodman, and Herbert H. Hoover. "Preliminary Results of NACA Transonic Flights of the XS-1 Airplane with 10-Percent-Thick Wing and 8-Percent-Thick Horizontal Tail." NACA RM L8I29, 1948.

Drake, Hubert M., Milton D. McLaughlin, and Harold R. Goodman. "Results Obtained During Accelerated Transonic Flight Tests of the Bell XS-1 Airplane in Flights to a Mach Number of 0.92." NACA RM L8A05a, 1948.

Goodman, Harold R., and Hubert M. Drake. "Results Obtained During Extension of U.S. Air Force Transonic-Flight Tests of XS-1 Airplane." NACA RM L8I28, 1948.

Goodman, Harold R., and Roxanah B. Yancey. "The Static-Pressure Error of Wing and Fuselage Airspeed Installations of the X-1 Airplanes in Transonic Flight." NACA RM L9G22, 1949.

Hamlin, Benson. *The Design Conception of Supersonic Flight.* Amherst, NY: The Amherst Museum/Niagara Frontier Aviation and Space Museum, 1996.

Mattson, Axel T. "Force and Longitudinal Control Characteristics of a 1/16-Scale Model of the Bell XS-1 Transonic Research Airplane at High Mach Numbers." NACA RM L7A03, 1947.

United States Air Force. *Air Force Supersonic Research Airplane XS-1 Report No. 1.* Wright Field, OH: USAF Air Materiel Command, January 9, 1948.

Williams, Walter C., and De E. Beeler. "Results of Preliminary Flight Tests of the XS-1 Airplane (8-Percent Wing) to a Mach Number of 1.25." NACA RM L8A23a, 1948.

Williams, Walter C., Charles M. Forsyth, and Beverly P. Brown. "General Handling Qualities Results Obtained During Acceptance Flight Tests of the Bell X-1 Airplane." NACA RM L8A09, 1948.

Young, James O. *Meeting the Challenge of Supersonic Flight.* Edwards AFB, CA: Air Force Flight Test Center, 1997.

Bell X-1A

Drake, Hubert M., and Wendell H. Stillwell. "Behavior of the Bell X-1A Research Airplane During Exploratory Flights at Mach Numbers Near 2.0 and at Extreme Altitude." NACA RM H55G25, 1955.

Powell, J.L. "X-1A Airplane Contract W33-038-ac-20062, Flight Test Progress Report No. 15, Period from 9 December through 20 December 1953." Bell Aircraft Corporation Report No. 58-980-019, February 3, 1954.

Bell X-2

Stiffler, Ronald. *The Bell X-2 Rocket Research Aircraft: The Flight Test Program.* Edwards AFB, CA: Air Force Flight Test Center, August 12, 1957.

Douglas X-3 Stiletto

Day, Richard E., and Jack Fischel. "Stability and Control Characteristics Obtained During Demonstration of the Douglas X-3 Research Airplane." NACA RM H55E16, 1955.

Douglas Aircraft Company, Flight Testing Division. X-3 test reports:

"Flight Report No. 7," 1953.

"Flight Report No. 8," 1953.

"Flight Report No. 23," 1953.

Douglas Aircraft Company, "Model X-3 Mock-up Conference Airplane Descriptions and Illustrations." Santa Monica, CA: Douglas Aircraft Company, December 6, 1948.

Fischel, Jack, Euclid C. Holleman, and Robert A. Tremant. "Flight Investigation of the Transonic Longitudinal and Lateral Handling Qualities of the Douglas X-3 Research Airplane." NACA RM H57I05, 1957.

Fleming, Frank N. "Evolution of the Configuration of the X-3 Supersonic Research Aircraft." Santa Monica, CA: Douglas Aircraft Company, August 1, 1949.

Keener, Earl R., Norman J. McLeod, and Norman V. Taillon. "Effect of Leading-Edge-Flap Deflections on the Wing Loads, Load Distribution, and Flap Hinge Moments of the Douglas X-3 Research Airplane at Transonic Speeds." NACA RM H58D29, 1958.

Marcy, William L. "High-Speed Loads Measured on the Douglas X-3 Research Airplane." NACA RM H57L08, 1958.

Marcy, William L., Harriet J. Stephenson, and Thomas V. Cooney. "Analysis of the Vertical-Tail Loads Measured During a Flight Investigation at Transonic Speeds of the Douglas X-3 Airplane." NACA RM H56H08, 1956.

NACA HSFRS, X-3 Progress Report Memorandums for Research Airplane Projects Leader:

"Progress Report for the X-3 Research Airplane for the Period November 1 to November 30, 1953."

"Progress Report for the X-3 Research Airplane for the Period July 1 to July 31, 1954."

"Progress Report for the X-3 Research Airplane for the Period August 1 to August 31, 1954."

"Progress Report for the X-3 Research Airplane for the Period September 1 to September 30, 1954."

"Progress Report for the X-3 Research Airplane for the Period October 1 to October 31, 1954."

NACA HSFRS, X-3 Status Reports for Chief of Research:

"X-3 Status Report for Period 14 September to 18 October 1952."

"X-3 Status Report for Week Ending 25 October 1952."

"X-3 Weekly Status Report Week Ending 25 April 1953."

"X-3 Weekly Status Report Week Ending 2 May 1953."

"X-3 Weekly Status Report Week Ending 20 June 1953."

"X-3 Weekly Status Report Week Ending 18 July 1953."

"X-3 Weekly Status Report Week Ending 25 July 1953."

"X-3 Weekly Status Report Week Ending 1 August 1953."

"X-3 Weekly Status Report for Week Ending 1 November 1953."

"X-3 Weekly Status Report for Week Ending 15 November 1953."

NACA HSFRS Memorandum for Chief of Research. "X-3 Airplane Visit of Harold F. Kleckner of the Douglas Company to Langley on October 18, 1951."

NACA HSFRS Memorandum for Chief of Research. "Proposed Modifications of X-3 Airplane to Rocket Power and Air Launch." October 24, 1952.

NACA HSFS. "Flight Experience with Two High-Speed Airplanes Having Violent Lateral-Longitudinal Coupling in Aileron Rolls," NACA RM H55A13, 1955.

Stephenson, Harriet J. "Flight Measurements of Horizontal-Tail Loads on the Douglas X-3 Research Airplane." NACA RM H56A23, 1956.

Northrop X-4 Bantam

Drake, Hubert M. "Stability and Control Data Obtained from First Flight of X-4 Airplane." NACA RM L9A31, 1949.

Matthews, James T., Jr. "Results Obtained During Flights 1 to 6 of the Northrop X-4 Airplane (A.F. no. 46-677)." NACA RM L9K22, 1950.

NACA HSFRS. X-4 Progress Memorandums for NACA Research Airplanes Project Leader:

"Acceptance of the X-4 Airplane." n.d.

"Progress Report on Acceptance Tests of X-4 Airplanes from January 1 to January 14, 1949."

"X-4, January 14 to June 10, 1949."

"X-4, June 17 through July 1, 1949."

"X-4, June 20, 1949."

"X-4, July 16 through July 29, 1949."

"X-4 Airplanes July 30 through August 12, 1949."

"X-4 Airplanes July 31 through August 12, 1949."

"X-4, August 27 to September 14, 1949."

"X-4 Airplanes October 8 to October 21, 1949."

"X-4, November 19 to December 2, 1949."

"X-4, December 3 to December 16, 1949."

"X-4, December 31, 1949, to January 1, 1950."

"X-4, January 27 to February 24, 1950."

"X-4, February 24 to March 24, 1950."

"X-4, May 5 to May 19, 1950."

"X-4, July 15 to July 28, 1950."

"X-4, August 26 to September 8, 1950."

"X-4, September 8 to September 22, 1950."

"X-4, September 22 to October 6, 1950."

"X-4, October 6 to October 20, 1950."

"X-4, November 3 to November 17, 1950."

"X-4, November 17 to December 1, 1950."

"X-4, December 15 to December 29, 1950."

"X-4, May 18 to June 1, 1951."

"X-4, June 16 to June 29, 1951."

"X-4, June 30 to July 13, 1951."

"X-4, July 14 to July 27, 1951."

"X-4, July 28 to August 10, 1951."

"X-4, August 11 to August 25, 1951."

"X-4, September 22 to October 5, 1951."

"X-4, October 6 to October 19, 1951."

"X-4, October 20 to November 2, 1951."

"X-4, November 3 to November 16, 1951."

"X-4, January 26 to February 8, 1952."

"X-4, February 9 to February 22, 1952."

"X-4, March 8 to March 21, 1952."

"X-4, March 22 to April 4, 1952."

"X-4, April 5 to April 18, 1952."

"X-4, April 19 to May 2, 1952."

"X-4, May 17 to May 30, 1952."

"X-4, May 31 to June 13, 1952."

"X-4, June 28 to July 11, 1952."

"X-4, July 12 to July 25, 1952."

"X-4, August 9 to August 22, 1952."

"X-4, September 5 to October 1, 1952."

"X-4, October 1 to November 1, 1952."

"X-4, November 1 to December 1, 1952."

"X-4, January 1 to January 31, 1953."

"X-4, February 1 to February 28, 1953."

"X-4, March 1 to March 31, 1953."

"X-4, April 1 to April 30, 1953."

"X-4, May 1 to May 31, 1953."

"X-4, July 1 to July 31, 1953."

"X-4, August 1 to August 31, 1953."

"X-4, September 1 to September 30, 1953."

Sadoff, Melvin, and A. Scott Crossfield. "A Flight Evaluation of the Stability and Control of the X-4 Swept-Wing Semitailless Airplane." NACA RM H54G16, 1954.

Sadoff, Melvin, and Thomas R. Sisk. "Summary Report of Results Obtained During Demonstration Tests of the Northrop X-4 Airplanes." NACA RM A50I01, 1950.

Valentine, George M. "Stability and Control Data Obtained from Fourth and Fifth Flights of the Northrop X-4 Airplane (A.F. No. 46-676)." NACA RM L9G25a, 1949.

Williams, Walter C. "Results Obtained from Second Flight of X-4 Airplane (A.F. No. 46-676)." NACA RM L9F21, 1949.

Williams, Walter C. "Results Obtained from Third Flight of Northrop X-4 Airplane (A.F. No. 46-676)." NACA RM L9G20a, 1949.

Bell X-5

Banner, Richard D., Robert D. Reed, and William L. Marcy. "Wing-Load Measurements of the Bell X-5 Research Airplanes at a Sweep Angle of 58.7°." NACA RM H55A11, 1955.

Bell Aircraft Corporation. "Bell X-5 Ready for Flight Tests." June 14, 1951.

Bellman, Donald R. "Lift and Drag Characteristics of the Bell X-5 Research Airplane at 59° Sweepback for Mach Numbers from 0.60 to 1.03." NACA RM L53A09c, 1953.

Briggs, Donald W. "Flight Determination of the Buffeting Characteristics of the Bell X-5 Research Airplane at 58.7° Sweepback." NACA RM L54C17, 1954.

Campbell, John P., and Hubert M. Drake. "Investigation of Stability and Control Characteristics of an Airplane Model with Skewed Wing in the Langley Free-Flight Laboratory." NACA TN No. 1208, 1947.

Childs, Joan M. "Flight Measurements of the Stability Characteristics of the Bell X-5 Research Airplane in Sideslips at 59° Sweepback." NACA RM L52K13b, 1953.

Donlan, Charles J., and William C. Sleeman. "Low-Speed Wind-Tunnel Investigation of the Longitudinal Stability Characteristics of a Model Equipped with a Variable-Sweep Wing." NACA RM L9B18, 1949.

Finch, Thomas W., and Donald W. Biggs. "Preliminary Results of Stability and Control Investigation of the Bell X-5 Research Airplane." NACA RM L52K18b, 1953.

Green, Warren E. *The Bell X-5 Research Airplane*. Wright-Patterson AFB, OH: Wright Air Development Center, March 1954.

Kress, Robert W. "Variable-Sweep Wing Design." AIAA Paper No. 83-1051, 1983.

Martin, James A. "Longitudinal Flight Characteristics of the Bell X-5 Research Airplane at 59° Sweepback with Modified Wing Root." NACA RM L53E28, 1953.

NACA HSFRS, X-5 Flight Research Summaries:

"Investigation of Flight at Speeds Below Minimum Drag, Flight No. 60." January 27, 1953.

"Investigation of Flight at Speeds Below Minimum Drag, Flight No. 61." January 29, 1953.

"Investigation of Flight at Speeds Below Minimum Drag, Flight No. 63." February 6, 1953.

NACA HSFRS, X-5 Progress Memorandums for Chief of Research:

"Progress Report for the X-5 Research Airplane for the Period May 3 to May 16, 1952."

"Progress Report for the X-5 Research Airplane for the Period July 12 to July 25, 1952."

"Progress Report for the X-5-1 Research Airplane for the Period July 26 to August 8, 1952."

"Progress Report for the X-5-1 Research Airplane for the Period October 1 to November 1, 1952."

"Progress Report for the X-5-1 Research Airplane for the Period July 1 to July 31, 1955."

"Progress Report of Engineering and Instrumentation for the X-5 Airplane During the Period August 25 to September 7, 1951."

"Progress Report of Engineering and Instrumentation for the X-5 Airplane During the Period December 1 to December 14, 1951."

"Progress Report of Engineering and Instrumentation for the X-5 Airplane During the Period December 15 to December 28, 1951."

"Progress Report of Engineering and Instrumentation for the X-5 Airplane During the Period December 29, 1951, to January 11, 1952."

NASA Langley Research Center. "Summary of NACA/NASA Variable-Sweep Research and Development Leading to the F-111 (TFX)." NASA LRC Working Paper LWP-285, 1966.

Nugent, Jack. "Lift and Drag of the Bell X-5 Research Airplane in the 45° Sweptback Configuration at Transonic Speeds." NACA RM H56E02, 1956.

Perry, Robert L. *Innovation and Military Requirements: A Comparative Study.* RAND Report RM-5182PR. Santa Monica, CA: The RAND Corporation, 1967.

Reed, Robert D. "Flight Measurements of Horizontal-Tail Loads on the Bell X-5 Research Airplane at a Sweep Angle of 58.7°." NACA RM H55E20a, 1955.

Rogers, John T., and Angel H. Dunn. "Preliminary Results of Horizontal-Tail Load Measurements of the Bell X-5 Research Airplane." NACA RM L52G14, 1952.

United States Air Force. "Report of Major Aircraft Accident—X-5, 50-1839A." Edwards AFB: AFFTC, October 27, 1953.

Videan, Edward N. "Flight Measurements of the Dynamic Lateral and Longitudinal Stability of the Bell X-5 Research Airplane at 58.7° Sweepback." NACA RM H55H10, 1955.

Douglas D-558-1 Skystreak

Angle, Ellwyn E., and Euclid C. Holleman. "Longitudinal Frequency-Response Characteristics of the D-558-I Airplane as Determined from Experimental Transient-Response Histories to a Mach Number of 0.90." NACA RM L51K28, 1952.

Barlow, William H., and Howard C. Lilly. "Stability Results Obtained with Douglas D-558-1 Airplane BuAero No. 37971 in Flights up to a Mach Number of 0.89." NACA RM L8K03, 1949.

Beeler, De E., Donald R. Bellman, and John H. Griffith. "Flight Determination of the Effects of Wing Vortex Generators on the Aerodynamic Characteristics of the Douglas D-558-I Airplane." NACA RM L51A23, 1951.

Bellman, Donald R. Letter to NACA Headquarters. "Looseness of Stabilizer Mountings for the D-558-I Airplane." November 5, 1952.

Bellman, Donald R. Letter to NACA Headquarters. "Reply to Request for Information on D-558-I Vertical-Tail Load Investigation." January 12, 1953.

Douglas Aircraft Company. "Skystreak World's Speed Records." El Segundo, CA: DAC, September 19, 1947.

Heinemann, Edward H. "The Development of the Navy-Douglas Model D-558 Research Project." El Segundo, CA: Douglas Aircraft Company, November 17, 1947.

Hyatt, 1st Lt. Abraham, United States Marine Corps Reserve. "Proposed High-Speed Research Airplane." USN Bureau of Aeronautics Memorandum AER-E-225-AH. September 22, 1944.

Keener, Earl R., and Mary Pierce. "Tabulated Pressure Coefficients and Aerodynamic Characteristics in Flight on the Wing of the Douglas D-558-I Airplane for a 1g Stall, a Speed Run to a Mach Number of 0.90, and a Wind-Up Turn at a Mach Number of 0.86." NACA RM L50J10, 1950.

Keener, Earl R., James R. Peel, and Julia B. Woodbridge. "Tabulated Pressure Coefficients and Aerodynamic Characteristics Measured in Flight on the Wing of the Douglas D-558-I Airplane Throughout the Normal-Force Range at Mach Numbers of 0.67, 0.74, 0.78, and 0.82." NACA RM L50L12a, 1951.

NACA, "NACA Aircraft Accident Investigation Report Douglas D-558-1 Airplane, BuNo 37971." Muroc, CA: NACA Muroc Flight Test Unit. May 3, 1948.

Sadoff, Melvin, William S. Roden, and John M. Eggleston. "Flight Investigation of the Longitudinal Stability and Control Characteristics of the Douglas D-558-I Airplane BuAero No. 37972 at Mach Numbers up to 0.89." NACA RM L51D18, 1951.

Soulé, Hartley A. Letter to NACA Headquarters. "Request for Comments on Abandonment of D-558-I Vertical-Tail Load Investigation." December 19, 1952.

Thompson, Jim Rogers, William S. Roden, and John M. Eggleston. "Flight Investigation of the Aileron Characteristics of the Douglas D-558-I Airplane BuAero No. 37972 at Mach Numbers Between 0.6 and 0.89." NACA RM L50D20, 1950.

Williams, Walter C. "Flight Measurement of the Stability Characteristics of the D-558-1 Airplane BuAero No. 37971 in Sideslips." NACA RM L8E14a, 1949.

Williams, Walter C. "Limited Measurements of Static Longitudinal Stability in Flight of Douglas D-558-1 Airplane, BuAero No. 37971." NACA RM L8E14, 1948.

Douglas D-558-2 Skyrocket

Ankenbruck, Herman O., and Chester H. Wolowicz. "Lateral Motions Encountered with the Douglas D-558-II All-Rocket Research Airplane During Exploratory Flights to a Mach Number of 2.0." NACA RM 54I27, 1954.

Ankenbruck, Herman O., and Theodore E. Dahlen. "Some Measurements of Flying Qualities of a Douglas D-558-II Research Airplane During Flights to Supersonic Speeds." NACA RM L53A06, 1953.

Brunn, Cyril D., and Wendell H. Stillwell. "Mach Number Measurements and Calibrations During Flights at High Speeds and at High Altitudes Including Data for the D-558-II Research Airplane." NACA RM H55J18, 1956.

Dahlen, Theodore E. "Maximum Altitude and Maximum Mach Number Obtained with the Modified Douglas D-558-II Research Airplane During Demonstration Flights." NACA RM L53B24, 1953.

Fischel, Jack. "Effects of Wing Slats and Inboard Fences on the Longitudinal Stability Characteristics of the Douglas D-558-II Research Airplane in

Accelerated Maneuvers at Subsonic and Transonic Speeds." NACA RM L53L16, 1954.

Fischel, Jack, and Cyril D. Brunn. "Longitudinal Stability Characteristics in Accelerated Maneuvers at Subsonic and Transonic Speeds of the Douglas D-558-II Research Airplane Equipped with a Leading Edge Wing Chord-Extension." NACA RM H54H16, 1954.

Fischel, Jack, and Donald Reisert. "Effects of Several Wing Modifications on the Subsonic and Transonic Longitudinal Handling Qualities of the Douglas D-558-II Research Airplane." NACA RM H56C30, 1956.

Fischel, Jack, and Jack Nugent. "Flight Determination of the Longitudinal Stability in Accelerated Maneuvers at Transonic Speeds for the Douglas D-558-II Research Aircraft Including the Effects of an Outboard Wing Fence." NACA RM L53A16, 1953.

Fischel, Jack, Robert W. Darville, and Donald Reisert. "Effects of Wing-Mounted External Stores on the Longitudinal and Lateral Handling Qualities of the Douglas D-558-II Research Airplane." NACA RM H57H12, 1957.

Sjoberg, S.A., James R. Peele, and John H. Griffith. "Flight Measurements with the Douglas D-558-II (BuAero No. 37974) Research Airplane: Static Longitudinal Stability and Control Characteristics at Mach Numbers up to 0.87." NACA RM L50K13, 1951.

Sjoberg, S.A. "Preliminary Measurements of the Dynamic Lateral Stability Characteristics of the Douglas D-558-II (BuAero No. 37974) Airplane." NACA RM L9G18, 1949.

Consolidated Vultee XF-92A Dart

Holleman, Euclid C. "Flight Measurements of the Lateral Response Characteristics of the Convair XF-92A Delta-Wing Airplane." NACA RM H55E26, 1955.

Holleman, Euclid C., John H. Evans, and William C. Triplett. "Preliminary Flight Measurements of the Dynamic Longitudinal Stability Characteristics of the Convair XF-92A Delta-Wing Airplane." NACA RM L53E14, 1953.

Redd, Joseph W., Jr., Maj. Charles E. Yeager, and Lt. Col. Frank K. Everest. "Performance Flight Tests of the XF-92A Airplane, USAF S/N 46-682, with a J33-A-29 Power Plant." AFFTC Technical Report No. 53-11. Edwards AFB, CA: Air Force Flight Test Center, 1953.

Sisk, Thomas R., and Duane O. Muhleman. "Lateral Stability and Control Characteristics of the Convair XF-92A Delta-Wing Airplane as Measured in Flight." NACA RM H55A17, 1955.

Sisk, Thomas R., and John M. Mooney. "Preliminary Measurements of Static Longitudinal Stability and Trim for the XF-92A Delta-Wing Research Airplane in Subsonic and Transonic Flight." NACA RM L53B06, 1953.

II. Autobiographies, Biographies, and Memoirs

Bridgeman, William, and Jacqueline Hazard. *The Lonely Sky*. New York: Henry Holt and Company, Inc., 1955.

Cebeci, Tuncer. *Legacy of a Gentle Genius: The Life of A.M.O. Smith*. Long Beach, CA: Horizons Publishing, Inc., 1999.

Connor, Margaret. *Hans von Ohain: Elegance in Flight*. Reston, VA: American Institute of Aeronautics and Astronautics, 2001.

Crossfield, A. Scott, and Clay Blair, Jr. *Always Another Dawn: The Story of a Rocket Test Pilot*. New York: Arno Press, 1972.

Everest, Lt. Col. Frank K., as told to John Guenther. *The Fastest Man Alive*. New York: E.P. Dutton, 1958.

Glennan, T. Keith, edited by J.D. Hunley and in association with Roger D. Launius. *The Birth of NASA: The Diary of T. Keith Glennan*. NASA SP-4105. Washington, DC: NASA, 1993.

Golley, John (in association with Frank Whittle and with technical assistance from Bill Gunston). *Whittle: The True Story*. Washington, DC: Smithsonian Institution Press, 1987.

Grierson, John. *Jet Flight*. London: Samson Low, Marston & Co., Ltd., 1944.

Heinemann, Edward H., and Rosario Rausa. *Ed Heinemann: Combat Aircraft Designer*. Annapolis, MD: Naval Institute Press, 1980.

Hoover, Robert A. "Bob," with Mark Shaw. *Forever Flying*. New York: Orion, 1996.

Johnston, A.M. "Tex," and Charles Barton. *Tex Johnston: Jet-Age Test Pilot*. Washington, DC: Smithsonian Institution Press, 1991.

Lundgren, William R. *Across the High Frontier: The Story of a Test Pilot—Major Charles E. Yeager, USAF*. New York: William Morrow, 1955.

Meyer, Corwin H. *Corky Meyer's Flight Journal: A Test Pilot's Tales of Dodging Disasters—Just in Time*. North Branch, MN: Specialty Press, 2006.

Nahum, Andrew. *Frank Whittle: Invention of the Jet*. Duxford, U.K.: Icon Books, 2004.

Peebles, Curtis, ed. *The Spoken Word: Recollections of Dryden History: The Early Years*. SP-2003-4530. Washington, DC: NASA, 2003.

Phillips, W. Hewitt. *Journey in Aeronautical Research: A Career at NASA Langley Research Center*. Washington, DC: NASA, 1998.

Späte, Wolfgang. *Top Secret Bird: The Luftwaffe's Me 163 Comet* [*sic*]. Missoula, MT: Pictorial Histories Publishing Company, 1989.

Stoliker, Fred, Bob Hoey, and Johnny Armstrong. *Flight Testing at Edwards: Flight Test Engineers' Stories 1946–1975*. Edwards AFB, CA: Flight Test Historical Foundation, 1996.

Whittle, Sir Frank. *Jet: The Story of a Pioneer*. New York: Philosophical Library, 1954.

Yeager, Chuck, and Leo Janos. *Yeager: An Autobiography*. New York: Bantam, 1985.

Young, James O., ed. *The Men of Mach One: A Supersonic Symposium*. Edwards AFB, CA: Air Force Flight Test Center, 1990.

Ziegler, Mano. *Rocket Fighter*. Garden City, NY: Doubleday and Co., Inc., 1963.

III. Miscellaneous Sources

Abzug, Malcolm J., and E. Eugene Larrabee. *Airplane Stability and Control: A History of the Technology That Made Aviation Possible.* Cambridge, U.K.: Cambridge University Press, 1997.

Alegre, Gregory. *Campini Caproni*, no. 5 of the Ali d'Italia series. Turin: La Bancarella Aeronautica, n.d.

Aronstein, David C., and Albert C. Piccirillo. *Have Blue and the F-117: Evolution of the "Stealth Fighter."* Reston, VA: American Institute of Aeronautics and Astronautics, 1997.

Ball, John, Jr. *Edwards: Flight Test Center of the USAF.* New York: Duell, Sloan, and Pearce, 1962.

Becker, John V. *The High-Speed Frontier: Case Histories of Four NACA Programs, 1920–1950.* NASA SP-445. Washington, DC: NASA, 1980.

Boyne, Walter J., and Donald S. Lopez, eds. *The Jet Age: Forty Years of Jet Aviation.* Washington, DC: National Air and Space Museum in association with the Smithsonian Institution Press, 1979.

Bradley, Robert E. "The Birth of the Delta Wing." *American Aviation Historical Society* (winter 2003).

Brown, Capt. Eric, RN. "An Ill-Fated 'Swallow'…but a Harbinger of Summer." *Air Enthusiast* 10 (July 1979).

Burnet, Charles. *Three Centuries to Concorde.* London: Mechanical Engineering Publications Limited, 1979.

Constant II, Edward W. *The Origins of the Turbojet Revolution.* Baltimore: The Johns Hopkins University Press, 1980.

Divine, Robert A. *The Sputnik Challenge: Eisenhower's Response to the Soviet Satellite.* New York: Oxford University Press, 1993.

Emme, Eugene M., ed. *The History of Rocket Technology: Essays on Research, Development, and Utility.* Detroit, MI: Wayne State University Press, 1964.

Fries, Sylvia Doughty. *NASA Engineers and the Age of Apollo.* NASA SP-4104. Washington, DC: NASA, 1992.

Gray, George W. *Frontiers of Flight: The Story of NACA Research.* New York: Alfred A. Knopf, 1948.

Gorn, Michael H. *Expanding the Envelope: Flight Research at NACA and NASA.* Lexington, KY: The University Press of Kentucky, 2001.

Hallion, Richard P. "Before B-2: The History of the Flying Wing," Part 1: "to 1945"; Part 2: "since 1945." *Air Power History* 41, nos. 3–4 (fall–winter 1994).

Hallion, Richard P. "Convair's Delta Alpha." *Air Enthusiast Quarterly* 2 (February 1977).

Hallion, Richard P. "Lippisch, Gluhareff, and Jones: The Emergence of the Delta Planform and the Origins of the Sweptwing in the United States." *Aerospace Historian* 26, no. 1 (spring 1979).

Hallion, Richard P. *On the Frontier: Flight Research at Dryden, 1946–1981.* SP-4303. Washington, DC: NASA, 1985.

Hallion, Richard P. "Richard Whitcomb's Triple Play." *Air Force Magazine* 93, no. 2 (February 2010).

Hallion, Richard P. "Rocket Dreams." *World War II* 23, no. 4 (October–November 2008).

Hallion, Richard P. "Serendipity at Santa Monica: The Story of the Douglas X-3." *Air Enthusiast Quarterly* 4 (October 1977).

Hallion, Richard P. *Supersonic Flight: Breaking the Sound Barrier and Beyond—The Story of the Bell X-1 and Douglas D-558.* London: Brassey's, 1997 ed.

Hallion, Richard P. "X-4: The Bantam Explorer." *Air Enthusiast Quarterly* 3 (June 1977).

Hallion, Richard P., and Michael H. Gorn. *On the Frontier: Experimental Flight at NASA Dryden.* Washington, DC: Smithsonian Books, 2003.

Hallion, Richard P., ed. *NASA's Contributions to Aeronautics*, vol. 1: *Aerodynamics, Structures, Propulsion, Controls*. NASA SP-2010-570-Vol 1. Washington, DC: NASA, 2010.

Hansen, James R. *Engineer in Charge: A History of the Langley Aeronautical Laboratory, 1917–1958*. NASA SP-4305. Washington, DC: NASA, 1987.

Hansen, James R. *The Bird Is on the Wing: Aerodynamics and the Progress of the American Airplane*. College Station, TX: Texas A&M University Press, 2004.

Hunley, J.D., ed. *Toward Mach 2: The Douglas D-558 Program*. NASA SP-445. Washington: DC: NASA SP-4222, 1999.

Jenkins, Dennis R. *X-15: Extending the Frontiers of Flight*. NASA SP-2007-562, Washington, DC: NASA, 2007.

Knaack, Marcelle Size. *Post–World War II Fighters*. Washington, DC: Office of Air Force History, 1986.

Launius, Roger D. "An Unintended Consequence of the IGY: Eisenhower, Sputnik, and the Founding of NASA." AIAA Paper No. 2008-860, 2008.

Libis, Scott. *Skystreak, Skyrocket, & Stiletto: Douglas High-Speed X-Planes*. North Branch, MN: Specialty Press, 2005.

Matranga, Gene J., C. Wayne Ottinger, Calvin R. Jarvis, and D. Christian Gelzer. *Unconventional, Contrary, and Ugly: The Lunar Landing Research Vehicle*. NASA SP-2004-4535. Washington, DC: NASA, 2004.

Miller, Jay. *The X-Planes X-1 to X-45*. Hinckley, U.K.: Midland Publishing, 2001.

Page, Brian R. "The Creation of NASA." *Journal of the British Interplanetary Society* 32 (1979).

Pavelec, Sterling Michael. *The Jet Race and the Second World War*. Annapolis, MD: Naval Institute Press, 2007.

Peebles, Curtis. "Risk Management in the X-Planes Era: D-558-II vs. X-1A at Mach 2." *Quest* 11, no. 4 (2004).

Peebles, Curtis. *Road to Mach 10: Lessons Learned from the X-43A Flight Research Program*. Reston, VA: AIAA, 2008.

Rivas, Brian. *A Very British Sound Barrier: DH 108—A Story of Courage, Triumph, and Tragedy*. Newark, U.K.: Red Kite/Wing Leader Publishers, 2012.

Rotundo, Louis. *Into the Unknown: The X-1 Story*. Washington, DC: Smithsonian Institution Press, 1994.

Schatzberg, Eric. *Wings of Wood, Wings of Metal*. Princeton, NJ: Princeton University Press, 1998.

Schlaifer, Robert, and S.D. Heron. *Development of Aircraft Engines and Fuels*. Boston: Harvard Business School, 1950.

St. Peter, James. *The History of Gas Turbine Development in the United States…A Tradition of Excellence*. Atlanta, GA: International Gas Turbine Institute of the American Society of Mechanical Engineers, 1999.

Smith, G. Geoffrey. *Gas Turbines and Jet Propulsion for Aircraft*. New York: Aircraft Books Inc., 1946.

Swenson, Loyd S., Jr., James M. Grimwood, and Charles C. Alexander. *This New Ocean: A History of Project Mercury*. NASA SP-4201. Washington, DC: NASA, 1966.

Taylor, John R. *Jane's Pocket Book of Research and Experimental Aircraft*. New York: Collier Books, 1976.

Thompson, Milton O., and Curtis Peebles. *Flying Without Wings: NASA Lifting Bodies and the Birth of the Space Shuttle*. Washington, DC: Smithsonian Institution Press, 1999.

Winter, Frank H. "'Black Betsy': The 6000C4 Rocket Engine, 1945–1989." Paper presented at the 23rd Symposium on the History of Astronautics, 40th International Astronautical Congress of the International Astronautical Federation. Malaga, Spain: October 1989.

Witkin, Richard. *The Challenge of the Sputniks*. New York: Doubleday Headlines Publications, 1958.

Young, James O. *Meeting the Challenge of Supersonic Flight.* Edwards AFB, CA: Air Force Flight Test Center History Office, 1997.

Index

Numbers in **bold** indicate pages with illustrations and figures

G

X